Manual of
FORMULAS

Recipes, Methods
and Secret Proce~~~~

Popular Science Publishing

reprinted by Lindsay Public

MANUAL
OF FORMULAS

RECIPES, METHODS
&
SECRET PROCESSES

EDITED BY RAYMOND B. WAILES, B.S.

Manual of Formulas

Recipes, Methods and Secret Processes

edited by Raymond B. Wailes

Originally published by
Popular Science Publishing Co., Inc.
New York

Copyright 1932 by
Popular Science Publishing Co., Inc.

Reprinted by Lindsay Publications Inc
Bradley IL 60915

ISBN 1-55918-036-6

5 6 7 8 9 0

1990

INTRODUCTION

WITHIN the following pages lies a wealth of information for the householder and the amateur experimenter. This entirely new compilation of formulas has been the result of an exhaustive research undertaken especially for POPULAR SCIENCE MONTHLY. The formulas and processes have been selected as most worthy for publication after a search through a veritable mountain of data, in the course of which thousands of formulas of less certain merit were discarded. Only those believed to be reliable and the ingredients for which are easy to obtain have been selected.

Since the Editor has striven here to include the greatest possible number of formulas of practical value, it has been manifestly impossible to test them all personally. They have been chosen, however, from the most authoritative sources available, and many were devised, tested, and recommended by U. S. Government scientists and industrial chemists of high standing. Available in this volume are many formulas and trade secrets never before published. Wherever possible, the actual formulas used in industry are given, revised as necessary to meet the requirements of home use.

Chemicals for use in compounding the formulas may be obtained from a number of chemical supply houses throughout the United States, many of which fill orders by mail. Often, however, the necessary ingredients for a formula may be obtained from your local drug store or hardware shop. It is advisable, for this purpose, to know other names under which a chemical may masquerade.

To illustrate this, one has only to go into a large paint or hardware store and demand copper sulphate. An inexperienced clerk probably will shake his head and say that the store does not carry it; but tell him that you mean ordinary bluestone and the chances are that he will smile and give it to you. Both names and also the term "blue vitriol" are used to designate the same chemical.

Many of the more common chemicals have at least two names under which they may be sold. This is, of course, confusing. If you ask for muriatic acid and receive hydrochloric acid in its place, you are likely to wonder if there isn't some difference, but both names indicate the same acid. So, in the same way, do not be surprised if, when you ask for water glass, you receive a bottle or can labeled "sodium silicate," or on asking for sodium silicate you receive a container labeled "sodium silicate solution." If you know one designation for a chemical, you can look it up in an unabridged dictionary or in the table of synonyms at the back of this book and quickly learn any others.

Another important consideration is the price paid per pound. In the paint store you can probably get a pound of copper sulphate for twenty-five cents, whereas in a drug store you would have to pay at least twice as much for the same quantity. There is a good reason for this variation. The copper sulphate called "bluestone" or "blue vitriol" in the paint store is an impure salt often contaminated with other chemicals. The chemical sold in a drug store, however, will be absolutely pure.

Often the cheaper type of salt, designated by the term "technical," will be found to answer the purpose just as well as the pure and more expensive kind. Whenever pure chemicals are required, those known and marked "C. P." (chemically pure) or "U. S. P." (United States Pharmacopœia) should be used. For this purpose never use those marked "technical" or "tech.," as it is usually abbreviated. If in doubt, use the purer grade.

It is wise to buy small quantities of expensive chemicals and larger quantities of cheaper chemicals. It is costly to purchase cheap chemicals in small amounts. Take copper sulphate, a pound of which in the technical grade may cost about a quarter. If you require only an ounce, it may cost you ten or fifteen cents. It will obviously be wiser to buy a full pound, especially as this chemical has many uses and is easily stored.

MANUAL OF FORMULAS

ADHESIVES

How to Make Glue

The following glue formulas, with directions for mixing, were developed at the Forest Products Laboratory by the laboratory personnel and are available for the free use of the people of the United States and are taken from U. S. Dept. Agr., Department Bulletin #1500.

#1—Casein	100 parts
Water	220 to 230 "
Hydrated lime..	20 to 30 "
Water	100 "
Silicate of soda.	70 "
Copper chloride.	2 to 3 "
Water	30 to 50 "

The 220 to 230 parts of water added to the casein is approximately the right amount to use with Argentine (naturally soured) casein; but if a different casein is used the water requirement will lie somewhere between 150 and 250 parts by weight. The correct amount for different caseins must be determined by trial.

The formula presupposes that a high calcium lime will be used. A lime of lower grade may be used, but a proportionately larger amount of it will be needed, or the water resistance of the glue will be sacrificed. It is suggested that for the first trial the user try 25 parts of lime. If this does not give good results the amount can be varied within the limits specified.

The density of the silicate of soda used should be about 40° Baumé, with a silica-soda ratio of from 3 to 3.25.

Copper sulphate can be substituted for copper chloride.

Place the casein and water in the bowl of the mixing machine and rotate the paddle slowly, stirring the mixture until all the water has been absorbed and all the casein moistened. If the casein is allowed to soak beforehand it is more readily dissolved in the mixing process. Mix the hydrated lime with water in a separate container. Stir this mixture vigorously at first, but just before it is added to the casein stir just enough with a gentle rotary motion to keep the lime in suspension. Pour the milk of lime quickly into the casein.

When casein and lime are first combined they form large, slimy lumps, which are balls of dry casein coated with partly dissolved casein. These break up rapidly, becoming smaller and smaller, and finally disappear. The solution, in the meantime, is becoming thin and fluid. At this point stop the paddle and scrape the sides and bottom of the container, and then stir again. If a deposit of casein remains unacted on, it may cause more lumps later.

When about two minutes have elapsed since the lime and casein were united, it may be noticed that the glue has begun to thicken a little. Add the sodium silicate now, or else the glue will become too thick. The glue will momentarily become even thicker, but this thickness will soon change to a smooth and fluid consistency.

Continue the stirring until the glue is free from lumps. This should not take more than 15 or 20 minutes from the time the lime was added. If the glue is a little too thick, add a small amount of water. If the glue is too thin, it will be necessary to start over again, using a smaller proportion of water.

The copper salt may be added at any one of several times during the mixing process. If added as a powder before the casein is soaked, it may have a corrosive action upon the metal container. The copper salt, if added as a powder, should be thoroughly mixed with the casein before the addition of the lime. Copper salt may be placed in solution and conveniently stirred into the moistened casein immediately before the lime is added or after all the other ingredients have been combined. If the copper solution is added at the end of the mixing period, pour it into the glue in a thin stream and stir the mixture vigorously. Continue stirring until any lumps, which may have formed by the coagulation of the glue and the copper solution, are broken up and until a smooth violet-colored glue is obtained.

Glue prepared by formula No. 1 has proved to be exceptionally strong and durable, even under wet or damp conditions.

#2—Casein .... 100 parts
    Water .... 200 "
    Sodium hydroxide
      (caustic soda) .... 10 "
    Water .... 50 "

Bring the casein and water together according to the directions for mixing glue prepared by formula No. 1. Dissolve the caustic soda in water in a separate container, and while the mixing paddle is revolving sprinkle the caustic-soda solution into the damp casein. Stir slowly until a thin, smooth glue has been obtained. The consistency of the finished product may be altered by adding more casein if it is too thin, or by adding water if it is too thick. Silicate of soda is sometimes added to thicken or to reduce the cost of the glue per unit of volume. This glue has exceptional strength when dry, but when exposed to moisture it weakens as rapidly as animal or vegetable glue.

#3—Blood albumin (90 per
      cent solubility) .... 100 parts
    Water .... 170 "
    Ammonium hydroxide
      (specific gravity
      0.90) .... 4 "
    Hydrated lime ...... 3 "
    Water .... 10 "

Pour the larger amount of water over the blood albumin and allow the mixture to stand undisturbed for an hour or two. Stir the soaked albumin until it is in solution and then add the ammonia while the mixture is being stirred slowly. Slow stirring is necessary to prevent foamy glue. Combine the smaller amount of water and the hydrated lime to form milk of lime. Add the milk of lime, and continue to agitate the mixture for a few minutes. Care should be exercised in the use of the lime, inasmuch as a small excess will cause the mixture to thicken and become a jellylike mass. The glue should be of moderate consistency when mixed and should remain suitable for use for several hours. The exact proportions of albumin and water may be varied as required to produce a glue of greater or less consistency or to suit an albumin of different solubility from that specified.

#4—Blood albumin (90 per cent solubility) ... 100 parts
Water .... 140 to 200 "
Ammonium hydroxide (specific gravity, 0.90) .... 5½ "
Paraformaldehyde 15 "

The blood albumin is covered with the water and the mixture is allowed to stand for an hour or two, then stirred slowly. The ammonium hydroxide is next added with more stirring. Then the paraformaldehyde is sifted in, and the mixture is stirred constantly at a fairly high speed. Paraformaldehyde should not be poured in so rapidly as to form lumps nor so slowly that the mixture will thicken and coagulate before the required amount has been added.

The mixture thickens considerably and usually reaches a consistency where stirring is difficult or impossible. However, the thickened mass will become fluid again in a short time at ordinary temperatures and will return to a good working consistency in about an hour. It will remain in this condition for 6 or 8 hours, but when the liquid finally sets and dries, as in a glue joint, it forms a hard and insoluble film.

This glue may be used in either hot or cold presses. When cold pressed, however, it has only moderate strength, and for that reason is not to be depended upon in aircraft construction where maximum strength is required. If hot pressed, it is high in strength and very water resistant.

Preparing Glutin Glue

Place a handful of flour in a piece of muslin and wash it with water, kneading the flour until the wash water is no longer milky from the starch. Glutin remains and should be placed on a glass dish to dry. To use, take a small flake, add a drop or two of water, and allow it to stand 5 or 10 minutes. Knead it until it is soft and then apply.

Yellow Glue

Glue chips are soaked several hours in water, after which the water is poured off and replaced by glacial (strong) acetic acid. The container should be placed in warm water and the glue stirred. If the glue is not to be used for veneering or sticking paper together, finely powdered calcium chloride can be stirred into it, using enough to keep the glue still plastic.

Thin Shellac Solution

A glue of rather thin consistency, having shellac for a base, is made by dissolving an ounce of borax in a pint of very hot water, and then stirring in two ounces of flake shellac until thorough solution is had. It is best to grind the shellac with a small amount of the borax water in a mortar, then add the remainder of the solution a little at a time.

Miscellaneous Glues

#1—Mix a handful of calcium oxide with 4 oz. of linseed oil; thoroughly lixiviate the mixture; boil it to a good thickness, and spread it on tin plates until cool. It will become very hard, but can be dissolved over a fire, like common glue, and is then fit for use.

#2—Granulated or flake glue 11½ lb.
Water .... 5 gal.
Calcium chloride ...... 5 lb.

Heat until calcium chloride is dissolved, then add any good grade of flake or ground glue, 11½ lb. Let soak for about two hours, then add ten gallons water. Boil and stir until thoroughly mixed. Then when cool, bottle. It should be kept bottled when not in use. If put up in bottles to sell about one-half liquid ounce of oil of sassafras should be placed in each gallon of glue. It keeps the glue from becoming moldy.

#3—Glue, cut in small pieces, 3 parts, water 8 parts; let stand for several hours; then add hydrochloric acid ¾ part and sulphate zinc 1 part; expose the whole to a temperature of 178° to 192° F. during a period of 10 or 12 hours.

#4—Take the best glue; pour on water to cover; soak over night; melt over a gentle heat, and add fine plaster of Paris or white lead: mix well, and add a little acetic acid, carbolic acid or any ethereal oil to prevent putrefaction; adapted for flexible objects like leather; will not withstand boiling water.

#5—Take of best white glue 16 oz., white lead, dry, 4 oz., rain water 2 pints, alcohol 4 oz., with constant stirring dissolve the glue and lead in the water by means of a water bath; add the alcohol and continue the heat for a few minutes. Lastly pour into bottles while it is still hot.

#6—(A) A hot solution of 50 parts of glue in 60 parts of a 20-per-cent aqueous calcium-chloride solution. (B) A solution of 50 parts of glue in 60 parts of acetic acid. (C) Soak gelatin in acetic acid of 70 per cent until it swells up, then rub it up, adding a little water during the process.

#7—One pound fine isinglass and 1 pint rain water; boil and prepare an ordinary glue, then add slowly stirring continually, 2 oz. nitric acid; bottle, and it is fit for use. It will permanently adhere to wood, leather, paper, and everything else.

#8—Take gum arabic, 100 parts; starch, 75 parts, sugar, 21 parts. Dissolve the gum arabic in a little water; also dissolve the starch in a little water. Mix and add the sugar. Boil

on the water bath until a paste is formed of desired consistency.

#9—(A) Gum arabic 5 parts, sugar 3 parts, starch 2 parts; add very little water; boil, stirring until thick and white. (B) Glue, dissolved in water to the thickness of molasses; add a thickening of flour and water while the glue is boiling until about as thick as clear starch; apply to the moss or lichen, and to the surface to which it is to be attached.

Glue in Stick Form

Glue chips, about ½ pound, are soaked for several days in water. The water is then poured off and the glue melted over a moderate fire. To 1 pound of glue add ½ pound of sugar, mix thoroughly, and then pour the mass into suitable molds and allow it to stand for several days. In using the glue it is moistened with the tongue. Wrap the glue with waxed paper when removed from molds.

Waterproof Glue

Thick solution of glue...... 10 parts
Linseed-oil varnish .... 5 "
Litharge .... 1 "

The thick glue solution is made as above, omitting the sugar. Heat the whole for 15 minutes and use while hot.

Transparent Mucilage

#1—Oil sassafras .... 10 drops
Water .... 1 pt.
Gum dextrine .... 5 oz.

The water should be boiling. Make dextrine into a paste and stir until all is dissolved, after which add about ½ teaspoonful of oil of sassafras, then bottle. Eight oz. gum arabic can be substituted in place of the dextrine. This makes a wonderful mucilage and will stick to metal and wood as well as paper. To make thick mucilage add 4 oz. more of dextrine.

#2—Dextrine .... 40 gm.
    Aluminum sulphate .... 1 "
    Dissolve in water ...... 60 cc.
    Now add
    Glue .... 2 gm.

Heat the whole to about 100° F., with stirring, until the mass becomes silky and white.

Ordinary Mucilage

Dextrine .... 1 lb.
Gum arabic .... 4 oz.
Acetic acid .... 4 "
Water .... 1 qt.

Dissolve the dextrine in the water by boiling, strain and add the acetic acid and let cool, then add 4 oz. alcohol. Denatured alcohol can be used.

Bottle Label Paste

Rosin .... 1 lb.
Wax .... 2 "

Melt, apply to label and affix to bottle.

Celluloid

#1—Shellac .... 1 oz.
    Camphor .... 1 "
    Alcohol .... 4 "
    Apply warm.

#2—Ether .... 4 parts
    Alcohol .... 3 "

Use this as a solvent. Clamp, and let dry.

Paste with Glue

#1—White glue .... 1 oz.
    Corn starch ...... 2 "
    Water .... 1 pt.
    Sodium benzoate... ¼ teaspoon

Soak the glue in boiling water, mix the starch with small quantity of water and then gradually pour into the glue solution, stirring until thick, heating the while.

#2—Wheat flour .... 8 oz.
    Powdered alum ..... ¼ "
    Glycerin .... ½ "
    Oil of cloves......... 15 drops
    Water, about .... 1½ pt.

Bill Poster's Paste

Wheat flour .... 10 lb.
Water .... 5 pt.
Alum .... 5 oz.
Oil of sassafras .... ¼ "
    Mix using hot water.

Warm Water Paste

#1—Powdered dextrine ..... 23 lb.
    Powdered borax .... ¾ "
    Powdered alum .... 1¼ "
    Powdered gum acacia.... 1 "

Mix. Add water to the consistency desired. Heat gently and allow to cool.

#2—Flour .... 4 oz.
    Powdered gum
      arabic .... 1 "
    Glycerin .... 1 "
    Salicylic acid ..... ¼ teaspoon
    Water .... 1 qt.

Mix and boil for a few minutes, stirring to prevent burning, or use a double boiler.

Strong Mucilage

#1—Glue .... 5 oz.
    Granulated sugar .... 1 "
    Water .... 5 "

Heat the glue in the water until dissolved; add the sugar. Use more or less water according to thickness desired. Add soda benzoate, about ⅛ oz., to preserve.

#2—Gum arabic .... 2 oz.
    Water .... 32 "
    Glycerin .... 2 "
    Salicylic acid .... 90 gr.

This makes a light colored mucilage.

#3—Rye flour .... 4 oz.
    Powdered gum acacia.... ½ "
    Water .... 24 "
    Glycerin .... 1 "

Add a preservative.

#4—Dextrine .... 50 to 90 parts
    Alum .... 4 "
    Sugar .... 75 "
    Water .... 120 "

Oil of cloves, enough to give odor.

#5—Gum tragacanth .... 1 oz.
    Gum arabic .... 1 "
    Boiling water .... 64 "
    Carbolic acid .... 1 dr.

#6—Gum tragacanth .... 1 oz.
    Dextrine .... 3 "
    Water .... 1 pt.

Preserve with oil of wintergreen, oil of cloves, sodium benzoate or salicylic acid.

#7—Dextrine, 10 dr.; glucose, ½ dr.; in which is dissolved a solution of alum, 15 gr.; glycerin, 1 dr.; water, to make 2 oz.

#8—Dextrine .... 1 lb.
    Acetic acid .... 4 oz.
    Alcohol .... 4 "
    Water to make......... 1 qt.

Dissolve the dextrine in 1 pt. of boiling water, strain through flannel; add the acetic acid, and when nearly cold add the alcohol, stirring thoroughly, then add rest of water.

Mucilage in Stick Form

The glue sticks produced as follows are moistened and the wet surface applied to the paper to be united.

#1—Powdered white glue.. 10 parts
    Powdered gum arabic.. 2 "
    Sugar .... 5 "
    Water .... Sufficient

Mix the glue and gum, then stir in enough cold water to make the solution the consistency of thick syrup. Soak overnight to allow the glue and

gum to absorb the water, then add enough water to again bring it to a thick syrup. Pour into a flat bottom pan that has been chilled and cut into sticks of desired size when almost solid. If poured into molds the molds should first be well greased and then chilled by setting upon cracked ice.

#2—Glue, pure and best...... 6 oz.
    Sugar .... 2 "
    Glycerin .... ½ "

Mix as above, soaking the glue in water.

Commercial Mucilage

Dissolve ½ pound white glue in equal parts water and vinegar, and add ¼ as much alcohol and ½ oz. alum dissolved in a small amount of water. Soak the glue in cold water until it swells and softens. Pour off the water, then melt the glue to a thick paste in hot water, and add the vinegar, which should be hot. When cool add the alcohol and alum solution.

Transparent Glue for Glass

White gelatin .... 5 oz.
Acetic acid .... 5 "
Water .... 6 "

Soak the gelatin in the water for twelve hours or so, then heat the softened gelatin and water until the gelatin has dissolved, and then add the acetic acid. Water is then added until about a pint of glue is obtained. It is useful in cementing glass sheets together, or where a transparent mucilage or cement is desired. It is also useful in mounting photographs on glass, the adhesive being applied to the face of the photograph, which is then pressed against the underside of the glass. A roller is used to squeeze out the surplus cement. The glass surrounding the photo is washed with warm water, before the excess cement dries.

Glue for Celluloid

Shellac	2 parts
Alcohol	4 "
Spirits of camphor	3 "

Dissolve all by allowing to stand in a corked bottle in a warm place. Owing to the shellac, which imparts a slight color to the glue, it is not used on light colored celluloid objects. This glue, however, is useful in securing paper, leather, or metal to celluloid. Bleached shellac, if used, will make the product more nearly transparent. The alcohol used should be about 96% by volume.

Celluloid can be mended by moistening the broken edges with glacial acetic acid, allowing the acid to soften the celluloid by remaining in place for a short time, and then pressing the two parts together, and allowing to dry. Glacial acetic acid should not be confused with weak solutions of acetic acid. The glacial acetic acid contains little water, and will become a solid at low temperatures.

Library Paste

#1—Dextrine .... 100 gm.
Boracic acid .... 5 "
Water .... 80 cc.

Dissolve the boracic acid in the water, and then beat into the dextrine, using a little at a time. Use a double boiler and heat the dextrine-boracic acid water mass until creaminess sets in. Stir from time to time. Add about 10 cc. of glycerin and incorporate thoroughly. The paste is now ready for use, although as it will sour despite the presence of boracic acid, it is better to add about one or two grams of sodium benzoate or salicylic acid. It can be perfumed with methyl salicylate. High temperatures are avoided if a double boiler is used, thus escaping the risk of having the paste turn yellow when finished.

#2—Starch .... 2 dr.
Sugar .... 1 oz.
Gum acacia .... 2 dr.

After weighing out the above, add enough water to produce a thin paste, then transfer to a double boiler and add more water until very thin and cook until it thickens and reaches the proper consistency. The whole must be stirred while heating. Preserve with salicylic acid, oil of cloves, formaldehyde or carbolic acid.

#3—Starch .... 1 oz.
Gelatin (sheet) .... 3 dr.
Water .... 8 oz.

Treat as in previous preparation.

#4—Heat 2 parts of dextrine, 5 parts of water, 1 part of acetic acid, 1 part of alcohol together, with stirring until the whole becomes pearly and of the proper consistency.

#5—Dextrine .... 3 oz.
Powdered alum .... 1 dr.
Sugar .... ½ oz.
Water .... 4 "
Gelatin .... ¼ "
Oil of cloves.........15 drops

Dissolve all ingredients in the water, except the oil of cloves, stir and heat to boiling point, continue the boiling until dissolved and then add the oil of cloves.

#6—Starch .... 2 oz.
Gelatin .... ¼ "
Water .... 16 pt.
Oil of cloves.......... 16 drops

Mix starch and water, add the gelatin and heat gently over water bath until it thickens.

#7—Dextrine .... 1 lb.
Sugar syrup .... 2 oz.
Alum .... 1 "
Water .... 24 "
Sodium benzoate .... pinch

Mix the dextrine, alum, and sodium benzoate with a portion of water, rub to a smooth paste, add the syrup and balance of water and heat on water bath, stirring until it becomes pearly.

Common Paste

Dissolve one part gum arabic in 8 parts of water, warming to dissolve. Add 4 parts of sugar, one of corn starch, and boil to desired thickness. Add a pinch of boracic acid to keep it from becoming mildewed.

Simple Paste

#1—White dextrine, 1 lb.; water, enough to make a stiff paste; and add 1 oz. salicylic acid or benzoate of soda, after heating.

#2—White dextrine	1 lb.
Powdered tragacanth..	2 "
Flour	6 "
Alum	2 oz.
Boric acid	2 "
Oil of cloves	20 drops

To each pound of this powder add 4 pints of hot water and half a pound of glycerin and stir well until dissolved, heating to facilitate mixing.

#3—Flour	4 oz.
Gum arabic	1 "
Glycerin	1 "
Water	2 pt.

Grind in a mortar, boil, and while hot, strain. Preserve with pinch of sodium benzoate or salicylic acid.

Thick Paste

#1—Heat the following to desired consistency:

Dextrine	2 parts
Acetic acid	1 "
Water	5 "
Alcohol	1 "

#2—Wheat flour	4 oz.
Nitric acid	1 dr.
Boric acid	10 gr.
Oil of cloves	5 drops
Carbolic acid	½ dr.

Stir flour and water together, mixing thoroughly, and add the other ingredients. Heat, adding the nitric acid a drop at a time, followed by vigorous stirring. Remove from fire when desired plasticity is produced.

#3—Flour	1 lb.
Dextrine	2 "
Boric acid	2 oz.
Glucose	5 dr.
Water	1½ qt.

Dissolve the acid in the water, then the glucose. Beat in the dextrine and flour and heat in a double boiler. Add oil of sassafras to perfume.

Paste for Labels

To affix labels on metal containers:

#1—Dissolve sheet gelatin in glacial acetic acid, using a very low flame.

#2—Dextrine	2 oz.
Acetic acid	1 "
Water	5 "
Heat to dissolve, and add	
alcohol	1 "

Flour-rosin Paste

Boil 4 lb. of rye flour in 2 gal. of water. Dissolve 3 oz. of rosin in alcohol, using heat if necessary, and limit the alcohol to about 6 oz. or less. Stir the rosin solution into the flour paste, and continue to heat while stirring, thoroughly to incorporate the rosin in the mixture. Remove from fire and, as the mixture slowly cools, add some perfume material such as oil of sassafras, beating the oil in.

Wall Paper Paste

Rye flour	4 lb.
Cold water	½ gal.
Boiling water	1½ "
Pulverized rosin	2 oz.

Make flour and water into a batter free from lumps; then pour into boiling water. Boil if necessary, and while hot stir in the pulverized rosin a little at a time. This paste is exceedingly strong, and will stick heavy wall paper or thin leather. If the paste be too thick, thin with a little hot water.

Envelope Mucilage

Gum arabic	1 part
Starch	1 "
Sugar	4 "

Water, sufficient to produce the desired consistency.

The gum arabic is first dissolved in water, the sugar added, then the starch, breaking up all lumps, after which the mixture is boiled for a few minutes in order to dissolve the starch, after which it is thinned down to the desired consistency with more water.

Mounting Paste

White dextrine	1 lb.
Gum arabic	1 oz.
Water	1½ pt.
Acetic acid	1 oz.
Oil of wintergreen........	20 drops
Oil of cinnamon..........	20 drops
Salicylic acid	20 gr.

The dextrine and the gum, which should be pulverized, are dissolved in the water, and then the salicylic acid added and dissolved. This liquid is heated with the dextrine, and when the whole has become pasty, which should require a quarter of an hour, the acetic acid is added, stirring in slowly. The heating is continued, taking care not to boil the mass. The paste will soon become pearly, and should then be removed from the fire and the perfume oils added while it is cooling. It should be stirred thoroughly while the oils are being added.

Some manufacturers of pastes, such as this, ripen the product by allowing it to age in a cool place for several weeks, but if the paste is to be used continuously after making, this can be omitted. If the paste is too thick, water, or glycerin, or both, can be added to thin it. The glycerin, if added, will also keep the paste moist, by abstracting water from the air.

Paste for Leather

Four parts by weight of glue are allowed to soften in 15 parts of cold water for some hours, and then gently heated until the solution becomes clear. Sixty-five parts of water are now added, with constant stirring. In another vessel 30 parts of starch are stirred in 20 of cold water, so that a thin milky fluid is obtained without lumps. Into this the boiling solution of glue is poured, with constant stirring, and the whole kept boiling. Cool and add 10 drops of carbolic acid. This paste is of extraordinary adhesive power, and may be used for leather, paper, or card-board.

ART AND DECORATION

Etching on Metal

In etching, the metal plate is covered with a ground, or protective wax or pitch coating, the desired design scratched through this and the whole plate immersed or covered with the etching fluid. If only one side of the plate is to be etched, the ground or protective wax can be applied, using heat to melt it, and when cold, building up a dam about the plate to retain the etching mixture which is then poured in the tray of wax thus formed. In all cases it is best to heat the surface of the plate as well as the wax in applying, as this will tend to drive off the adsorbed air and moisture which is always present on a metal surface. After etching, the ground is removed by heating, and then the small amount remaining is removed by appropriate solvents such as gasoline, benzol, toluene, carbon tetrachloride, or alcohol. The grounds used for etching are:

Gum mastic .... 16 parts
Burgundy pitch .... 50 "
White wax .... 125 "
Asphalt .... 200 "

The whole is melted over a low fire and when cold thinned with turpentine, about 500 parts of which will be required.

Another ground:

Asphaltum .... 4 parts
White wax .... 3 "

A simple liquid ground is asphaltum varnish. This can be made by dissolving asphaltum in gasoline or benzene.

The following resists strong etching acids quite well:

Asphaltum .... 4 parts
Pitch .... 1 "
Wax .... 4 "

Etching Upon Steel

In etching metals the usual procedure is to clean the surface and then apply a thin film of wax. This is best done by warming the metal and brushing on a thin film of melted wax, allowing the surplus wax to run off. When cold, scribe or write through the wax the desired data. The object is then placed in one of the following acid etching baths, or if the object to be etched is flat, the bath can be applied to the wax, covering the scribed portions. Care should be taken not to allow the chemical etching solution to run onto the uncoated or unprotected metal surface as it will, of course, act upon this.

Muriatic acid ... 3 parts by volume
Nitric acid ...... 1 " " "

When these two are well mixed the result is called aqua regia and will attack gold as well as the common metals. This acid mixture may be used or a mixture of varying proportions of each can be taken.

#1—Iodine .... 1½ oz.
     Iron filings .... ¾ dr.
     Water .... 6 oz.

Digest until the iron is dissolved. This is a good but rather expensive etching fluid.

#2—Dissolve in 150 parts of vinegar, sulphate of copper, 30 parts; alum, 8 parts; salt, 11 parts. Add a few drops of nitric acid. According to whether this is allowed to act a longer or shorter time, the steel may be engraved upon deeply or the surface may be given a frosted appearance.

#3—Ammonium persulphate.. 20 gm.
     Water .... 100 cc.

#4—Copper ammonium chlo-
         ride .... 12 gm.
     Strong hydrochloric acid 5 cc.
     Water .... 100 "

#5—Copper sulphate .... 2 oz.
     Alum .... ½ "
     Salt .... ½ "

Mix with ½ pt. of vinegar and 40 drops of nitric acid. This can also be used to give steel a frosted surface.

#6—Nitric acid .... 62 parts
     Water .... 125 "
     Alcohol .... 187 "
     Copper nitrate .... 8 "

This can be used for fine lines upon polished steel.

#7—Iodine .... 2 gm.
     Potassium iodide .... 6 "
     Water .... 40 cc.

#8—Silver acetate .... 2 parts
     Alcohol .... 125 "
     Nitric acid .... 65 "
     Nitric ether .... 16 "
     Oxalic acid .... 1 "
     Water .... 125 "

Etching on Copper

#1—Alcohol .... 3 parts
    Nitric acid .... 8 "
    Silver nitrate .... 8 "
    Water .... 5 "

Wash the plate with dilute nitric acid. Then apply the solution for 3 minutes, and wash with alcohol. Repeat if necessary.

#2—White vitriol ...... 1 to 5 parts
    Common salt ..... 1 "
    Concentrated sul-
      phuric acid ...... 100 "
    Nitric acid .... 200 "

Mix together. The sulphuric acid should be poured carefully into the nitric acid, not the reverse.

#3—Nitric or sulphuric acid.. 1 part
    Potassium bichromate
      saturated solution .... 2 "
    Water .... 5 "

Etching on Brass

#1—Nitric acid, 8 parts; mixed with water, 80 parts; into this mixture pour a solution of potassium chlorate, 3 parts, in water, 50 parts.

#2—A mixture of fuming nitric acid and concentrated nitric acid will eat brass or copper violently and can be used to make holes in thin sheets of these metals. Do not inhale the brown fumes produced.

#3—Hydrochloric acid .... 12 parts
    Water .... 12 "
    Mix and in this mixture
      dissolve antimony
      chloride .... 2 "

Coloring Glassware

Vases, bottles, bulbs, test tubes, and other glassware intended for novelty purposes can be frosted with the aid of sodium silicate solution (waterglass). At the same time, they may be tinted any desired color by adding water soluble dye to the sodium silicate. Since this viscid liquid, which sticks so firmly to glass, is inexpensive, a sufficient quantity may be used to allow the glassware to be dipped bodily. If desired, just the lower part or one side of the glassware may be treated, depending upon the intended effect. After being dipped, the glass should be immersed in a concentrated and boiling hot solution of epsom salts or of ammonium chloride, preferably the latter.

Painting on Porcelain

Brianchon's process consists of melting

Rosin .... 30 parts
Bismuth subnitrate .... 10 "

When these are thoroughly incorporated together, add 40 parts of oil of lavender and stir until mixed. Remove from the source of heat and then add 35 parts of oil of lavender, when the flux is ready for use. The salts and oxides of antimony, chromium, cobalt, copper, iron, silver, uranium, zinc, etc., are used as coloring substances. Gold produces iridescent colors. The desired mix is painted on and fired.

Black: Stannic sulphide .. 5 parts
    Cobalt oxide ...... 1.6 "
    Stannic oxide .... 1.6 "
Blue: Cobalt oxide .... 1 part
    Stannic oxide .... 1 "
    Lead glass #1........ 1 "
    Lead glass #2........ 4 "
Lead Glass #1: Sand....... 1 part
             Borax ..... 1 "
             Minium .... 2 "
Lead Glass #2: Sand....... 1 part
             Minium .... 2 "
Brown: Calcined zinc sul-
      phate .... 8 parts
    Calcined manganous
      sulphate .... 1 "
    Calcined iron sul-
      phate .... 12 "
    Potassium nitrate.. 26 "

Heat until decomposed. Wash soluble material out and use the regulus, mixing it with 2½ times its weight of lead glass #1.

Green: Heat mercury chromate until chromium oxide is formed and mix with 3 parts of lead glass #1.

Gold (Gilding)

#1—Powdered gold is mixed with borax and gum-water, and the solution applied with a camel's-hair pencil. Heat is then applied until the borax fuses, which fixes the gold.

#2—Gold, 6 parts; aqua regia, 36 parts. Dissolve, then add tin, 1 part; next add sulphur, 3 parts; oil of turpentine, 1 part. Mix and rub until the mixture becomes hard; then add oil of turpentine, 4 parts.

Gold: Uranium nitrate	10	parts
Bismuth oxide	4	"
Boracic acid	4	"
Orange: Uranium oxide ...	2	parts
Silver chloride ...	1	"
Bismuth oxide ...	1	"
White: Minium	1	part
Boric acid	1	"
White sand	1	"

Glazing Paint for Pottery

#1—Water-glass	100	parts
Red lead (minium)...	20	"
Fine sand	5	"

Mix. The thick paint obtained is brushed on the ware and burned on.

#2—Soda ash	80	parts
Fine sand	70	"
Clay	10	"

To Cut Pottery

Using a Bakelite-Carborundum cutting disc spun in the lathe, pottery may be cut as easily as wood. This disc, which is about one-sixteenth or one-eighth of an inch thick, is mounted on the head stock of a buffing wheel or lathe, and spun. The pottery is held to the wheel which cuts through without chipping. The disc sharpens and trues itself in cutting, a smooth wheel always being at the service of the potter. Heretofore a metal disc has been used which is fed with water and emery, Carborundum, or diamond powder.

Drilling China

To drill china use a copper drill and emery, moistened with turpentine. To drill glass, use a steel drill tempered as hard as possible and camphor and water as a lubricant or camphor and turpentine.

Body Material for Stoneware

Ball clay	14	parts
China clay	10	"
Stone	8	"

Body Material for Earthenware

Ball clay	13	parts
China clay	9½	"
Flint	5½	"
Cornwall stone	4	"

To Preserve Flowers

Many substances and formulas have been suggested and even patented which, it is claimed, if added to the water in which flowers have been placed after cutting, will assist materially in keeping them fresh for a longer time than would be the case if the water were not so treated. Recent experiments at the Boyce Thompson Institute have shown that many such agents are without effect on the flowers.

One method by which flowers may be made to preserve their appearance for some time, however, is to immerse them in molten paraffin until all bubbles have ceased to come off. Many flowers will not stand this treatment, but some are little affected.

Dipping the entire flower in an alcoholic solution of gum dammar or Canada balsam has been used to preserve flowers. The alcohol evaporates and the gum, which is nearly transparent, is left behind on the outside of the flower, thus effectively keeping out the air and keeping the moisture in. The following has also been used. The glycerin allows the flowers to be handled quite freely.

Gelatin, 11 oz.; concentrated glycerin, 9 oz. The gelatin is softened by first soaking it in cold water, and then dissolving it in the glycerin, with the latter heated to 212° F. When properly prepared, this varnish is colorless, and when cold resembles wax in color, and is pliable.

Preserving Leaves

Spread the leaves, and press in a suitable pan with alternate layers of fine dry sand heated as hot as the hand can bear, and set aside to cool. When the sand has cooled, the leaves may be removed, smoothed under a hot iron, dipped for a moment in clear varnish, and allowed to dry in the air. The varnish can be made as in previous process.

Changing Color of Flowers

The colors of many flowers can be changed chemically. Red roses can be bleached white by exposing them to the fumes from burning sulphur. In carrying out this operation the flower must be dampened thoroughly and held for several minutes in the vapors from the burning sulphur. A box placed over the flowers, under which the sulphur is burned, makes a suitable gassing chamber. The petals often become variegated, considerably enhancing the effect. Sulphur gases such as the sulphur dioxide or trioxide, work by uniting with the red coloring matter and producing a compound that is colorless, or white. Another method is to allow a dilute solution of an acid, such as sulphuric or muriatic (hydrochloric), to act upon sodium sulphite. Sulphur dioxide is copiously evolved.

Some flowers placed over ammonia gas also undergo a change in color. This is best accomplished by placing the flowers under a box in close proximity to a basin of ammonium hydroxide or strong ammonia water. Many purple colored flowers are affected with ammonia gas, becoming green, the red colors, if they contain same, are turned green and the red become black.

Dilute nitric acid sprinkled over flowers will also change many of their colors by oxidation. This process, however, destroys their use for certain purposes, and, at the same time, changes some of the petals to a worthless pulpy mass.

Red roses that have been turned white by sulphur trioxide or dioxide gas can be brought back to red by immersing them in dilute cold sulphuric acid.

To Bleach Leaves

Mix about a teaspoon of bleaching powder (calcium hypochlorite) in a quart of water and add sufficient vinegar or dilute sulphuric acid to cause the evolution of chlorine gas. Allow the leaves to remain for about ten minutes or until they have become whitened. Wash carefully in clear water and dry between sheets of paper.

To Color Celluloid

The usual organic dyes are not suitable for coloring celluloid articles, as they do not penetrate into the material and are less permanent than some colorants of a chemical type. To color celluloid, wash the surface with soapy water to free it of grease, then rinse off the soapy water and use the following solutions to obtain the desired color:

Black: Immerse in a solution of nitrate of silver. Allow to dry in sunlight.

Yellow: First immerse in a solution of lead nitrate, then in a concentrated solution of potassium chromate.

Brown: Dip in a solution of permanganate of potash made strongly alkaline by the addition of sodium carbonate.

Blue: Dip in a solution of indigo neutralized by the addition of soda.

Red: First dip in a dilute solution of nitric acid; then in a solution of carmine to which ammonia has been added.

Green: Dip in a solution of copper acetate.

Papier-mâché

The base of this substance, which is often used to mold objects, is paper waste, pulped with starch, dextrine, a small amount of water-glass, glue, lime water, etc. After pressing into molds, it is coated with linseed oil and baked to make a glossy, hard, non-fluffing coating. Clay, chalk, or other fillers are sometimes added.

Bleaching Ivory Objects

Discolored ivory may be restored to its original condition by three methods. In the first, the ivory objects are placed in a wide-mouthed glass jar into which oil of turpentine is poured until the ivory is covered. Then, the mouth of the jar is covered with a bladder membrane and the whole container is exposed to the sunlight for from one to two weeks. Another method, particularly suitable for knife and fork handles, umbrella handles, and similar ivory objects, is to immerse them in a mixture of one part of peroxide of hydrogen and two parts of water for from one half to one hour, if necessary even longer, until the ivory is sufficiently bleached. Then polish them by rubbing briskly with a woolen cloth.

If the ivory has become yellow through handling or contact with dishwater, it is advisable to begin by immersing in alcohol, gasoline or carbon tetrachloride. After drying, rub vigorously with a rag dipped in 3 per cent peroxide of hydrogen or a 5-10 per cent solution of citric acid. After the bleaching is completed, the ivory should be rinsed with clean water and then rubbed dry. If the ivory forms the handles of knives or forks, care should be taken to protect the metal parts by coating them with vaseline and then wrapping them with paper to prevent the grease from spreading. If necessary, this process can be repeated two or three times. The whiteness of piano keys can also be restored by this process.

Transferring Designs to Paper or Cloth

To transfer designs to paper or cloth use one of the following solutions:

#1—Tincture of green soap   1 part
     Potassium carbonate ..   ½ "
     Water ....   1 pt.

#2—Sal soda ....   1 oz.
     Water ....   8 "

#3—Varnish remover, liquid   1 part
     Water ....   1 "

#4—Tincture of green soap. 1 teaspoon
     Spirits of turpentine...1   "
     Water ....   1 pt.

#5—Soap ....   4 gm.
     Glycerin ....   20 drops
     Alcohol ....   10 cc.
     Water ....   10 "

Saturate the print with the liquid, dry with a blotter. Lay print face down on paper or object to which it is to be transferred. Lay piece of newspaper on top and rub with a spoon or blunt article.

A picture transfer fluid is made of 1 bar of common soap dissolved in 1 gallon water, then add ½ pint of turpentine. Apply to any printed picture with small brush, then lay clean white paper or cloth over picture and rub quite hard with bowl of teaspoon. To transfer on glass or dishes first varnish the glass or dish with white varnish and let dry. Then wet picture as before, and lay same face down on the glass or dish and rub on back of picture.

Sun Pictures on Leaves or Fruit

If a monogram, insignia, or single initial cut from metal foil is varnished and then applied to a mature leaf, or a fruit that is almost ripe but has not yet developed the color, the parts covered will not be exposed to the sun's rays and will not develop as fully as the region outside the metal leaf. The image or figure produced often will be quite plain and have a pleasing shading. It is important that metal foil such as tin foil, and that an adhesive such as varnish, be used so that the cut-out will not be washed off by the rains.

Dyeing Flowers

Package dyes, sold in many drug stores for dyeing cloth, are suitable for dyeing flowers. The wool dyes produce the best results when cut flowers are treated. The flowers are severed, making a slanting cut on the stem, and then immersed in the solution of the dye in water.

Only white flowers can be colored the original color of the tinted water, but many combinations can be made. Yellow flowers can be made into orange, saffron, green, and other colors. Pink can be changed to lilac, red to purple, and so on through the list of colors and shades.

To Transfer Pictures

#1—Prepare a liquid by using 1½ dr. of common yellow soap in a pint of hot water, adding when nearly cold, 3½ fl. oz. of turpentine and shake thoroughly.

#2—Soap powder, 1 oz.; water, 1 pt. Mix and dissolve by boiling, take off the fire and add 1 pt. turpentine. Proceed as directed in other formulas.

#3—Brush creosote over the picture. Moisten the paper, upon which the picture is to be transferred, with a solution made by dissolving one ounce of oxalic acid in a pint of water. Then apply the picture soaked in the creosote, face downward on the oxalic acid soaked paper, and rub the back with a spoon. Remove the picture carefully while still damp.

Mosaic Gold for Bronzing

Mosaic gold is used in bronzing powders and can be prepared experimentally as follows:

A mixture of equal parts of powdered tin and of sulphur is mixed with one-eighth of its volume of powdered ammonium chloride. The mixture is then placed in a porcelain crucible, covered with a 2 mm. layer of powdered ammonium chloride, and the covered crucible heated with a Bunsen burner. As a result of the reaction, the ammonium chloride vaporizes as a white smoke, and stannic sulphide (mosaic gold) sublimes as a brilliant yellow crystalline deposit on the crucible lid. If larger quantities are taken, enough of the mosaic gold can be recovered to be available for use in a gilding compound.

Plastic Modeling Clay

Plastic clays that do not dry out are made by kneading the clay, which may be of any color, with glycerin so that its plasticity has not been seriously impaired. This will dilute the water and allow the vaseline or pe- troleum jelly, which is added next, to make a thorough incorporation with the clay. The amount of vaseline to be added can be an amount sufficient to render it sufficiently pliable. The working in should be thorough; a food chopper can be used for this. If the mixture is too thin, it can be built up to the desired stiffness with whit- ing which will of course cause the product to have a lighter color if much is used.

Wax	100 parts
Whiting	75 "
Turpentine	13 "
Lard	7 "

The lard, and then the turpentine, is added to the melted wax after which the whiting is stirred in. It can then be removed from the heating vessel and kneaded on a bread board.

Plastic Molding Materials

Suitable puttylike materials that can be used in taking impressions, du- plicating rosettes, or filling cracks in wood are:

#1—Plaster of Paris and sawdust made into a paste with glue water.

#2—Glue	13 parts
Litharge	4 "
White lead	8 "
Plaster of Paris	10 "
Sawdust	1 "

Dissolve the glue in a small amount of hot water. This glue solution is mixed with small portions of the other materials until a putty has been formed.

Coloring Plaster for Casts

In coloring plaster for casts the pig- ments used are the salts of the metals, lead, copper, and iron, either alone or in combination. The plaster is mixed very thoroughly with a watery solu-

tion of the salt, and then a little for- maldehyde is added to fix the color.

Wax Casts of Figures

One of the best ways of making plaster casts of metals, figures, or or- namental objects is to prepare the molds in wax. A special wax for tak- ing impressions is a mixture of 4 oz. of beeswax and 1 oz. of olive oil, melted together. To this is added 4 oz. of sifted starch, which is worked into the liquid until the whole takes on a doughlike consistency. When cold the mass is quite hard.

To use the wax, take a sufficiently large piece and warm it. Then make an impression of the object, being sure to moisten the metal before it is pressed into the wax. When cold, gently tap the reverse of the wax and the metal will fall out. Plaster of Paris and water may be poured di- rectly into this mold. This method will give a perfect replica in the metal, and a number of copies can be easily prepared.

Fixing Fluid for Charcoal Drawings

A fixing fluid for charcoal drawings is prepared by dissolving beeswax in spirits of turpentine. This solution must be applied to the back of the paper.

Hardening Plaster Casts

Casts made of plaster of Paris can be hardened by soaking them in a so- lution made by dissolving one part of alum in six parts of hot water. A very small cast should be allowed to stay in the alum water for at least an hour and larger casts for several days or a week.

Hardener for Paper Ornaments

Paper ornaments, boxes, and novel- ties can be hardened and strengthened by painting them with boiled linseed oil. This treatment should be repeated until the oil will no longer penetrate. The drying may be hastened by placing the paper articles in a moderately warm oven, but care should be taken not to heat them to too high a temperature. Carpenter's glue, prepared by dissolving it in water, draining off the excess water, dissolving the resulting mass with heat, and adding acetic acid in such a quantity that the glue will remain fluid can also be used.

Hardener for Plaster of Paris

Carpenter's glue diluted with twice its usual amount of water, forms an efficient hardener for use with plaster of Paris.

Varnish for Drawings

Coat the drawings with collodion to which stearic acid has been added.

#1—Collodion .... 100 cc.
    Stearine .... 20 gm.

The solution is flowed over the drawings while they are tacked down. Allow to dry and make another application to the back of the drawing in the same manner. This will prevent the drawing from curling up, which is usually caused by a greater tension pulling the paper fibers together on one side than the other side.

#2—Canada Balsam .... 1 oz.
    Turpentine .... 8 "
    Dissolve.

Show Bottles

These formulas have been used at various times for filling the glass globes seen in drug store windows. As such colored solutions are often desired for show purposes, making glass tubing visible, to attract attention, etc., the following formulas are given. Use distilled water for exceptionally clear liquids:

Green:
  #1—Copper sulphate ..... 2 oz.
     Salt (not iodized)... 4 "
     Water .... 1 pt.

  #2—Copper sulphate .... 3 gm.
     Hydrochloric acid ... 4.5 "
     Water ....450 cc.
Red:
     Potassium iodide ... 7.5 gm.
     Iodine .... 7.5 "
     Hydrochloric acid ... 60 "
     Water ....4500 cc.
Pink:
     Cobalt nitrate or chloride .... 1 oz.
     Water .... ½ gal.
     Add ammonia water drop by drop until a clear pink solution is formed.
Blue:
  #1—Copper sulphate ..... 48 gm.
     Sulphuric acid ...... ·6 "
     Water ....450 cc.

  #2—Sulphate of Copper.. 28 parts
     Alum .... 28 "
     Sulphuric acid .... 26 "
     Distilled water ......950 "

Dissolve the alum and blue vitriol in the water, carefully add the sulphuric acid, and filter if necessary.

Yellow: Use a solution of potassium chromate or potassium dichromate.

Artificial Snow Paint

Flaked mica, such as is sold as "Christmas tree snow," is mixed with a thin clear varnish, a lacquer, or a dilute solution of celluloid dissolved in amyl acetate or acetone. This varnish, when applied to objects, dries and leaves the mica in shiny plates which reflect the light in many directions. Ornamental objects coated with this mica-lacquer can be used as Christmas tree decorations.

Another method that requires more

time to apply is to coat the articles with clear varnish, or lacquer, and while the varnish or lacquer is sticky, sift the pulverized mica upon the varnish, to which it adheres. If a base of precipitated chalk, zinc white, whiting, or other white pigment is first applied, using a varnish or glue adhesive, the mica will then resemble deep snow. The mica can be sifted on top of this, after giving the white pigment another coating of adhesive.

A paint spray gun can be used to apply the adhesive varnish, which of course must be thinned out with an appropriate solvent to enable it to flow through the nozzle.

Frosting or Etching Glass

To make frostwork on glass dissolve a small quantity of dextrine in strong epsom salt solution, sulphate of zinc or any other readily crystallizing salt; filter the solution through white blotting paper and coat glass panes uniformly thin with the clear filtrate, using a fine, broad brush; leave them lying in a horizontal position.

As the water slowly evaporates handsome crystalline patterns, closely resembling frostwork, will develop on the glass panes, which adhere so firmly to the glass that they will not rub off easily. As a fixative, use shellac or thin spar varnish.

To write on glass mix in a lead dish 30 parts of ammonium fluoride, 15 parts of water and 6 parts of sulphuric acid; warm, and add, after cooling, 6 parts of strong hydrofluoric acid and 1 to 2 parts of gum arabic in solution. Steel pens or goose quills may be used to do the writing.

#1—Ammonium fluoride, 1 part; barium sulphate, 3 parts; water, enough to make a paste. This is made into a semi-liquid mixture, and may be applied with a common pen.

#2—To obtain mat designs on glass, take sodium fluoride, 35 parts; potassium sulphate, 7 parts; zinc chloride, 15 parts; hydrochloric acid, 65 parts; water, 1,000 parts. Dissolve the sodium fluoride and the potassium sulphate in half the water; dissolve the zinc chloride in the remaining water and add the hydrochloric acid. Preserve these two solutions separately. For use, mix a little of each solution and use as an ink.

#3—Sodium fluoride, 1 oz.; glacial acetic acid, 4 cc.; water, $1\frac{1}{2}$ pints. Dissolve the sodium fluoride in water and add the acetic acid. The article to be etched is first coated with etching varnish, which is scratched off where a pattern is desired, and then immersed in the solution. The fluid is sometimes applied by a rubber stamp.

#4—Ammonium fluoride, barium sulphate, hydrofluoric acid, enough to make a paste.

#5—Shellac .... 2 parts
      Alcohol .... 15 "
      Borax .... 3 "
      Water .... 5 "

Easter egg dye sufficient to color. Dissolve the shellac in the alcohol, the borax in the water and mix. This solution can be used to write on glass.

Frosted Appearance on Glass

Dissolve 1 oz. of gum arabic in 1 qt. of water. Then add Rochelle salts until the water will dissolve no more. Let stand for 12 hours in a cool place and filter. Clean the glass, lay it flat and flow on the solution. When dry, varnish with a thin spar varnish.

Chipped Effect on Glass

Dissolve glue in water. Heat, using small flame. While hot, add 1 oz. of alum for each pound of glue. Apply this glue to the glass. In a half hour, apply a second coat. Allow to harden for 24 hours. Place the glass in an oven at a temperature of about 100° F.

Allow to remain for a few hours and remove. The glue will detach itself, removing particles of glass.

Etching Aluminum

A dilute solution of hydrochloric acid, one part of acid in one or two parts of water, etches aluminum rapidly. For slow etching, dilute the acid with five parts of water. Heat the metal and cool it with molten wax. When this is cold, scratch on the design or lettering, cutting right through the wax film to the metal. Apply the solution and when the metal has been etched deeply enough, wash thoroughly with water and remove the wax with boiling water.

Enamel Solutions

#1—Feldspar .... 60 lb.
    Quartz .... 52 "
    Borax .... 80 "
    Fluorspar .... 8 "
    Soda ash .... 20 "
    Calcspar .... 8 "
    Saltpeter .... 8 oz.
    Cobaltic oxide .... 7 "
    Manganese dioxide .... 14 "

The above is ground, and when being added to the ball mill, 9% of clay is incorporated.

#2—Feldspar .... 56 lb.
    Quartz .... 40 "
    Soda ash .... 20 "
    Borax .... 60 "
    Saltpeter .... 9 "
    Fluorspar .... 12 "
    Manganese oxide ...... 2 "
    Cobalt oxide .... 8 oz.

Use 10% clay on introducing into ball mill.

White Enamel Powder

#1—Boracic acid powder ... 12 lb.
    Quartz .... 40 "
    Cryolite .... 18 "
    Red lead (minium).... 14 "
    Soda ash ....2½ "
    Saltpeter ....1¼ "

Just as the above mixture is being ground in the mill, 10 lb. of stannic (tin) oxide are added to every 100 lb. of the above batch.

#2—Powdered glass .... 30 parts
    Tin oxide .... 6 "
    White arsenic .... 2 "
    Borax .... 6 "

Green Enamel

#1—Quartz .... 52 lb.
    Feldspar .... 30 "
    Borax .... 65 "
    Soda ash .... 20 "
    Saltpeter .... 12 "
    Fluorspar .... 15 "
    Copper oxide black..... 12 "

Three per cent of white clay is also added when grinding.

#2—Chromic oxide .... 4 parts
    Borax .... 10 "
    Glass .... 9 "
    Lead carbonate .... 9 "
    Cobalt oxide .... 2 "
    Tin oxide .... 1 "

Red Enamel

#1—Quartz .... 5 lb. 6 oz.
    Feldspar .... 12 "
    Boric acid .... 8 "
    Red lead .... 14 "
    Cryolite .... 2 "
    Soda ash .... 4 "
    Potassium carbonate.. 4 "
    Tin oxide .... 2 "
    Iron oxide (red).....3½ "
    Magnesium carbonate 2 oz.

#2—Mosaic gold .... 65 parts
    Glass .... 30 "
    Borax .... 4 "

Yellow Enamel

#1—Feldspar .... 15 lb.
    Quartz .... 23 "
    Sand .... 35 "
    Boric acid .... 48 "
    Cryolite .... 23 "
    Minium ....160 "

Saltpeter ....1½ lb.
Magnesium carbonate... 10 oz.
Soda ash .... 14 lb.
Tin oxide .... 20 "
Antimony oxide .... 21 "

#2—Lead chromate .... 1 part
Flint .... 1 "
Borax .... ¼ "
Red lead ....2¾ "

#3—Uranium oxide .... 1 part
Red lead ....4½ "
White glass .... 1 "
Flint (quartz) ....1½ "

Dark Blue Ground Coat

Feldspar .... 120 lb.
Borax .... 80 "
Quartz .... 72 "
Cryolite .... 30 "
Saltpeter .... 7 "
Cobalt oxide .... 7½ "
Manganese dioxide.... 1 "

Four per cent clay is added to the above when charging the mill.

Black Ground Coat

Feldspar .... 35 lb.
Borax .... 75 "
Quartz .... 60 "
Soda ash .... 27 "
Fluorspar .... 15 "
Potassium nitrate .... 12 "
Manganese oxide ..... 15 "
Cobalt oxide .... 2½ "
Cupric oxide .... 3 "

To every 100 lb. of the above, 9 or 10 lb. of clay is also mixed.

To Color Electric Light Bulbs

#1—Beat the white of an egg to a froth and then mix it with a pint of water. Strain through a cloth and be sure that no bubbles remain on the surface. Clean and polish the light bulbs and then dip them in the solution. Hang up with a string to dry and then dip them again.

#2—Water-glass, syrupy .... 1 part
Water .... 4 "
Easter egg dye to color.

#3—Amyl acetate .... 1 part
Alcohol .... 1 "

#4—To color bulbs red use fuchsine red dye. For blue, use anilin blue. For yellow, use napthol yellow. For violet, use methyl violet, dissolving the dyes in a liquid solvent.

#5—White shellac .... 3 oz.
Powdered rosin .... 1 "
Benzoin .... 1 dr.
Alcohol .... 10 oz.
Anilin dye (any color).. enough

Not good on high wattage lamps.

Applying Transfers

When decorative transfers or decal-comania designs have to be applied on woodwork, furniture, and novelties of any kind, it helps a good deal to use an electric iron which has been allowed to reach a gentle heat. Thin blotting paper should be placed over the transfer. The warmth dries the cement quickly, and the edges do not tend to curl away from the wood.

Plastic Material

A plastic material that is unusually adhesive, dries hard, and can be carved, sandpapered, or colored is made by mixing:

Whiting ....1¼ cup
Linseed oil .... 2 teaspoons
Clear spar varnish...... 3 "
Thick liquid glue....... ¼ pt.

The whole should be thoroughly mixed, which is best done with a spatula or thin bladed knife upon a board or marble slab. The material can be applied with a brush if a bit more linseed oil is added, or with modeling tools if used stiff. A confectioner's icing gun is useful in applying the composition to objects.

The uses of the material are many. Picture frames, lamp stands, shades, turned vases, shade pulls, and other objects of art can be coated with the material, forming ropes, scrolls, beads, crowns, spatter effects, etc. When dry, the material becomes hard and can be colored with lacquer or colored varnishes. For a quick drying material, four hour spar varnish should be used.

Gold or aluminum bronze can be mixed with the plastic material to form the metallic colored effects, or they may be applied to the plastic which has been applied to the object, by a dusting-on process, thus decreasing the amount of metallic powder used.

It is also useful in filling cracks, and building up small pieces of wood work which would require hand carving or delicate fitting.

Another plastic mass can be made from:

White lead .... 16 parts
Fine sawdust .... 4 "
Plaster of Paris .... 20 "
Litharge .... 6 "
Glue, sufficient.

The powders are first mixed together, and enough glue is added to make them into a paste or slurry which is of a rather thin consistency if it is to be applied with a brush, or a stiff body if it is to be molded, or applied with bladed tools.

The sawdust and also part of the white lead and litharge can be replaced by burnt umber or other mineral color if a colored material is desired.

AUTOMOBILES

Sealing Punctured Tires

The preparations used for filling pneumatic tires usually contain one of these five substances:

1. A finely ground fiber, either mineral or vegetable.
2. Water.
3. A material for holding the fibers in suspension.
4. A preservative, this being added when a vegetable fiber or an organic liquid is used.
5. A substance that tends to lower the freezing point of the mixture.

Some of the items used in puncture sealing compounds are: asbestos fibers, flax, wood fibers, mica, cork, moss, leaves, paper pulp, and bran.

Among the liquids used to hold the fibers in suspension are molasses, starch water, dextrine, glucose, glue, water-glass, soap, gum arabic.

The compounds used to lower the freezing point are those universally used in other arts—alcohol, calcium chloride, glycerin, and salt.

Preservatives are boric acid, carbolic acid, formaldehyde, and creosotes.

The actual quantities of the different substances have been found to vary over a wide range in the commercial fillers or sealers, but the following formula should prove to be a good one that will really work:

Place one lb. of glue in three pt. of water and allow to soak for several hours. Heat the water to dissolve the glue. Add one qt. of molasses, and two handfuls of short asbestos fibers or shredded asbestos, and a half teaspoon of carbolic acid or formaldehyde. Then add a pint of alcohol and shake well.

To Deodorize Gasoline

Gasoline (straight) .... 1 qt.
Oil of lavender .... 1 dr.
Potassium dichromate ..... 1 oz.
Sulphuric acid .... 1 "
Water .... 1 qt.

Dissolve the acid in the water, taking care to avoid spattering as the mixture will become hot. When

AUTOMOBILES

warm, add the potassium dichromate and dissolve. Add this oxidizing solution to the gasoline and allow to stand throughout the day, shaking from time to time. Pour off the upper layer of gasoline into another container, add the same amount of water, shake well, and after settling, again pour off the gasoline and wash it with water a second time. The oil of lavender can then be added to the gasoline, and distributed throughout the liquid by shaking.

The sulphuric acid and the potassium dichromate produce chromic acid which removes the unsaturated compounds in the gasoline. Although gasoline cannot be completely deodorized, this operation, together with that of adding a substance which by virtue of its own odor will mask the offending odor, effectively produces the desired result.

Freezing Points of Automobile Radiator Solutions

Freezing Temperature Fahrenheit	Denatured Alcohol	Wood Alcohol	Distilled Glycerin	Ethylene Glycol
20°	15%	12%	22%	16%
10°	25%	20%	32%	25%
0°	30%	29%	40%	32%
—10°	35%	34%	47%	39%
—20°	40%	40%	54%	44%

The percentages above are by volume. Thus, 25 parts by volume of denatured alcohol and 75 parts of water will freeze at 10° F. (22 degrees below the freezing point of water). Ordinary alcohol is denatured alcohol.

The following table gives the freezing points, percentages, and specific gravities of denatured alcohol and glycerin solutions. To ascertain the temperature at which a radiator solution will freeze, determine the specific gravity of a sample, using a sensitive hydrometer or a pycnometer bottle,

and compare the specific gravity values with those of the freezing points. Thus, an alcohol solution having a gravity of .9710, freezes at about 10 degrees F. (22 degrees below freezing, which is 32° F.). For inaccuracies, it is best to add a trifle more of the substances to give ample protection against freezing.

Fahr. Freezing Point	Denatured Alcohol		Glycerin	
	% by Volume	Specific Gravity	% by Volume	Specific Gravity
30°	5	.9928	..	....
20	15	.9811	22	1.058
10	25	.9710	32	1.08
Zero	30	.9654	40	1.1
—10	35	.9591	47	1.115
—20	40	.9518	54	1.14

Storage Battery Solution

The following table gives the percentage of sulphuric acid and water solutions and their specific gravities. The sulphuric acid in batteries should have a gravity of 1.200, or about 31% of sulphuric acid (concentrated) and the rest water. The acid should be poured into the water, very slowly and with stirring. Considerable heat is produced in mixing. The gravity should always be taken when the solution is at room temperature. If the water is poured into the acid, it will float, and probably will be boiled or spattered out.

Auto Top Dressing

Mix a solution of benzol and asphaltum to the consistency of milk and to each pint of the resulting mixture add about two or three tablespoons of linseed oil. The linseed oil is added to make the dressing more flexible.

Automobile Body Polish

#1—Heat 5 lb. of cedar oil in a double boiler and add 4 oz. of paraffin wax and when melted take off the fire and add 1 lb. turpentine.

#2—Benzol .... 1 qt.
    Paraffin oil .... 5 gal.
    Raw linseed oil .... 5 "
    China wood oil .... ½ "
    Kerosene .... 1 qt.
    Oil of cedar .... 4 oz.

Mix oil, linseed and china wood oil together. Mix benzol and kerosene, then add to the first mixture and mix together. Oil of mirbane (nitrobenzene) or oil of citronella can be used instead of the oil of cedar.

#3—Cedar oil .... 1 lb.
    Turpentine .... 1 pt.
    Ammonia water .... 1 "
    Venice turpentine ..... 2 oz.

Dissolve the Venice turpentine in the turpentine and mix with the remainder. Polish with a dry cloth after applying.

Valve Grinding Compound

This compound is prepared with ground emery powder and vaseline, equal parts mixed to a paste. Different grades or finenesses of emery powder can be used for grinding the valves, a coarse powder and vaseline being used to start or grind away the ridges, after which a finer powder is used as a polish.

Windshield Fluid to Prevent Mist

The following produces a liquid that will keep windshields and glass free from moisture and rain. Heat 1½ gal. water to boiling. Add 1½ oz. sodium oleate and 1 oz. glycerin. Boil for five minutes. Place cloth or felt in this and boil for ten minutes. Dry without wringing. The cloth or felt is then ready for use. Moisten glass and rub the wiper across it ONCE. When rain or moisture comes in contact with the glass it runs off in an unbroken film, affording clear visibility.

To Stop Leaks in Radiators

#1—Dilute shellac with its own volume of water. Use one cup of this diluted shellac solution, adding it to the water in the radiator.

#2—Dissolve 2 lb. gum sandarach and 1 lb. gum mastic in one gallon alcohol. Add a few drops oil of sassafras and color with anilin dye. Use about ⅓ pint for each gallon of water in radiator.

#3—Castile soap .... 9 oz.
    Glycerin .... 1 "
    Water .... 8 "

#4—Glycerin .... 1 oz.
    Water .... 5 "
    Ground flaxseed .... ½ "

#5—Glycerin .... 4 oz.
    Alcohol .... 4 "
    Oleic acid .... 2 "

Mix the alcohol with the acid and then add the glycerin.

Hydraulic Brake Fluid

The liquid compressant used in the hydraulic brakes of the modern automobile consists of equal parts of denatured alcohol and castor oil. The alcohol thins the oil and acts as an anti-freeze. The castor oil lubricates the piston and is the fluid through which the pressure is transmitted.

BEVERAGES

Fruit Juices

Fruit juices in concentrated form may be prepared at home in a manner similar to that of making simple grape juice, which consists in pressing and heating the juice to concentrate and sterilize it. Strawberry and red raspberry juices can be concentrated and preserved in this manner, although their flavor is impaired and their color is changed after heating to concentrate and sterilize. Orange and lemon juices cannot be concentrated or sterilized at home. Pineapple juice entails special methods of preserving when home manufacture is attempted. The fruits which can be successfully handled are sour cherries, grapes, red and black currants, blackberries, and black raspberries.

In clarifying fruit juices, the slimy sediment which usually forms when the juice is concentrated or allowed to settle after concentrating is removed by filter paper, but the pores of the filter paper are clogged to such an extent that frequent renewal of the paper is necessary. One effective way in which this time consuming changing of filter papers can be eliminated is to add about one or two per cent of kieselghur, or diatomaceous earth to the juice before filtering. When the juice is filtered, the kieselghur settles upon the filter paper and acts as a protective layer between the pores of the paper and the slimy sediment which is to be filtered out. In this manner the sediment does not clog the pores or minute interstices of the paper and the sediment is removed much more quickly than if the diatomaceous earth were not used.

Freezing in a mechanical refrigerator offers a good method of concentrating small quantities of fruit juices. The cold produced will freeze out some of the water as ice crystals, which are then removed and discarded, the syrupy liquid left being more concentrated than the juice used before freezing.

Ripe Sweet Fruit Wine

Fruit	4 to 6 lb.
Sugar	3 to 5 "
Water	1 gal.
Cream of tartar	1¾ oz.

1½ lb. of raisins can be used instead of a pound of sugar. This recipe is for ripe sweet fruits such as blackberries, apricots, grapes, cherries, gooseberries, currants, strawberries, apples, raspberries, peaches.

Dried Fruit Wine

Dried fruits	5 to 7 lb.
Cream of tartar	½ oz.
Water	1 gal.

The fruit may be raisins, figs, dates, prunes, or mixtures of these.

Black Cherry Wine

Twenty-four pounds of small black cherries, 2 pounds of sugar to each gallon of liquor; bruise the cherries but leave the stones whole, stir well, and let the mixture stand 24 hours, then strain through a sieve, add the sugar, mix again, and stand another 24 hours; pour juice in barrels.

Grape Wine

♯1—Grape juice		1 qt.
Water		3 "
Brown sugar		2½ lb.
♯2—Grape juice		1 gal.
Sugar		1 lb.

Let stand 3 days, skim and to each gallon add 1 lb. sugar. Let stand 3 days, skim and strain and add 1 lb. sugar to every gallon.

Damson Wine

One gallon of boiling water to every 8 pounds of bruised fruit, 2½ pounds of sugar to each gallon of juice. Well bruise the fruit and pour the boiling water on it; let it stand 48 hours. Then strain the mixture into a barrel and put in the sugar.

Ginger Wine

Sugar	9 lb.
Whole bruised ginger	4 oz.
Raisins ......(½ box)	7 "
Lemons cut & sliced	4
Water	3 gal.

Heat all but lemons. Cool and add lemons and then yeast.

Ginger Beer

Cream tartar	2 oz.
Sugar	2 lb.
Ginger powdered	3 oz.
Water	1½ gal.

Boil. When cool add yeast.

Damson Wine

Damsons	10 lb.
Sugar	3 "
Water	1½ gal.

Strawberry Wine

To 1 qt. of strawberry juice add 1 qt. water and 1 lb. sugar; stir well and let it ferment in an open jar. When it has stopped fermenting syphon off, bottle and cap.

Non-Alcoholic Drinks

The following formulas and recipes might be of considerable interest to those who desire to delve a bit into home-made beverages of this class:

Artificial lemonade liquid is made of sugar syrup, 200 parts; tartaric acid, 15 parts; distilled water, 100 parts; lemon oil, tincture of vanilla to suit.

Lemonade powder is made of sodium bicarbonate, 17 dr.; tartaric acid, 2 oz.; sugar, 4 oz.; oil lemon to suit taste.

Effervescent lemonade powder contains sodium bicarbonate, 65 parts; tartaric acid, 60 parts; sugar, 125 parts; lemon oil enough to flavor. Rub in. Dissolve in water.

Concentrated soft drinks consist of both tablets and an emulsion in tubes. The emulsion is made as follows:

Gum tragacanth	1 lb.
Glycerin	4 "
Water	5 qt.

Rub the gum with the glycerin to a smooth paste, add the water and mix well. Incorporate the flavoring oils by thorough agitation, using sufficient flavoring oils to produce the flavor and strength desired.

The tablets are made of:

Citric acid	5 lb.
Tartaric acid	5 "
Sugar XXXX	2 "

One tablet is placed in a glass of water with 5 to 8 drops of the flavored emulsion from the tube. Stir well and add sugar to sweeten. The tablets should be cut to a size to be determined by taste of finished product.

To make lemon beer, take boiling water, 1 gallon; 1 lemon, sliced; 1 oz. of bruised ginger; yeast, 1 teacup; sugar, 1 lb. Let stand 12 to 20 hours and it is ready for use.

Strawberry cordial contains one quart strawberries, 1 lemon, 1 orange, 3 pints water, 1 pound sugar; mash the strawberries through a sieve; add juice of lemon and orange and the water, and work together; let stand 2 hours; put the sugar into a bowl and pour the juice over it, stirring till sugar is dissolved.

The following is used for producing home-made lemonade:

Tartaric acid	1 oz.
Oil of lemon	20 min.
Tincture of curcumi....	1 dr.
Sugar (XXXX)	1 lb.

Mix the tincture and oil with a few ounces of the sugar, then add to the bulk and sift. Add one ounce to a pint of cold water and stir.

Orangeade powder consists of:

#1—XXXX Sugar		14 oz.
	Oil of orange	60 drops
	Baking soda	3½ oz.

The above is the carbonate portion of the whole mixture. For use, take about 145 gr. of the above mixture and dissolve in water, then add either 30 gr. of citric acid or about 32 gr. of tartaric acid, either being finely powdered. The resulting mixture will be effervescing.

#2—Powdered citric acid... 1 lb.
　　Oil of sweet orange.... 2 dr.
　　Azo-orange anilin dye.. 12 gr.

Rub the dye with the oil and then gradually add the acid. Half an ounce should be added to a gallon of water. Sweeten to taste. Orange cake coloring can be used for the dye.

To make artificial lemonade take:
　　Loaf sugar .... 2 lb.
　　Tartaric acid .... ½ oz.
　　Essence of lemon ..... 30 drops
　　Essence of almond..... 20 "

Dissolve the tartaric acid in two pints hot water, add the sugar, and lastly the lemon and almond essence; stir well and cover with cloth, leave until cold. Two teaspoons are used to each glass of water. It can be colored pink by adding confectioner's dye.

For orange syrup use sugar syrup, 1 gal.; citric acid solution, 1 oz.; orange extract, 2 oz. Use 1 oz. to a glass of water.

Cherry kola syrup is made of sugar syrup, 1 gal.; kola extract, 1 oz.; elixir of cocoa, 1 oz.; vanilla extract, 1 oz.; burnt sugar, 4 oz.; wild cherry extract, 1 oz.; cherry coloring, 1 oz.; citric acid solution, 1 oz. Mix and let stand two weeks before using.

Koka kola syrup contains sugar syrup one qt.; burnt sugar, 2 oz.; fluid extract of kola, 1 oz.; elixir of cocoa, 1 oz.; vanilla extract, a teaspoon; extract of cinnamon 10 drops; citric acid solution, 1 oz. Age in wood several weeks before using.

To make blood wine syrup take sugar syrup, 1 gal.; oil of bitter almonds, 2 drops; wild cherry flavor, 2 oz.; clove oil, 3 drops; pure vanilla extract, 20 drops; citric acid solution, 1 oz. Mix and let stand for 10 days and then add cherry coloring to give it a deep red color. Use 1 oz. to a glass of water.

Ginger Wine

　　Sugar .... 19 lb.
　　Raisins .... 9 "
　　Lemons .... 4 "
　　Bruised ginger .... 9 oz.
　　Water .... 17 gal.

Boil 16 lb. of the sugar in the water. Macerate the ginger with the remaining 3 lbs. of sugar, add this to the water and sugar. Then add the 9 lb. of raisins which have been passed through a meat chopper. Add lemons, sliced. When cool add yeast (½ cake) and let stand 3 weeks.

Ginger Beer

　　Ginger, bruised ....1½ lb.
　　Sugar .... 20 "
　　Lemons, sliced .... 1 doz.
　　Honey .... 1 lb.
　　Water .... 17 gal.

Prepare similar to ginger wine, but bottle when mixed.

Package Pop

This old fashioned beverage is made by dissolving the following mixture in 1½ gallons of hot water, and allowing to cool. Yeast is then added and the liquid bottled.

　　Cream of tartar .... 3 oz.
　　Ginger, bruised .... 1 "
　　Sugar .... 24 "
　　Citric acid .... ¼ "

Fruit Punch

　　1 small can crushed pineapple
　　Juice of 4 oranges
　　Juice of 3 lemons
　　2 cups of sugar
　　4 cups hot water
　　1 bottle ginger ale

Prepare a syrup of the water and sugar and boil fifteen minutes, cool, add fruit and ginger ale, add enough ice-water to make three and one-half quarts of punch. This fills eight and one-half water-glasses or twenty-five punch-glasses.

Grape juice lemonade is made of juice of 3 lemons, ⅓ cup sugar, 2 cups grape juice and ice water to make 1 qt. Combine ingredients in the order given. Chill for half an hour. Serve in each glass a thin slice of lemon from which the seeds have been removed. This quantity will serve six water-glasses or eighteen punch-glasses.

Effervescing Beverages

Sparkling raspberry powder:

XXXX sugar	2 lb.
Bicarbonate of soda....	2 oz.
Tartaric acid	2 "
Essence of raspberry...	4 dr.

Rub the essence up with the sugar and mix this with the soda and acid. Pack in air-tight bottles.

Sparkling drink powder:

XXXX sugar	1 lb.
Carbonate of magnesium	3 oz.
Citric acid	1 "
Oil of bitter almonds...	3 drops

Vanilla flavoring, quantity sufficient. Mix the carbonate, sugar and acid and rub in the oil of almonds and sufficient essence of vanilla to give a slight flavor.

Orangeade powder:

Sugar (XXXX)	5 lb.
Citric acid	3 oz.
Oil of orange peel......	⅛ "

Rub the oil up with the sugar and then add coloring if same is to be used. Cake coloring is excellent. Mix in the citric acid last. Use one teaspoon to a glass of water. It should be mixed as wanted. The drink is not effervescent.

To Age Beverages

Suspend a cloth sack containing activated charcoal in the liquid for several weeks. The charcoal will absorb the off odors and eliminate disagreeable tastes.

CARE OF CLOTHING

Waterproofing Cloth

Aluminum acetate has been used for waterproofing cloth, the usual procedure being to immerse the well cleaned material in a solution of aluminum acetate of 4 to 5 degrees Baumé strength. The material is soaked for a period of about twelve hours and then dried in a warm room. The cloth is then introduced into a soap solution made up of about five pounds of soap in 13 gallons of water, the excess liquid wrung out and the cloth then given a bath in a 2% alum solution, followed by drying. This latter process precipitates aluminum stearate into the fibers of the cloth.

Another process, somewhat similar to the one above, consists in first immersing the cloth in a solution of:

White soap chips..........	10 lb.
Dextrine	20 "
Water	16 gal.

To cause thorough solution, the above is heated. After passing the cloth into this first solution, it is hung to drain and while still wet immersed in:

Zinc sulphate (white vitriol)	6 lb.
Dissolved in water..........	9 gal.

The material is then removed after thorough penetration by the second solution, and dried, any coarse precipitated particles being brushed out.

Another method uses the following formula:

Lead acetate (sugar of lead)	1 lb.
Tannic acid	2 oz.
Sodium sulphate (Glauber's salts)	1 "
Alum	10 "
Water	1 gal.

These are the amounts of ingredients required but the procedure is to dissolve the sodium sulphate and the alum in one half of the water; then in the other half of the water dissolve the sugar of lead. Mix the solutions when they have dissolved their respective constituents, and allow the precipitate or cloud to settle. To the clear solution add the tannic acid crystals and the liquid, after solution of the tannin, is filtered through paper and used on the clothing.

The following can also be used on paper or cloth:

Lime	10	parts
Sal soda	10	"
Rosin	27	"

The sal soda is dissolved in half of the water and the lime is formed into lime water by dissolving in the remaining half of the water. The two solutions are then mixed and heated. The rosin is then warmed to melt it and poured very slowly into the heated caustic solution which is produced by the interaction of the soda and the lime. Stir the whole until the rosin is intimately mixed. The product results in a somewhat pasty mass of which one part is taken and dissolved in 10 parts of water and the paper or cloth is immersed therein. Without drying, the cloth or paper is then passed into another solution made by dissolving one part of alum in 10 parts of water, the operation being complete except for drying or ironing out.

Here is still another method by which cloth can be waterproofed:

Dissolve at a moderate heat 35 parts of stearic acid in 850 parts denatured alcohol. Pour the solution on 1100 parts of pulverized alum and heat the whole to a temperature of 98° F. For waterproofing cotton and linen fabrics immerse them in a solution of 1 part of the precipitate which forms from this process dissolved in 100 of water, and then dry them. For silk use 1 part of the precipitate in 200 of water.

Or the following mixture, which somewhat stiffens the fabric, can be used:

Shellac	500	parts
Sandarac gum	175	"
Turpentine	50	"
Castor oil	15	"
Alcohol	2,000	"

Waterproofing Straw Hats

The following simple varnishes, with alcohol as a solvent, will stand moderate dampness, unless prolonged.

#1—Bleached shellac	75	parts
White rosin	15	"
Venice turpentine	15	"
Castor oil	2	"
Alcohol	250	"

#2—Gum sandarac	135 gm.
Gum elemi	45 "
Castor oil	11 "
Rosin, bleached	45 "
Alcohol	1,000 cc. (1 qt.)

#3—White shellac	4 oz.
Gum sandarac	1 "
Gum thus	1 "
Alcohol (denatured)	1 pt.

Waterproofing Shoes

This treatment is especially good when applied to hunting boots, hiking shoes, or golf shoes.

#1—Vaseline, 1 lb., beeswax, two ounces. #2—Neutral wool grease, eight ounces, petrolatum, four ounces, paraffin wax, four ounces.

In each case melt the ingredients together by warming carefully and stir thoroughly. The grease will penetrate better if applied warm, but it should never be hotter than can be borne by the hand. Grease the welt and the edge of the sole thoroughly, as this is where shoes leak most, and impregnate the sole with the grease.

The sole is best waterproofed by letting the shoe stand for 15 minutes in a shallow pan containing enough of the melted waterproofing material to cover the entire sole. Rubber heels must never be allowed to stand in the grease as it softens the rubber.

Use any of the following mixtures which have been melted with the aid of heat. Apply to the shoes:

#1—Neutral wool grease... 8 oz.
  Dark petrolatum ..... 4 "
  Paraffin wax .... 4 "

#2—Petrolatum .... 16 oz.
  Beeswax .... 2 "

#3—Petrolatum .... 8 oz.
  Paraffin wax .... 4 "
  Wool grease .... 4 "
  Crude turpentine gum. 2 "

#4—Tallow .... 12 oz.
  Cod oil .... 4 "

Fireproofing Clothing

The following formulas are said to be used in fireproofing clothing:

#1—Ammonium sulphate .. 27 parts
  Borax .... 3 "
  Boracic acid .... 1 "
  Water .... 200 "

#2—Zinc sulphate .... 1 part
  Epsom salts .... 1 "
  Sal ammoniac .... 1 "

Mix with three times their weight of ammonium hydroxide. Suitable for white cloth only.

#3—Sodium tungstate, 30 parts; borax, 20; wheat or rice starch, 60. The ingredients are mixed with water.

Clothing Cleaners

#1—The following will not burn or explode:

Gasoline .... 2 gal.
Carbon tetrachloride ...... 3 "
Chloroform .... 8 oz.
Methyl salicylate .... 2 "

As the methyl salicylate (artificial oil of wintergreen) is used as an odorant, it can be omitted or substituted by other odoriferous substances.

Apply with sponge or soft cloth, rubbing toward the inside of the spot and not in a circle. When the goods are rubbed with a circular motion a ring of lighter shade is left, no matter what sort of cleaning preparation is used. This point is well to remember in using any cleaning solution. Place a white blotter under the garment to be cleaned. This absorbs the dissolved-out greases.

#2—Ammonia water .... 1 oz.
  Tincture of green soap. 3 "
  Sodium carbonate ..... 2 dr.
  Borax .... 2 "
  Alcohol .... 1 oz.
  Water .... 2 pt.
Mix.

#3—Alcohol .... 1 part
  Acetone .... 1 "
  Aqua ammonia .... 1 "
Shake well.

Straw Hat Cleaner

First use soap and water to remove the grease and dirt, then expose the wet hat in fumes from burning sulphur, or the following procedure can be used:

Mix together equal parts of oxalic acid crystals and flowers of sulphur and dissolve one-half teaspoon of the mixture in half a cup of cold water or simply use the crystals alone dissolved in water. Clean the hat with a soft brush dipped in the solution and dry in the sun. Repeat.

Hats also may be cleaned with peroxide of hydrogen applied with a brush, repeating if necessary. Fuller's earth or powdered magnesia may be used as a dry cleaner. Rub the powder in with a tooth brush, allow it to remain for several days and then brush it off. The dirt will be removed with the cleaning material. Slightly dampened corn meal also may be used. Apply, dry in the sun, and then brush off.

#1—Sodium bisulphite .... 10 parts
    Glycerin .... 5 "
    Alcohol .... 10 "
    Water .... 75 "

Lay aside in a damp place and then apply.

#2—Citric acid .... 2 parts
    Water .... 40 "

Shoe Polish

#1—Dark yellow wax ..... 1 oz.
    Oil of turpentine....... 3 "
    Palm oil .... 1 "
    Oil of mirbane........ 15 min.

Melt the wax and oil together; add the turpentine and when nearly cool, the oil of mirbane. This makes a tan polish. The oil of mirbane is used as a scenting material, and is also known as nitrobenzene.

#2—First use a cleaner, or mild bleacher which is composed of:

Gum tragacanth .... 2 dr.
Oxalic acid .... 3 "
Water .... 32 oz.

Mix and dissolve. It should be colored yellowish with anilin yellow, saffron, turmeric, etc.

Then for the polish use:

Yellow wax .... 4 oz.
Linseed oil, raw.......... 6 "
Oil of turpentine......... 20 "
Soap (laundry yellow).... 2½ "
Water, hot .... 28 "

Melt the wax on a low fire. Then add the oils, and then beat in the water in which the soap has been dissolved.

#3—Wax paraffin .... 1 part
    Stearic acid .... 2 "
    Linseed oil .... 1 "
    Turpentine .... 6 "
    Soap (brown) .... 1 "
    Water .... 10 "

Melt the wax and stearic acid and the oil. Then incorporate the soap dissolved in the water. Beat well. Add oil of mirbane if desired.

#4—Yellow wax .... 1 oz.
    Palm oil .... 1 "
    Turpentine .... 3 "

#5—Oleic acid .... 1 part
    Yellow soap .... 3 "
    Palm oil .... 1 "

Heat to dissolve.

#6—Yellow wax .... 9 parts
    Turpentine .... 6 "
    Yellow soap .... 2 "
    Hot water .... 3 "

#7—Beeswax .... 2 oz.
    Linseed oil .... 3 "
    Turpentine .... 10 "

Dissolve by heat and add 1¼ ounces yellow soap shavings. Dissolve in 14 ounces of hot water.

For Black Polish

#1—Beeswax .... 1 lb.
    Ceresin .... 1 "
    Carnauba wax .... 6 oz.
    Turpentine .... 3 pt.
    Yellow soap .... 6 oz.
    Oil-soluble black anilin
       dye .... enough to color
    Water ....sufficient

Add the anilin dye, water and soap to the previous ingredients which should be melted on a low fire.

#2—Lampblack .... 1 oz.
    Shellac .... 3 "
    Alcohol .... 1 pt.

Let stand several days before using. Shake before using.

#3—Ozokerite .... 5½ oz.
   Ceresin (yellow) ..... 2 lb.
   Carnauba wax .... 5½ oz.
   Beeswax .... 11 dr.
   Oil of turpentine ..... 4 pt.
   Lampblack .... 2 lb.
   Oil-soluble anilin dye.. ½ dr.

Melt the first four ingredients, add the turpentine and stir well; then thoroughly combine the mixture.

White Shoe Dressing

#1—Zinc white .... 2 oz.
   White shellac .... 3 "
   Borax .... 1 "
   Sugar .... 2 "
   Glycerin .... ½ "
   Water .... 10 "
   Pipe clay .... 3 "

Dissolve the borax in the water and add the shellac and boil until dissolved, take off the fire and add the sugar and glycerin and finally add the pipe clay and stir well, then add the zinc white.

#2—Water .... 136 parts
   Fine pipe clay....... 450 "
   Bleached shellac ..... 136 "
   Borax, powdered .... 70 "
   White soap .... 8 "
   Bluing .... 3 "

Mix as in the previous formula.

#3—Pipe clay .... 1 lb.
   Spanish whiting ...... ½ "
   Zinc white .... 6 oz.
   Precipitated chalk .... 4 "
   Gum arabic .... 2 dr.

Mix the powders and make into a cream with water, then add oil of cedar or oil of cloves to keep the gum from souring.

Carbon Tetrachloride

Most of the solvents prepared by diluting carbon tetrachloride come under the head of cleaning fluids generally designed for small scale home use. The purpose of the dilution in these cases is usually the lowering of the cost per unit volume, so that the diluents are confined almost entirely to benzol, and various grades of naphtha. The object, as a rule, is to have enough carbon tetrachloride present in the mixture to render it non-inflammable, but several so-called safe solvents have been found where the compounder's zeal in lowering costs was evidently greater than his respect for fire hazard.

The addition of these hydrocarbons to carbon tetrachloride does not materially change its corrosive action on metals; such mixtures also have much the same health hazard as does carbon tetrachloride. Cleaning fluids so prepared are no more apt to affect dyes and fabrics than is carbon tetrachloride alone. Claims are sometimes made that these mixtures are actually better solvents than carbon tetrachloride, but carbon tetrachloride may generally be considered a more active solvent than the naphthas.

The principal points to be considered in preparing such a mixture are, first, to have the proportion of carbon tetrachloride sufficiently great that the mixture is free from fire hazard; and, second, to use such a diluent that the mixture will remain non-inflammable throughout its evaporation range. Benzol fulfills this latter requirement to an ideal degree. Its boiling point is very close to that of carbon tetrachloride, and the fact that it is a chemical individual gives it a very narrow distillation range. Mixtures of benzol and carbon tetrachloride, therefore, evaporate without material change in composition.

The principal object in using carbon tetrachloride in cleaning fluids is to reduce or eliminate fire hazard. Since most of the practical diluents are inflammable, there is always some minimum proportion of carbon tetrachloride which must be present to insure non-inflammability. In the case of benzol, this proportion has been found to be 70 volumes of carbon tetrachloride for each 30 volumes of benzol. The mixture, therefore, contains 70% by volume carbon tetrachloride and 30% benzol.—From "Carbon Tetrachloride," Roessler and Hasslacher Chemical Co.

Dry Cleaning

Benzine soap stock, extensively used in dry cleaning, is made by mixing one pound of soft soap or shaved soap with one gallon of benzine (petroleum benzine). This mixture alone is useful in cleaning coat linings and fine fabrics by hand.

An alcohol soap stock is made by mixing 3 parts of the benzine soap stock with one part of denatured alcohol. It is useful where perspiration stains and body greases have soiled the garments. Alcohol-benzine soap stock is a mixture of:

Benzine soap stock......... 1 part
Benzol .... 1 "
Denatured alcohol .... 1 "

A pyridine solution consists of pyridine, 1 part; oleic acid, 9 parts. This is useful for removing stains made by salad or other oils.

Carbon disulphide is effective in removing certain kinds of tars, road oils and stains caused by smoke or imperfect combustion.

Alcoholic oleic solution, which is a mixture of denatured alcohol, 1 part, and oleic acid, 1 part, is useful on leather goods.

Hexalin soap is effective on sugar stains, perspiration stains, food stains, and some paints. Its formula calls for:

Triple distilled oleic acid.... 3 pt.
Hexalin (cyclo hexanol).... 1 qt.
Carbon tetrachloride ...... 1 "

Mix, and add slowly, 10 oz. of strong ammonium hydroxide (28%),

with constant stirring. Then add 1½ pints of water, preferably distilled. This is a dry cleaner's material.

Removing Paint from Clothing

Carbon tetrachloride, benzene, toluene, can be used to loosen the vehicle which, with brushing, will release the pigment which causes the stain.

A solution of carbon tetrachloride, 2 parts, denatured alcohol, 2 parts, triple distilled oleic acid, 1 part, can be used with success by the home cleaner. If the garments are well covered with paint stains, then use the following:

Acetone .... 1 part
Benzol .... 1 "

The above is not to be used on rayon. Benzol is also sold under the name benzene, and is different from benzine.

To Remove Rust Stains

#1—Use the following mixed with a little water:

Cream of tartar.......... 1 part
Oxalic acid .... 1 "
Tin chloride .... ½ "

#2—Wet the material with a solution of 5% sodium sulphide and then wash in water without the use of soap. Then treat the stain with a 5% solution of oxalic acid until the stain is removed and wash in water until the material is entirely free from the chemicals.

#3—Cream of tartar....... 1 lb.
      Oxalic acid .... ½ "

Mix. To use moisten the spot and place some of the powder on it for about ten minutes. Wash thoroughly in clear water.

A 20% solution of hydrofluoric acid also is used to remove rust stains from clothing. The 20% solution is applied to the stain, and after disappearance, is washed away with water, followed with weak ammonia water, and then followed by another washing with water.

Dry Cleaning Gloves

Put the gloves upon a board, make a mixture of fuller's earth and pulverized alum, and apply the powder to both sides of the glove with an ordinary stiff brush. Wipe the powder off, cover the glove with dry bran and brush off.

Removing Stains

Argyrol stains can be removed by applying potassium iodide solution followed by hypo crystals.

Blood stains can be removed in water with ammonia.

Candle drippings are removed with lard and benzol.

Cod liver oil stains are removed with soap dissolved in amyl acetate.

Enamel stains are removed with amyl acetate and acetone.

Fruit stains are removed by pouring boiling water through the garment from a height of several feet. Use peroxide of hydrogen.

Grass stains are removed with ether or soap and alcohol.

Gum stains are removed with carbon tetrachloride, benzol.

To remove ink stains apply hydrogen peroxide and hold in steam issuing from a kettle until yellowish. Repeat. Then apply oxalic acid solution and wash with water. Repeat if needed.

To remove iodine stains use sodium thiosulphate.

Lacquer stains can be removed easily with amyl acetate (banana oil), lacquer thinner.

To remove mercurochrome stains, 1st, boil ¾ hour in soapy water, and, 2nd, apply benzaldehyde, then a 25% hydrochloric acid solution. Rinse thoroughly afterward.

Mildew is removed in one minute with Javelle water, but *not* from silk or wool.

Paint or varnish is removed with carbon tetrachloride, benzol, Stoddard's Solvent, amyl acetate; *not* for Rayon, which should be scrubbed with two parts carbon tetrachloride, two of alcohol, one part of oleic acid.

Perfume can be removed with alcohol.

Perspiration stains are removed with soapy water and hydrogen peroxide.

Scorched stains are removed with potassium permanganate followed by hydrogen peroxide.

Shoe polish stains are removed the same as candle drippings, or use benzol.

Javelle Water

Washing soda	1 lb.
Boiling water	1 qt.
Chloride of lime	½ lb.
Cold water	2 qt.

Dissolve the soda in boiling water. Let this mixture settle and put the clear lime water into the dissolved soda water. Bottle and keep in dark place. Will remove stains from cotton but do not use on silk or wool.

Dyes for Wool

Scarlet: For 50 pounds of wool, use cream of tartar, 1 pound 9 ounces; cochineal, pulverized, 12½ ounces; tin chloride, 8 pounds, dissolved in water. After boiling this dye, enter the goods, work well for 15 minutes, then boil for 1½ hours, slowly agitating the goods while boiling, wash in clean water, and dry in the shade.

Pink: For 60 pounds of goods, take alum, 5 pounds 12 ounces; boil and immerse the goods 50 minutes; then add to the dye powdered cochineal, 1 pound 4 ounces; cream of tartar, 5 pounds; boil and enter the goods while boiling, until the desired color is produced.

Blue: For 1 lb. of goods: Alum, 2½ oz.; cream of tartar, 1½ oz.; water. Boil together, then boil the goods in it for an hour. Prepare some warm water with indigo extract, immerse goods, and boil. Add more indigo if desired.

Green: For 1 lb. of goods: Fustic, 1 lb.; alum, 3½ oz. dissolved in water. Steep the goods until a good yellow is obtained. Remove the fustic, and add extract of indigo a very little at a time, until the desired green is obtained.

Scarlet: For 2 lb. of goods: Well pulverized cochineal, 1 oz.; cream of tartar, 1 oz.; tin chloride, 1 oz. in ½ pt. water. Boil together, then put in the goods for ten minutes, then boil for 1 hour. Stir while boiling. Finally, wash in clear water.

Dyes for Silks

Buff: Boil ¾ lb. of annatto, ½ lb. potassium carbonate in 3 gallons of water. Put the goods in this and let boil for 10 minutes. Stir well. Remove the goods, and put them into cold clear water, and rinse. Dry without wringing.

Green: Take equal quantities of yellow oak and hickory bark, make a strong yellow bath by boiling, and shade to the desired tint by adding a small quantity of extract of indigo.

Black: Take 2 gal. of vinegar and boil with 2 lbs. of iron sulphate, 2 lb. of logwood chips and 2 oz. of chopped nutgalls. Let the mixture boil until it is dark. Drain off the liquor, and boil the goods in this until they are the shade desired. Rinse in water, and dry.

Blue: Dip goods in 1 lb. of iron sulphate in 1 gallon water. Dye the goods afterward in 3 oz. alum, indigo extract (sufficient to produce desired shade), and 1 gal. of water.

Yellow: Boil ½ lb. of oak bark in 1 gallon of water for ½ hour. Strain and add 6 oz. of alum. Dip silk goods in this dye.

Orange: For 40 pounds of goods, take 2 lbs. lead acetate, and 1 gallon boiling water. When cool, enter the goods, and dip for 2 hours, wring them out, make a fresh dye with potassium bichromate, 4 pounds; madder, 1 pound, and immerse until the desired color is secured. The shade may be varied by dipping in lime-water.

Crimson: For 1 lb. of goods: Dip the goods in an alum fixing bath, then in a dye bath of cochineal, 3 oz.; nutgalls, bruised, 2 oz.; cream of tartar, ¼ oz.; water, 1½ gal. Boil together 10 minutes, then allow to cool. When cool put in the goods, boil for 1 hour. Wash and dry.

Dyes for Cotton

Blue: For 5 lb. of goods: Bichromate of potash, ¾ lb., dissolved in boiling water; put in the goods, and dip 2 hours; then take out and rinse. Make a dye with logwood, 4 lb.; dip in this 1 hour, air, and let stand in the dye 3 or 4 hours. Wash and dry.

Green: For 40 pounds of goods, use fustic, 10 pounds; blue vitriol, 10 ounces; soft soap, 2½ quarts; and logwood chips, 1 pound 4 ounces. Soak the logwood overnight and heat twelve hours later, adding the other ingredients. When quite hot it is ready for dyeing; immerse the goods. Different shades may be obtained by allowing the goods to remain in the dye for different lengths of time.

Yellow: For 40 pounds of goods, use sugar of lead, 3 pounds 8 ounces, water, 3 gallons. Dip for several hours. Make a new dye with bichromate of potash, 2 pounds, water, 3 gallons. Dip until the color suits, wring out and dry. Repeat the operation for a deeper yellow.

Crimson: For 50 lbs. of goods. Prepare with 15 lbs. sumach and 10 lbs.

alum. Dye with $6\frac{1}{4}$ lbs. cochineal. Dip for twenty-four hours in the sumach; remove, make up a hot solution of alum; wash in this for 2 or 3 hours; lift; wash in 2 clear waters; then boil the cochineal, add the goods until desired shade is formed, then wash and dry.

Black: Immerse for 24 hrs. in 18 lbs. sumach soaked in water overnight. Then dip in a solution of iron sulphate, 1 pound to a gallon of water. Wash and dry.

Cinnamon or Brown: Immerse in a solution of blue vitriol, 2 ounces, water, 1 gallon, for 15 minutes; then wash in limewater. This will make a beautiful sky blue of much durability. The fabric should next be run through a solution of potassium ferricyanide, 1 ounce, and water, 1 gallon.

Disinfecting Clothes

Clothes worn by a person suffering from or exposed to a contagious disease, or bed linen, may be disinfected previous to washing by immersion in one of the following solutions for one hour:

A 5-per-cent dilution of the commercial solution of formaldehyde (formalin).

A 1-per-cent solution of phenol (pure carbolic acid).

A $\frac{1}{2}$-per-cent solution of liquor cresolis compositus.

Infected clothing may also be readily sterilized by immersing in boiling water for 10 minutes.

Woolen goods may be disinfected by immersing in water maintained at a temperature of 165° F. for 20 minutes. If the goods are then carefully washed and dried, no undue shrinkage of the garments should result and the infectious agents of disease except those due to spore-forming bacteria, such as anthrax or gas gangrene, will have been destroyed.

The person who handles the infected garments should wear some form of apron to protect the clothing, and this apron should be disinfected immediately after the soiled clothes are handled. Also the hands and forearms should be thoroughly scrubbed with soap, water, and a nail brush for 10 minutes by the clock, and thoroughly rinsed in either the phenol solution or the cresolis solution mentioned above or in a 1 to 1,000 solution of bichloride of mercury.

These precautions are necessary in order to prevent the germs on the clothes being carried to the mouth of one handling the clothes or indirectly to the mouths of others.—From Farmers Bull. 1497, U. S. Dept. Agr.

CEMENT

Litharge-Glycerin Cement

A cement valuable for a number of purposes for which ordinary cement would be neither practical nor desirable is that known as litharge-glycerin cement. It is produced by adding to a mixture of six parts of ninety-five per cent pure glycerin and one to three parts water sufficient litharge (PbO) to form a paste of any desired consistency. Some operators omit the water entirely.

The resultant cement forms a chemical compound which, when it sets, becomes of incredible hardness. It hardens rapidly, remaining soft for only about ten minutes. The addition of ten per cent inert matter such as silica, Fuller's earth and iron oxide will delay the setting time considerably and prevent cracking to an extent. These materials have no effect on the cement's final set and strength.

Litharge-glycerin cement will withstand a high degree of combined heat and moisture. Its most conspicuous feature, however, is its resistance to practically all acids, provided they are not of full strength. Its chief use is in paper mills. The acid-resisting properties of litharge-glycerin cement make it valuable for lining the digesters or sulphite liquor tanks, both for cementing the bricks or tile and for the facing or lining.

Another common use of this cement is for forming water-tight connections between iron pipes and porcelain fittings; also for cementing glass aquariums, brass wick holders on lamps, etc.

Where large metal surfaces are to have an exceptionally glossy finish it is useful for filling in any indentations that the glossy finish would make doubly prominent. For this purpose many locomotive tenders are coated with litharge-glycerin cement before the red-lead priming coat is applied. It makes a good foundation for the finishing coat and adheres well.

Stone Cement

Where a cement is desired that has a little elasticity, the two parts of rosin and one part of plaster of Paris cement can be used, also incorporating in it about one-fourth as much paraffin wax as there is plaster of Paris. The wax should be added to the heated batch and worked in while cooling off. The mix can be cast and when ready for use, heated to cause it to work up into a soft consistency. It is then applied to the heated surfaces to be united.

Semi-Plastic Cement

Four oz. of rosin melted with two oz. of beeswax to which a small candle half an inch in diameter has been added makes a good air-tight covering for joints which are not subject to vibration or strain. The rosin and the wax can be stirred with the candle, the latter melting and uniting as the stirring is in progress. This makes a good bottle stopper seal; dip the corks of the bottles into the hot mixture.

Iron Cement

Three parts of fine iron or steel filings mixed with half their weight of sulphur and sal ammoniac will, upon the addition of water, set to a hard mass due to the oxidation or rusting of the iron, accompanied by a reversion to the sulphide. Several drops of alcohol added to the mixture before the water is added will enable the water to be stirred in quite easily; but without this alcohol, the water wets the mass only with difficulty. Standard cements now on the market consist of iron filings with other ingredients such as those above. It is only necessary to use a magnet to attract the iron filings to show that the basic substance is iron. Iron filings taken from about a grindstone or emery wheel, washed free from grease with gasoline and then alcohol, provide excellent material for this cement.

Waterproof Cement

Beeswax .... 1 oz.
Resin .... 3 "
Plaster of Paris............ 5 "

Talc or talcum powder can be substituted in place of plaster of Paris with good results. To make, melt the beeswax and resin in any metal receptacle over fire. When melted, stir in plaster of Paris and stir well until all lumps are taken up. This can be formed in cakes or sticks. Apply to any torn canvas, metal, or wood by melting and either pouring on or applying with brush. It is suitable for aquariums.

Insulating Cement

Rosin, five parts; beeswax and red ochre, of each 1 part; plaster of Paris, ¼ part. A cheaper formula gives rosin, 14 parts; red ochre, 2 parts; plaster of Paris, 1 part.

Acid Proof Cement

The following can be used in cementing metals to concrete, or porcelain, such as sink traps into bowls, stone electroplating tanks, etc.

#1—Powdered asbestos ..... 2 oz.
    Barium sulphate .... 3 "
    Solution potassium silicate .... 2 "

Mix the asbestos and barium and make into a paste with the silicate solution. It is claimed that if ordinary water-glass (sodium silicate solution) is used instead of the potassium silicate solution, the cement will take much longer to harden or set up.

#2—Rosin .... 1 part
    Wax .... 1 "
    Sifted sand .... 2 "

#3—Rosin .... 1 part
    Sulphur .... 1 "
    Fire clay .... 2 "

Molding Cement

The body of this cement is composed of shellac, 5 or 6 parts, with rosin, 2 parts, and fine sawdust or wood flour, 3 parts. The whole is thinned and worked up to the desired brushing or molding consistency with turpentine, 1 part, or as much as is needed to bring about the fluidity of the product desired.

Plaster of Paris Cement

If alum (potassium aluminum sulphate) is mixed with plaster of Paris before adding water, the plaster is modified, producing a plaster composition preferred by many to straight plaster of Paris.

Pitch Cement

Coal or water gas tar pitch when mixed with one-fourth its weight of beeswax and a small amount of tallow yields a product that can be applied while hot, using a brush.

Cementing Paper or Leather to Iron

#1—Flour .... 1 lb.
    Glue .... ¼ "
    Sugar .... ½ "
    Borax .... ½ oz.
    Sal ammoniac .... ½ "
    Alum .... ¼ "

Soak the glue in three pints of water overnight, then mix the flour with one quart of water, and then mix all together and heat to boiling over low fire, then remove.

#2—Starch .... 10 gm.
    Dextrine .... 5 "
    Zinc chloride .... 1 "
    Water .... 50 cc.

Heat until whole thickens.

#3—Dissolve with heat, glue, 20 parts, water, 15 parts. Then add, glacial acetic acid, 5 parts, alum, 5 parts, and heat slowly.

Cement for Iron

Sal ammoniac, pulverized... 1 lb.
Flour of sulphur.......... 2 "
Iron borings .... 80 "

Mix to a paste with water in quantities as required for immediate use.

Heat-resisting Cement

Clay .... 4 parts
Fine iron filings........... 2 "
Manganese dioxide .... 1 "
Salt .... 1 "
Borax .... ½ "

Mix portion with water, apply and heat to harden.

Marble Cement

Rosin .... 4 oz.
Yellow wax .... ½ "

Melt, add plaster of Paris, 2 oz. Heat parts to be joined and apply the cement.

Water-glass Cement

A water-glass cement which will dry quickly and will have a good body, not requiring several applications to build up a mass, even though in the liquid form, can be made from:

Water-glass syrupy .... 5 parts
Precipitated chalk .... 4 "
Zinc white .... 4 "

The cement made in this manner is white, but the addition of umber will give it a characteristic brown color. If umber is used the precipitated chalk should be reduced to an amount equal to the umber, if very heavy coloring is desired.

Sorel's Cement

Mix zinc oxide with half its bulk of fine sand, add a solution of zinc chloride of 1.260 specific gravity, and rub the whole thoroughly together in a mortar. The mixture must be applied at once, as it hardens very quickly.

Waterproof Bichromate Cement

Prepare a flour paste, and allow it to become cold. Prepare a quantity of thin glue, add 10 gr. of potassium dichromate to each gill of glue, bring it to a boiling temperature, and then pour it into the cold paste while stirring. Use warm and expose to strong sunlight afterwards. It is acid resistant.

Rubber Cements

For the preparation of non-inflammable rubber cements, as a solvent for rubber cements for impregnating fabrics, and as a diluent for sulphur chloride in curing rubber, carbon tetrachloride has found extensive use. The non-inflammability of the solvent is especially advantageous.

Rubber cements cannot be made very well by using the vulcanized rubber articles such as inner tubes, soft rubber tubing, or rubber dam, owing to the fact that they have been cured, and solution of the rubber by appropriate solvents is slow. However, for experiment, the following, caoutchouc, gutta percha, gum rubber, unvulcanized rubber, or crepe rubber, should be used. Rubber materials frequently found about the household or laboratory are sometimes suitable for making cements, and these can be used if time is given to allow the solvent thoroughly to soften and dissolve the rubber.

#1—Rubber .... 100 parts
  Rosin .... 10 "
  Shellac .... 8 "

Carbon bisulphide, enough to dissolve and make a cement.

#2—Gutta percha .... 10 parts
  Asphaltum .... 1 "

Dissolve in carbon bisulphide or a mixture of equal parts of carbon bisulphide and carbon tetrachloride.

#3—Rubber .... 2 parts
  Gum mastic .... 7 "
  Chloroform .... 50 "

The mastic is added to the chloroform solution of rubber. Several weeks will be required to effect solution of the rubber.

#4—Dissolve 1 part of sulphur and 3 parts of pure caoutchouc in 6 parts of alcohol and 100 parts of bisulphide of carbon, and evaporate to the consistency of a thin paste. Join the fractured edges with the cement and heat the whole to about 310° F. for several hours.

#5—Asphalt .... 1 part
  Rosin .... 1 "
  Gutta percha .... 4 "
  Carbon disulphide .... 20 "

A vulcanizing solution can be made of:

Sulphur chloride .... 18 gm.
Carbon bisulphide .... 300 cc.
Benzine (petroleum benzine) 400 "

Apply to the rubber cement or rubber articles with a glass rod and allow to remain over night.

Oil-proof Cement

The following cement will be found to produce an impervious layer between joints on gasoline, water or oil lines.

Powdered iron .... 1 part
Portland cement .... 1 "
Litharge .... 1 "

The above is mixed, using as much of each substance, by weight, as the others, and then mix with shellac or water-glass (sodium silicate solution) to make a paste of the required consistency. It becomes hard in about twenty minutes.

China Cement

#1—Glue, 8 oz.; water, 4 oz. Soak four hours, then dissolve on water bath and add 6 oz. acetic acid.

#2—Quicklime, 10 parts; whiting, 100; solution of water-glass, 25. This cement hardens slowly.

#3—Linseed oil .... 3 oz.
     Litharge .... 2 "
     White lead .... 1 "
     Gum copal .... 1 "

#4—White lead .... 10 parts
     Kaolin .... 6 "
     Linseed oil .... 5 "
     Driers .... trace

Warm the oil and mix in the other ingredients.

#5—Manganese dioxide ... 8 parts
     Zinc white (oxide of
       zinc) .... 10 "
     Water-glass solution .. 2 "

This cement hardens in a short time. It can be used on stoves, furnaces, etc., as it will withstand heat.

#6—Stir plaster of Paris into a thick solution of gum arabic till it becomes a viscous paste. Apply with brush to broken edge and press the parts tightly together.

Metal Cement

The formula below is intended to be used only for light metals where a strain is not present. It is not adapted to unite sheets of metal if they are to be united at their edges, by means of lapping.

Gum copal .... 1 oz.
Boiled linseed oil .... 2 "
Dry white lead............ 1 "
Litharge .... 2 "

Boil the linseed oil and copal together until dissolved, mix the white lead and litharge and stir into the oil-gum mixture. Apply warm to the parts to be mended. The cement can also be used to affix metal rods in holes in cement, porcelain, stove, or wood.

Jewellers' Cement

Gelatin .... 50 parts
Mastic varnish .... 25 "

Dissolve the gelatin in a small amount of water and alcohol. The mastic varnish is prepared by pouring alcohol over finely-powdered mastic and dissolving this in as small a quantity of alcohol as possible. The two solutions are then mixed together, stirring well.

Cement for Rubber Articles

The following is Chatterton's Compound and is used in cementing rubber articles together. It is a good insulator and can be used as a plastic insulation. It is warmed for use. It is made by heating the following: if vulcanized rubber be used, the heating will require considerable time.

Stockholm tar	1 part	
Rosin	1 "	
Rubber in shreds	3 "	

Dental Cement

Mix strong syrupy phosphoric acid with aluminum phosphate by heating. For use, mix with oxide of zinc, to the consistency of putty. The cement sets in two minutes.

Zinc amalgam consists of pure zinc filings combined with twice their weight of mercury, a gentle heat being employed to cause amalgamation. It is best applied as soon as made. Its color is gray, and it is said to be effective and durable.

Another dental cement is made of powdered glass, 5 parts; borax, 4 parts; silicic acid, 8 parts; zinc oxide, 200 parts. Powder very finely, and mix; tint with a small quantity of golden ocher or manganese. The compound, mixed, before use, with concentrated, syrupy zinc chloride solution, soon becomes as hard as marble, and constitutes a very durable tooth cement.

The following is Evan's Dental Cement, the color of which is said to be intermediate between that of silver and tin and does not easily darken.

Pure tin	2 parts	
Cadmium	1 "	
Beeswax	1 "	

The above is melted together in a porcelain crucible at a temperature not exceeding 600° F. The alloy is then cast into thin sticks, and then filed to procure shavings and small slivers of the metal. These are mixed with pure mercury to form an amalgam and palmed or triturated to cause thorough amalgamation. The excess of mercury is squeezed out, preferably through chamois, and the amalgam then applied immediately.

Transparent Cement

If the handles of certain kinds of tooth brushes are dissolved in amyl acetate, often called banana oil, or pear oil, a transparent cement results which has many uses. Only those tooth brushes should be used which have the transparent handle. A small handle of a child's size of brush will dissolve, accompanied first with intense swelling, in about two ounces of amyl acetate, finally forming a very viscous liquid which can be thinned with more of the solvent. Several coats of this transparent cement need to be applied to the objects before a coating of sufficient strength and protection is produced. It can be applied with a knife or brushed on like varnish. Alcohol, if allowed to come into contact with the cement, turns it white. The color of the tooth brush used will have no result on the resulting cement. It is used to protect maps, tables, blue prints, charts, etc. which are constantly being referred to and during which operation the finger is traced across the paper.

The following cement has been used to cement small specimens to microscope slides, or cementing covers over specimens.

#1—Dissolve, in the cold, gum arabic 2 gr., water 1 oz., then add glacial acetic acid 3 minims, and then the least possible amount of sugar. Filter through filter paper and repeat the operation in a few weeks. This cement has been found to stand the test of use for many years, being quite unaffected by the balsam used in microscopy, is also invisible, even under the highest powers of magnification.

#2—White dextrine	6 oz.	
Dilute acetic acid	1 "	
Oil of cloves	10 drops	
Glycerin	1 oz.	
Water	16 "	

Mix the dextrine thoroughly with 6 oz. of cold water, add 8 oz. of boiling water, boil 5 minutes, stirring constantly; add hot water sufficient to make 14 oz. When it is cold add the acetic acid, oil of cloves and glycerin. The oil must be thoroughly mixed with the paste.

Casein Cement

#1—Water-glass and casein cement for glass and porcelain. Casein 10 parts, solution of water-glass 60. To use, make into a paste with water and apply to the edges, binding the article together while drying. Care should be taken not to make the paste too thick or lumpy as this prevents a proper union of the edges. The cement must be applied as quickly as possible.

#2—Casein, in powder.... 5 oz.
    Quicklime, in powder. 1 "
    Camphor, in powder. 120 gm.

Mix. This powder to be made into a cream with sufficient water before using.

#3—Washed sifted sand.... 10 parts
    Casein .... 8 "
    Slaked lime .... 10 "

Mix with water. Allow to stand 15 minutes and then apply.

#4—A solution of casein in a concentrated aqueous solution of borax, made with cold water, makes a very tenacious cement. Or: Casein, in powder, 2 oz.; borax, in powder, 1 oz. Mix. Make into a paste with water when required.

#5—Sodium hydroxide .... $\frac{1}{2}$ oz.
    Water .... 4 "

The above solution is made and heated. While hot, dry casein is added to the mixture with stirring and heating, until no more will dissolve. Cool and then mix in $\frac{1}{2}$ oz. of powdered potassium dichromate. The cement is then placed in tightly stoppered bottles and used as desired.

Cement for Turning Lathe

The following cement is useful in mounting small irregular shaped objects to face plates, for turning in the lathe. The parts are mounted on the face plate by heating the cement and allowing to become cold. Heating likewise is used in removing the work, which can be cleaned of the cement by using alcohol, turpentine, gasoline, carbon tetrachloride or other solvent.

#1—Rosin .... 1 lb.
    Pitch .... $\frac{1}{4}$ "
    Whiting .... $\frac{1}{4}$ "

The whole is heated at a gentle heat, stirring to make good admixture.

#2—Rosin .... 1 lb.
    Beeswax .... 2 oz.

To Cement Wood to Metal

Lead acetate .... 50 gm.
Alum .... 5 "
Water .... 150 cc.
    Dissolve.
Gum arabic .... 8 gm.
Water .... 1000 cc.

Stir about 250 gm. of flour into the gum arabic solution and boil the mixture. The lead acetate-alum solution is then added to the mass and the whole boiled until the desired consistency is produced. The addition of water will serve to make the adhesive somewhat thinner.

Cement to Be Applied Hot

#1—If one part of plaster of Paris and two parts rosin are mixed, by warming the rosin to liquefy it, the resulting mixture will bind stone work or marble statuary. The parts to be cemented are heated, if possible, to drive out moisture and air. The cement is applied hot and the pieces pressed firmly together.

#2—Flake shellac, melted with the aid of heat, is smeared on the surfaces to be united. These should be heated so the melted shellac will flow freely and enter all crevices. When the surfaces are applied to each other the excess shellac is extruded and when cold can be removed with a scraper. Care should be taken not to use too much cement. Stone masons use this for outdoor work.

Aquarium Cement

This puttylike cement has had wide application in the making of aquariums of the type where angle iron is used. Equal parts of white sand, sifted fine, plaster of Paris and litharge are taken and well mixed. The sand should be washed with a strong stream of water and dried before mixing. Mix the three basic substances well and then incorporate rosin with the whole, using about one-third the amount of rosin as the amount of sand taken. The whole will keep without changing if placed in a well stoppered bottle. When required for use, linseed oil is added to the mixture so that a puttylike mass is obtained. Japan driers can be added to hasten the hardening of the oil, and boiled linseed oil, if taken, will also result in a product that will set quickly. Allow the cement to stand for several days after using, and before the fish are placed in the aquarium, test by filling with water and then make several changes of water before it is finally put into service.

Other aquarium cements are:

#1—Litharge .... 1 oz.
    Fine white sand...... 1 "
    Plaster of Paris...... 1 "
    Powdered rosin ..... 3½ lb.
    Spar varnish to make stiff.

#2—Take equal parts of flowers of sulphur, ammonium chloride, and iron filings, and mix thoroughly with boiled linseed oil. Finally, add enough white lead to form a thin paste.

#3—Powdered graphite .... 6 parts
    Slaked lime .... 3 "
    Barium sulphate .... 8 "
    Spar varnish .... 7 "

#4—Mix equal parts of white and red lead with a little linseed oil and Japan driers.

Pliant Cement

The following is from The Chemist-Analyst:

The following formula gives a cement which is satisfactory as an adhesive in making gas-tight joints or in uniting two objects. It can be used on various substances. In no instance has it failed to adhere firmly if the surfaces were moderately dry. It appears not to be affected by chemical reagents in moderate concentrations.

Asphalt .... 1 part
Rosin .... 6 "
Rubber .... 3 "
Turpentine .... 1 "

An old inner tube from an auto tire serves as a satisfactory source of rubber. Cut it into narrow strips. Mix the rosin and asphalt and heat with a small flame until melted and then add the rubber. Heat the mass at as low a temperature as possible and still keep it fluid, until the rubber is nearly all melted. This should require two or three hours. The turpentine is then added and the mixture is heated two or three hours more; or until the mass becomes homogeneous. It should be stirred at intervals of fifteen to thirty minutes.

A satisfactory amount of the cement is made up as follows:

Asphalt .... 25 gm.
Rosin .... 150 "
Rubber .... 75 "
Turpentine .... 25 cc.

The materials should be heated in a vessel of about 1 qt. capacity. There is some tendency to froth when the rubber is added. It can be poured into molds made from wooden strips.

The cement is applied by holding in a small gas flame until it liquefies, or catches fire. It is then applied directly. If a gas flame is not available, a candle may be used.

The above formula gives a pliant cement that is somewhat sticky when cold. However, it will not adhere to the fingers when touched. A harder and less pliant cement may be made by increasing the amount of rosin.

Shellac Cement

One of the most useful cements for uniting metals, glass, leather, paper, china, wood, stone, or cloth, is made of flake shellac and oil of pine tar, or oil of cloves. It is easily manufactured at home.

Melt dry flake shellac in a clean tin container, or porcelain evaporating dish, using shellac about equal to the amount of the cement desired. Use a low flame, taking care not to decompose the shellac by a high temperature. The shellac will melt, and while in this condition, the oil of pine tar, or oil of cloves, or oil of cassia (oil of cinnamon cassia) is added. The amount used is not critical, although about one fifth of the amount of shellac should be taken for a trial.

Stir until a thorough admixture has been made, then pour into tin molds to cool. Tobacco cans cut apart will serve nicely. If they are rolled or bent into the shape of troughs, the ends can be closed by small pieces of the same tinned iron.

When the cement is cool, it will be in the form of sticks, and pliable according to the amount of oil used. The amount of oil depends upon the nature of the articles to be cemented. If the items are subject to movement or are not rigid when set up after cementing, then a softer cement should be used, and this should be made with more oil.

To make joints, clean the surfaces to be cemented from grease by washing in alcohol, then heat over a Bunsen or alcohol flame sufficiently to melt the cement (about 140° C.). Then, having spread the cement, heat again until it becomes fluid, press the parts together with a slight sliding motion in order to squeeze out the surplus cement and air bubbles. When cooled the joint is ready for use. If the joints are not successful, do not condemn the material with which they are made; make a new joint, and give a new trial to the cement.

To cement rubber, hard rubber, wood, or ivory to glass or metals, heat the glass or metal to a temperature about 150° C., spread the soft cement, reheat, and press the rubber to the heated part and keep for a few minutes under slight pressure by putting weight on material.

Do not heat cement and spread over a cold surface. The parts will never cement together.

To cement wood to wood, heat some soft cement in an oil or paraffin bath to about 150° C. Heat the wood parts in an ordinary baking oven, kiln, or electric oven to about 160° C., then spread the cement on both parts with a stiff brush and bring the parts together with a slight motion. Reheat for fifteen minutes to 150° C., keeping the parts under slight pressure by a weight or clamps. Withdraw from heat. Pieces of wood cemented in this manner will not separate after being submerged under water.

For accurate turning and milling of small and irregular delicate pieces of metal on the face plate, where clamping should be avoided on account of the danger of springing or bending, heat the face or drill plate to the melting-point of medium cement and spread it on the heated surface from the stick. Place the metal pieces on the plate and let them sag through the cement to the surface of the plate. When cold the material can be worked.

To remove surplus cement from any article, rub it off with alcohol of any kind, or when possible put the material in an alcohol pot. Alcohol dissolves the cement, making a shellac varnish.

Celluloid Cements

These cements can be used for mending celluloid by applying to their edges until the parts have softened, and then squeezing the parts together and allowing them to dry. The solvents can also be used to make celluloid varnishes by dissolving scrap photographic film in them. As celluloid varnishes alone, they are not of much value, as too many coatings need to be applied.

#1—Amyl acetate .... 10 parts
    Celluloid .... 1 "

#2—Celluloid. .... 5 parts
    Amyl acetate .... 10 "
    Acetone .... 16 "
    Ether .... 16 "

#3—Dissolve 1 part of gum camphor in 4 parts of alcohol; dissolve an equal weight of shellac in strong camphor solution. The cement is applied warm.

#4—Celluloid .... 1 part
    Alcohol .... 10 "
    Camphor .... 1 "

#5—Make a solution of 2 parts shellac in 2 parts spirits of camphor and 6 to 8 parts of alcohol.

#6—Celluloid .... 5 parts
    Amyl acetate .... 25 "
    Acetone .... 25 "

#7—Celluloid .... 10 parts
    Ether .... 30 "
    Acetone .... 30 "
    Amyl acetate .... 30 "
    Camphor .... 3 "

Meerschaum Cement

A good cement for mending broken meerschaum pipes is prepared by mixing quicklime (calcium oxide) into a paste with the white of an egg, or dried egg albumen. The parts to be united are smeared with the cement, the pieces pressed tightly together to exude the surplus adhesive, and left a day or two until completely hardened.

Flexible Cements

#1—Shellac .... 5 parts
    Castor oil .... 1 "
    Alcohol .... 15 "

The shellac should be bleached if a colorless product is desired. Ordinary rubbing alcohol can be used as the solvent.

#2—Shellac .... 5 parts
    Castor oil .... 1 "
    Pyrogallic acid .... 1 "
    Alcohol .... 15 "

Add the castor oil to the solution of the remaining three substances.

#3—Lead oxide (litharge).. 1 part
    Castor oil .... 1.5 "
    Alcohol .... 3 "

The lead oxide (litharge) should be heated with the castor oil until combined. To the resulting product is added the alcohol, which may be of the rubbing type.

Skylight Cements

#1—Powdered heavy spar
    (barytes) .... 2 lb.
    Asbestos fibers (short) 3½ "
    Roofing paint .... 1 "

The heavy spar should be finely ground. Ordinary roofing paint can be used in the composition, using more of the paint if the product is too stiff.

#2—Red lead (powder).... 4 lb.
Litharge .... 8 "
White lead (dry)..... 12 "
Linseed oil .... ½ gal.
Varnish .... ½ "

If white lead paste, either soft or hard, is used, then the amount of linseed oil should be decreased proportionately, using the consistency of the paste as a guide in mixing.

Making Concrete

In a concrete mix, cement and water form a paste which, upon hardening, acts as a binder cementing the particles of sand and pebbles together into a permanent mass. The use of too much mixing water thins or dilutes the paste, weakening its cementing qualities. It is important that cement and water be used in proper proportions to get the best results. This is dependent upon the work.

The table given below shows at a glance the proportions of cement, sand, and concrete necessary for efficient construction. The ratios of the three substances used are given by volume. Thus 1:2:3 indicates that for every bag (one cubic foot) of cement, there should be mixed also two cubic feet of sand, and three cubic feet of gravel. The size of the gravel to be used depends upon the type of work.

	Mixture	Maximum Size Stone or Gravel
Building walls above foundation, when stucco finish will not be applied	1:2:4	1½"
Concrete floors	1:2:3½	1½"
Concrete roads and pavements	1:2:3½	2½"
Construction subjected to water pressure, such as reservoirs, tanks	1:2:3	1"
Culverts, dams, small retaining walls	1:2½:4	1½"
Fence posts	1:2:3	½"
Foundations subjected to heavy loading, impact, and vibration; engine beds	1:2:4	2"
Foundations for small engines	1:2½:5	2"
Hotbeds and cold-frames	1:2½:4	1½"
Mass concrete—large retaining walls, heavy foundations and footings	1:3:6	3"
Mass foundations	1:2½:5	3"
Pavement steps	1:2½:4	1½"
Poultry house floors and foundations	1:2:3½	1"
Reinforced concrete walls, floors, beams, columns, designed in combination with steel reinforcing	1:2:4	1"
Septic tanks	1:2:4	1"
Sidewalks	1:2½:4	1½"
Stable and barn floors	1:2:3½	1½"
Steps and stairways	1:2½:4	1"
Storage cellar walls	1:2½:4	1½"
Stucco	1:3:	¼"
Walls above ground	1:2:4	1½"
Walls of pits or basements exposed to moisture	1:2:3	1½"
Watering troughs and tanks	1:2:3	1"
Watertight walls	1:2:3	1½"
Well linings	1:2:3	1"

Putty

This familiar paste which hardens slowly after application is made from whiting (precipitated chalk), white lead, and linseed oil. It can be colored to suit the work, using practically any standard dry color. Common putty hardens as does paint, the linseed oil combines with the oxygen of the air to form its well known but complex oxidation products. When kept for any length of time, keep the putty under about half an inch of linseed oil as hardening will slowly occur throughout the whole mass.

Cement for Roof Flashings

Where sheet metal meets chimneys, or where there are open seams in tin roofs, and a repair is desired without the use of the soldering iron, use white lead and washed and dried sand mixed with as much boiled linseed oil and several drops of driers for a small job. If white lead paste is used, then only a small amount of linseed oil will be required for mixing. The sand acts as a filler, for if the white lead and oil be used without it, the joint will open up.

COSMETICS

Vanishing Cream

One of the simplest formulas for the preparation of cold cream is the following:

Stearic acid	60 gm.
Sodium hydroxide	2 "
Glycerin	60 "
Distilled water	300 cc.

The manner of mixing is perhaps as simple as the ingredients used in the preparation. Melt the stearic acid. This can be accomplished by using a double boiler, or better, a china bowl which is immersed in hot water. By heating the water, the stearic acid placed in the bowl will melt. Stearic acid usually has a melting point of

about 130° F. The acid should not be overheated, and a chemical thermometer (all glass) will enable one to make subsequent batches of cold cream all of the same consistency and pearliness.

After melting the stearic acid, dissolve the sodium hydroxide in about 60 cc. of water and allow to become warm, as in dissolving, heat is formed. The rest of the water should then be added to the caustic solution of soda. The caustic soda should then be poured into the melted stearic acid, stirring while the alkali is being added, and continuing to stir at least five minutes after the cream turns opaque. The glycerin is now added, and the whole batch is stirred until cold. It has been found that stirring, even after the cream has become cold, will develop an increased pearliness in the cream. Stirring should be performed with a wooden spatula, or wooden knife which can be whittled from soft pine. The use of a steel spatula sometimes colors the product. If a perfumed cold cream or vanishing cream is to be desired, the perfume is added with the glycerin. The exact amount of perfume is easily determined by experiment, and is variable because of the different perfumes used, the temperature at which it is added, and the degree of odor which is required. Although sodium hydroxide is sold as lye, household lye should not be used in this preparation. Pellets or sticks of chemically pure sodium hydroxide should be used. They should be kept in bottles securely corked, and should not be handled with the fingers while being weighed out.

A good cold cream or vanishing cream can also be made with sodium carbonate instead of sodium hydroxide. This substance can be handled with perfect safety and it keeps well. To make a cold cream with sodium carbonate, use:

Stearic acid	60 gm.
Sodium carbonate (anhydrous)	4 "
Glycerin	30 cc.
Water (distilled)	330 "

When using sodium carbonate as the saponifying agent in a cold cream, the cream should be stirred, but not whipped. Although whipping produces a pearly cream when sodium hydroxide is used, it will produce a somewhat fluffy and bubbly cream when sodium carbonate is used as the neutralizing agent.

The procedure in using this formula can be carried out by melting the glycerin and the stearic acid together. Dissolve the sodium carbonate in hot water. Add the carbonate solution to the melted mixture of glycerin and stearic acid, and stir. Bubbles of carbon dioxide gas are released, and the stirring should be continued until these no longer come off. If perfume is to be added, this should be incorporated when the last of the bubbles are passing off.

A softer cold cream than the two preceding types can be made by using potassium carbonate as a saponifying agent. A good formula is:

Stearic acid	60 gm.
Potassium carbonate	4 "
Water (distilled)	270 cc.

It is made in the same manner as the sodium carbonate vanishing cream, stirring to release the bubbles of gas which are produced.

The following cream needs no stirring to produce the pearliness so much desired in a cold cream. It is also very stable.

Spermaceti	75 gm.
White paraffin wax	135 "
White vaseline	540 "

These ingredients are warmed until they have become molten and placed in a container which can be heated by immersion in hot water. A hot solution of

Rose water	180 gm.
Borax	12 "
Oil of geranium	20 drops

is then poured into the melted first mixture, and the whole shaken without allowing it to cool. While still warm and limpid it is poured into the containers for dispensing.

Simple Cold Cream

Melt on a water bath, ½ oz. paraffin, 2 oz. lanolin, 7 oz. white petrolatum. Dissolve ½ oz. borax in 3 oz. water and add above while stirring briskly.

Skin Food and Bust Developer

Lanolin	2 oz.
Cold cream	14 "

Mix, using heat if necessary.

Simple Vanishing Cream

Stearic acid	25 gm.
Potassium carbonate	1 "
Water, warm	84 cc.

Dissolve the carbonate in the warm water, melt the stearic acid wax and mix with the carbonate solution. Beat until cold. Perfume and color to suit.

Cold Cream

The following proportions have been suggested, and yield a soft and white cream:

Liquid paraffin (paraffin oil)	61 parts
White beeswax	18 "
Rosewater	20 "
Borax	1 "

Perfume to suit.

The cream is compounded by dissolving the wax in the warmed paraffin and pouring in the borax dissolved in the warmed rosewater, with stirring, the perfume being added as the cream cools, heating while mixing.

As a perfume for cold cream, rose is favored. Genuine attar of roses, in conjunction with the rosewater present, reproduces exactly the odor of roses, but is very expensive. Cheaper synthetic rose-attars are obtainable.

Pink Cold Cream

A pure white is usually regarded as the ideal color for cold cream, but a slightly tinted cream may be obtained by working in a little alkanet or carmine with the cream as it cools. A trace of a suitable red coal-tar dye can also be used.

Corn Starch Cream

Stearic acid	4 oz.
Potassium carbonate	1 "
Corn starch	4 dr.
Glycerin	4 oz.

Water, sufficient quantity.

Mix the acid and potassium carbonate and heat on a water bath until saponified. Mix the starch with one ounce of cold water, add the glycerin, and heat until thoroughly cooked. Now, add the first mixture and four ounces of water, and heat and stir until a heavy smooth mass is obtained. Let it get cold, then beat with egg-beater until light and fluffy. Add suitable perfume.

As a matter of interest and for purposes of comparison, three formulas are shown in tabulated form below, parts being by weight:

Almond oil	47.3	61.0	50.0
Beeswax (white)	7.9	18.0	12.5
Spermaceti	7.9	none	none
Rosewater (undiluted)..	36.8	20.0	25.0
			(dild.)
Borax	none	1.0	1.0
Rose-oil	0.1	0.1	0.1
		(nearly)	
Soft paraffin (white)...	none	none	12.5

In addition to these, there are almost innumerable other formulas, including those in which oils other than almond are employed. Objection has been taken to the use of borax, but

its employment, owing to its saponifying action on the oil or wax, renders the production of the required emulsion extremely simple, a white cream resulting. It helps to preserve the cream, and the amount required is surely too small to be in any way injurious to the skin, especially if the cream is to be a cleansing cream only. Lanolin may be used as an alternative emulsifying agent, but the resulting cream lacks whiteness.

Another Cream

Stearic acid	4 lb. 12 oz.
Glycerin ....8½ lb.	
Witch-hazel	14 pt.
Strong ammonia water..	4 oz. 6 dr.
Alcohol #40	1 pt.
Oil of hyacinth	6 drops
Oil of jasmine (artificial)	4 dr.
Artificial musk (crystal).	20 gr.
Terpinol	2 oz.

Melt the stearic acid on a water bath at low temperature. Heat 2 lb. of glycerin with 12 pints of water to the same temperature; add the ammonia water; and pour slowly into melted stearic acid, with constant stirring. Mix remaining quantity of glycerin and heat to 80° C.; pour this into the first mixture, with constant stirring, continue the beating and stirring for about fifteen minutes. Remove and beat until cold. Alcohol #40 implies alcohol denatured by formula #40.

Liquid Almond Cream

Spermaceti	40 gr.
White wax	40 "
Oil sweet almond.........	1 oz.
Powdered castile soap......	75 gr.
Quince mucilage	2 oz.
Powdered borax	40 gr.
Distilled water	2 oz.
Alcohol #40	1 "
Distilled water to make....	1 pt.

Perfume to suit.

Melt spermaceti, white wax and almond oil in water-bath; dissolve borax and castile soap in 2 oz. hot water; beat gradually with the above; add last quince mucilage and alcohol, then balance of water, and keep on beating.

Quince mucilage is made by taking 1 oz. quince seed and 32 oz. hot water. Mix frequently for 24 hours and then strain through cheese cloth.

The following will give a satisfactory cream:

Spermaceti	6	oz.
White wax	2	"
Sweet almond oil	16	"
Borax	4	dr.
Glycerin	6	oz.
Orange flower water	2	"
Oil of neroli	10	drops
Oil of rose	6	"

Melt the wax, spermaceti and almond oil together at a gentle heat, dissolve the borax in the orange water and glycerin previously mixed; pour the solution, a little at a time, into the melted mixture. Stir the preparation without ceasing until all the solution has been fully incorporated, and a homogeneous product results. Add the essential oils, while whipping. The almond oil may be replaced by cottonseed, or paraffin oil; other perfumes may be used, such as rose water, for the orange flower water.

Greaseless Cream

#1—Stearic acid	4	oz.
Paraffin	½	"
Glycerin	12	"
Strong ammonia (26°)	½	"
Distilled water	16	"
Powdered borax	1	gm.
Concentrated flower oil	7	"

Fill the wooden bucket of an ice-cream freezer with scalding hot water; in the tin bucket, place 4 oz. stearic acid, ½ oz. of paraffin and 12 oz. glycerin; melt these all together by placing the tin bucket in the hot water.

Add to this mixture when dissolved ½ oz. stronger ammonia (26°), and turning the crank, stir for about 10 minutes, or until you have a perfect saponification. Then take 16 oz. warm, distilled water in which you have previously dissolved 15 gr. borax, add to the other mixture, and stir again thoroughly, mixing all together.

Allow this to stand about 24 hours, so it will drop, then add 100 minims of lilac oil and mix this again. Your cream is then ready to box. In warm weather you sometimes have to add more paraffin to make it stiffer. This makes a most excellent cream and guaranteed not to dry out.

#2—Pure stearic acid	18	oz.
Sodium carbonate	2	"
Borax	1	"
Lanolin	5	"
Glycerin	30	"
Water	100	"

Heat the acid, soda, borax, water and glycerin for about one-half hour, then add the lanolin and stir in perfume.

#3—Lemon scented cream is made like formula for greaseless cream, but before making saponification with borax and water, take out ½ oz. water, and dissolve in it ½ dr. citric acid and add this solution while hot to the cream the very last, after the cream is made.

Color yellow, to suit, and perfume with lemon cream oil 6 to 8 oz. to 100 lb.

#4—Mineral oil	1	gal.
Paraffin	1	lb.
White wax	3	"
Borax, powdered	3	oz.
Lukewarm water	1	gal.

Melt the wax and paraffin in mineral oil, dissolve the borax in lukewarm water, and then pour the two together; stirring briskly less than a minute; then perfume with rose oil. Witch-hazel can be used instead of water.

Same formula as previous, but eliminate two oz. of water, before adding the borax to the water; in this water dissolve 4 dr. citric acid. Add the borax to the balance of water, then color the water with R. and F. yellow, twice the shade you desire the cream, as the water and borax solution is only half the bulk. Then make saponification and add the citric acid solution hot. Perfume with 6 to 8 oz. lemon cream oil to one hundred pounds of the cream.

Cocoa Butter Cream

Cocoa butter	16	oz.
Yellow beeswax	½	"
White vaseline	12½	"

Melt cocoa butter and wax by hot water bath, or slow fire, then add vaseline. Perfume to suit, adding as it cools.

Another good cream contains:

Lanolin	1 dr.
Glycerin	1 oz.
White wax	1 "
White vaseline	3 "
Castile soap	½ dr.
Witch-hazel	1 oz.
Oil rose geranium	5 drops
Oil bitter almond	1 "
Terpinol	5 "

Cut the soap as small as you can, and dissolve it in the water by means of heat. Melt the wax on low fire, add the vaseline and lanolin, and when well mixed, put in the soap solution which has been well mixed with the glycerin. This should be added hot. Remove from the fire and stir until cold.

Cleansing Cream

Mineral oil	78	parts
White wax	5	"
Spermaceti	28	"
Trihydroxyethylamine stearate	20	"
Perfume	enough to suit	
Glycerin	4	parts
Water	92	"

The white mineral oil, spermaceti, wax, and TS should be heated to 200° F. Likewise the glycerin and the water should be heated to the same temperature. The glycerin-water solution should then be added to the first heated mixture very slowly, with constant stirring. When the cream begins to cool and set, the perfume is added. The whole is then allowed to stand overnight. The next morning the cream is stirred thoroughly and packaged. This cream is not affected by hot weather, the mineral oil being retained under this condition.

Hand Cleanser and Conditioner

Olive oil	8	parts
Mineral oil (white)	70	"
Trihydroxyethylamine stearate	14	"
Water	70	"
Perfume, enough to suit.		

The oils and the TS are heated to a temperature of 140° F., stirring until homogeneous. The water is then added while still continuing to stir, and while cooling, during which the stirring should not be stopped, the perfume is added. Thicker or thinner creams may be made by varying the amount of water used. This cream is useful in cleaning the hands when water is not available, a small amount of the cream being rubbed into the hands which are then wiped on soft cloth. The dirt, grease and grime are removed in this manner and the skin is left in a soothing, cooling condition, not liable to chapping during wet, cold weather.

Formulas using TS by courtesy of Glyco Products Co., Brooklyn, N. Y.

Almond Cream Lotions

#1—Tragacanth, powder ... 2 dr.
   Borax, powder .... 2 "
   Glycerin .... 5 oz.
   Water .... 27 "
   Oil of bitter almond... 15 "

Triturate the tragacanth with the glycerin to a smooth paste; dissolve the borax and ammonium chloride in a portion of the water; add this solution, the oil, and the remainder of the water to the mucilage. Can be colored with cochineal solution.

#2—Sweet almonds .... 24 oz.
   Rice flour .... 4 "
   Orris root, powder..... 4 "
   White castile soap powder 2 "
   Spermaceti .... ½ "
   Sweet almond oil ...... 2 "
   Oil of rose .... 15 drops
   Oil of bitter almond ... 1 dr.
   Oil of bergamot........ 2 "
   Rose water, sufficient quantity to make consistency desired.

Blanch the almonds in the usual manner, then rub to powder in a mortar, add the rice flour and orris root and beat with enough rose water to make a smooth paste. Melt the spermaceti, add the sweet almond oil and the soap, and with this gradually incorporate the previously prepared mixture. Finally add the volatile oils.

#3—Castile soap, powder... 2 dr.
   Boric acid, powder..... 1 "
   Tragacanth, powder.... 90 gr.
   Glycerin .... 6 oz.
   Water .... 26 "
   Oil of bitter almond... 20 drops

#4—Mineral oil .... 35 oz.
   White wax or beeswax.. 2 "
   Trihydroxyethylamine stearate .... 8 "
   Perfume (almond) .... 1 "
   Water .... 50 "

The oil, wax and TS are heated together to 140° F. and stirred until homogeneous. The water is also heated to 140° F. and run into the mixture, stirring thoroughly. Allow to cool and when the temperature has reached 105° F. add the perfume carefully drop by drop, stirring the mass until the perfume has become thoroughly distributed throughout the whole. Continue to stir until the lotion is cool.

Quince Lotion

Quince seed .... 2½ oz.
Boracic acid .... 1 "
Glycerin .... 4 "
Alcohol (tax-free No. 40) 12 "
Water enough for........ ½ gal.

Soak the quince seed in three pints of water and shake occasionally. Allow to soak at least a day. Then strain, using coffee strainer or cloth, add the boracic acid dissolved in the glycerin, and then add the alcohol. After the mixture has been made, add enough water to make the required one half gallon.

Witch-Hazel Lotion

Quince seed .... ½ oz.
Borax .... 20 gm.
Glycerin .... 2 oz.
Rubbing alcohol .... 2 "
Witch-hazel .... 28 "

Grind the quince seed in the glycerin and witch-hazel and allow to soak overnight. Strain through fine cloth, then add the water in which the borax has been dissolved. Lastly, add the rubbing alcohol.

Massage Cream

#1—Casein .... 8 oz.
    Sodium benzoate ...... 1 "
    Boric acid .... 1 "
    Rose water .... 2 "
    Glycerin .... 2 "
    Tincture orris .... 5 drops

Use enough carmine coloring to produce the shade desired. The glycerin can be increased if a softer paste is desired.

#2—Beeswax .... 1 oz.
    Hard paraffin .... 1 "
    Petroleum jelly, white 1½ "
    Liquid paraffin ..... 5 "
    Water .... 1½ "
    Borax .... 1½ dr.

The following is used for building up the flesh:

    Petroleum jelly, white. 4 oz.
    Beeswax .... 6 dr.
    Lanolin, hydrous....... 1 oz.
    Peach kernel oil....... ½ "

The following casein or milk-curd types are the rolling creams that roll up into little casein rolls during the massaging.

#1—Casein, dried .... 1 dr.
    Boric acid .... 5 gm.
    Glycerin .... 10 min.
    Carmine solution, enough to color
    Oil of bitter almond, enough to scent

#2—Casein, dried .... 30 gm.
    Boric acid .... 2 "
    Glycerin .... 5 cc.
    Water .... 25 "
    Carmine solution, enough to color

#3—Casein .... 2 oz.
    Water .... 7 "
    Liquid ammonia ...... ½ "
    Glycerin .... 1 "
    White petrolatum ..... 3 "
    Perfume as desired

Mix together the casein, water and glycerin, stir in the ammonia, warm to dissipate the ammonia, and when cold beat in the petrolatum.

#4—Stearic acid .... 10.0 gm.
    Sodium carbonate .... 0.5 "
    Glycerin .... 1.5 cc.
    Witch-hazel .... 50.0 gm.
    Distilled water ....100.0 cc.

Melt the stearic acid on the water-bath, add the sodium carbonate dissolved in the glycerin and 5 cc. of hot water. Continue the application of heat with constant stirring; then remove and add the water and then the witch-hazel. Beat while warm with an egg beater and drain from the container in which it is beaten while still warm and free flowing. If excessive drying out of the cream occurs, part of the water can be omitted and an equivalent amount of glycerin added.

#5—Corn starch .... 5 lb.
    Cocoa butter .... 1 "
    Stearic acid .... 6 oz.
    Formaldehyde .... 2 dr.
    Caustic potash .... ½ oz.
    Castile soap .... 5 "
    Water .... 5 gal.

Melt cocoa butter and stearic acid in hot water-bath. Dissolve starch in one gallon hot water; castile soap in 1 pint or more water; dissolve caustic potash in balance of water, adding the formaldehyde. Make saponification with caustic potash solution, then add the starch solution and lastly the soap solution, then add 1 dr. salicylic acid dissolved in alcohol Q. S.

Color; perfume.

Lemon massage cream, same as above, excepting use 6 to 8 oz. lemon cream oil to 100 lb., and color with R. and F. yellow.

Lanolin Cream

#1—Lanolin .... 2 oz.
    Tincture of quillaja ... 1 "
    Gelatin .... ¾ "
    Glycerin .... 4 "
    Water .... 15 "
    Perfume as desired

Dissolve the gelatin in the water by the aid of heat; triturate the wool-fat with the tincture in a warm mortar until emulsified; then add the gelatin and perfume while cooling and beating.

#2—Lanolin .... 2 oz.
  White petrolatum ..... 6 "
  Glycerin .... 4 to 8 "
  Perfume as desired

Casein Massage Cream

The basis of the massage creams that roll into balls or curds when applied to the face is casein, which is obtained from skimmed milk.

A suitable formula for the preparation of a cream is to use any amount of casein desired, rubbing it to a paste with ten percent of its weight of glycerin, adding about 1 or 2 percent of salicylic acid to preserve the whole and keep it from mildewing. Carmine or eosine can be added to the cream to give it a pink or red color.

The casein can be purchased as such, or it can be made from skimmed milk by warming the milk to a temperature of about 100° F. and adding ammonia water (ammonium hydroxide).

This will cause the fat to rise to the top of the liquid and about twenty-four hours later, this can be skimmed off. To the opaque liquid below should then be added acetic acid which will cause the formation of a precipitate of casein. Enough of the acetic acid should be added to give the liquid a strong odor, which should be ascertained after stirring. If not enough acid is added, all of the casein will not be precipitated.

The precipitated casein should then be placed in a fruit or berry strainer, and washed with water to remove the acid which adheres to it. The mass in the straining bag should be squeezed from time to time to allow the washing water to come into contact with every part of the casein. The casein is then dried at a low temperature. If dried hurriedly, hard lumps are formed which can be reduced to a powder only by grinding.

The casein will not necessarily have to be dried if made into a paste with the glycerin after it is washed free from the acetic acid, although the excess water should be squeezed out as much as possible.

The following formula produces a good product.

Skimmed milk .... 1 gal.
Powdered alum .... 1 oz.
Boric acid .... 3 dr.
Glycerin .... 3 oz.
Oil bitter almond.......... 20 drops
Oil rose geranium.......... 1 dr.

The milk is heated to about 100° F. and the alum which has been dissolved in half a gallon of water is then added to the milk, continuing to keep the whole at about 100 degrees. The liquid should not be boiled. After allowing to settle overnight, the top portion is poured off and discarded and the bottom precipitate of casein is stirred with a gallon of water, allowed to settle, and the water poured off. The process is again repeated, thus washing the casein free from alum. The casein is then collected, and strained, and the boric (boracic) acid added to it, followed by the glycerin, and finally the oils which have been dissolved in several ounces of rubbing alcohol. These are intimately mixed with the whole mass. The cream can be tinted with a solution of carmine, made by dissolving carmine powder in a small amount of water that has been made alkaline with ammonia water.

Astringent Lotions

These emollients reduce large pores and excess oiliness of the skin. They usually contain alum, which acts as the astringent principal. They are not difficult to prepare.

#1—Alum .... 1 oz.
    Potassium carbonate ... ¼ "
    Glycerin .... ½ "
    Rose water .... 10 "
    Distilled water enough to make
    1½ pints of total liquid

The water can be replaced partly with witch-hazel.

The following produces a good product:

#2—Alum .... 1 oz.
    Zinc sulphocarbolate ... 1 "
    Boracic acid .... ½ "
    Glycerin .... 1 qt.
    Distilled water ....1½ gal.
    Rubbing alcohol

The dry chemicals are dissolved in the water which should be warm, the glycerin being then added, followed by the rubbing alcohol. If the preparation is to be perfumed, then dissolve the perfume material in the alcohol. The product will not be clear unless it is filtered and intimately mixed.

#3—Boil together 1 quart of water and 2 handfuls of barley until the barley is soft, then strain and add 50 drops of tincture of benzoin.

#4—Distilled witch-hazel... ½ pt.
    Boric acid .... ½ oz.
    Glycerin ....1½ "
    Alcohol, rubbing ...... 3 "
    Perfume to suit
    Distilled water enough
      to make .... 20 "

#5—Zinc sulphocarbolate.... 30 gr.
    Alum .... ¾ oz.
    Borax .... ¾ "
    Glycerin .... ½ "
    Rose water .... 10 "
    Distilled water enough to
    make 20 oz. of lotion

Lotion for Oily Skin

#1—Sponge twice a day with a lotion made of ½ dr. boric acid; ½ oz. of alcohol, and 5½ oz. rose water.

#2—Zinc sulphocarbolate. 30 gr.
    Alcohol .... 4 fluidr.
    Glycerin .... 2 "
    Alum .... 30 gr.
    Orange-flower water.. 2 fluidoz.
    Rose water to make.. 6 "

The alcohol can be rubbing alcohol, or alcohol denatured by formula #40.

Shampoo Paste

Shredded toilet soap....... 50 parts
Potassium carbonate ...... 6 "
Water .... 75 "
Glycerin .... 25 "

Coarsely powder the soap and place it in a suitable vessel. Dissolve the potassium carbonate in the water and add it to the soap. Heat over a water-bath until dissolved, then add the glycerin. When thorough mixture is made, cool a small portion. If this is too stiff, add more water in sufficient quantity to thin to the desired consistency. Thoroughly incorporate and perfume as desired, beating or whipping the perfume into the mass.

Liquid Shampoo

#1—Toilet soap .... 2 oz.
    Glycerin .... 1 "
    Oil of bay........... 5 drops
    Water .... 8 oz.

Heat the soap with the glycerin and water at a low temperature to dissolve, then allow the solution to stand in a cool place. The top liquid may be syphoned or poured off to give a clear liquid. It should be noted that a drop in temperature may cause the shampoo to become opaque. This may be remedied by using more water.

#2—Shredded toilet soap... 4 oz.
  Potassium carbonate ...1⅛ "
  Alcohol (rubbing)...... 1 "
  Water enough to make 1 pint

Heat until thoroughly saponified. Remove from fire. Perfume with oil of rose geranium or oil of lavender while it is solidifying.

#3—Cocoanut oil .... 4 lb.
  Potassium hydroxide...1¼ "
  Alcohol #40 ....1½ pt.
  Glycerin .... 1 "

Dissolve the potassium hydroxide in about one gallon of water and when it has cooled somewhat but is yet still warm, add the warmed cocoanut oil with constant stirring. The amount of hydroxide here is enough to change all the oil to soap, but if when the mass cools, free oil is found floating upon the top, more of potassium hydroxide should be added, but do not exceed the amount as the soap will be prone to contain some free alkali. Allow to cool and to the semi-hard soap formed, add about a gallon of hot water, and then stir in the glycerin and the alcohol, the latter being colored if desired. The alcohol and the water will dissolve the soap. The liquid can then be allowed to settle, and the excess curd be separated, or it can be strained through several thicknesses of cheese cloth.

#4—Shaved castile soap.... 50 parts
  Potassium carbonate .. 6 "
  Water .... 75 "
  Glycerin .... 25 "

Shave the soap and heat it with the potassium carbonate dissolved in the water and then add the glycerin. Remove a portion and cool. If this portion is too stiff, add more water or glycerin, and stir to incorporate.

#5—Shaved castile soap .... 1 oz.
  Potassium carbonate ... 1 dr.
  Borax .... 2 "
  Bay rum .... 1 oz.
  Water .... 2 pt.
  Add bay rum last. Filter.

#6—Potassium carbonate...1½ oz.
  Water .... ½ gal.
  Dissolve and filter, then add
  Glycerin .... 4 oz.
  Alcohol, #40 .... 1 gal.
  Color to suit

For a cheaper preparation, use less alcohol and more water.

#7—Powdered castile soap.. 10 parts
  Potassium carbonate ... 6 "
  Water .... 15 "
  Glycerin .... 5 "

Dissolve the potassium carbonate in the water and add it to the soap. Heat over a water-bath until melted; then add the glycerin. When an even mixture is made, cool a small sample. If this is too firm, add water in sufficient quantity to thin to the desired consistency. Perfume if desired.

#8—Powdered borax .... 1 oz.
  Carbonate potassium ... 1 "
  Powdered camphor .... 20 gr.
  Oil rosemary .... 10 dr.
  Dissolve in 1 qt. of witch-hazel.

#9—Potassium carbonate.... 1 oz.
  Boric acid .... 1 "
  Witch-hazel or water... 1 pt.
  Bay rum .... 1 pt.

#10–Carbonate potash ..... 1 oz.
  Carbonate ammonia ... 90 gm.
  Borax .... 1 oz.
  Tincture green soap.... ½ "
  Bay rum .... 4 "
  Distilled extract witch-
    hazel .... 32 "

Shampoo Cream

#1—Dissolve 4 oz. white soap in 10 oz. water. While hot add ½ oz. glycerin and ½ oz. borax. Scent and color. A fine lathery preparation, that gives good results.

#2—Carbonate potash ..... 2 oz.
Borax .... 2 "
Powdered castile soap... 1 "
Carbonate ammonia ... ½ dr.
Oil neroli .... 20 drops
Mix. Dissolve in 3 pt. of soft water.

#3—Powdered borax ...... 3 oz.
Carbonate soda (dry).. 6 "
Soap bark (fine powder) 3 "
Perfume. Mix. Add above to 1 pt. of water.

#4—Castile soap .... 4 oz.
Water .... 6 "
Dissolve and add:
Potassium carbonate.... 1 oz.
Glycerin .... 2 "
Oil of lemon, several drops

Shampoo Paste

White castile soap shav-
ings .... 2 oz.
Ammonia water .... 2 "
Bay rum .... 1 "
Glycerin .... 1 "
Water .... 12 "
Dissolve the soap in the water by means of heat; when nearly cold stir in the other ingredients. Witch-hazel can be substituted for the water.

Clay Pack for Face

#1—Take 1 lb. Fuller's earth or ka-olin, rub with glycerin and a little water to a paste, then mix with equal parts or more of greaseless cream to desired consistency.

#2—Wales blue clay is also used.

#3—Fuller's earth .... 4 oz.
Hydrogen peroxide .... 4 "
Witch-hazel .... 14 "
Spirits camphor .... ½ "
Tincture of benzoin.... ½ "
Mix and apply as a pack in the usual manner.

#4—Hydrogen peroxide .... 4 oz.
Witch-hazel .... 4 "
Tincture of benzoin.... ½ "
Spirits of camphor..... ½ "
Fuller's earth .... 4 "
Carbolic acid (liquid).. 1 drop

#5—Fuller's earth .... 50 gm.
Glycerin .... 25 "
Borax .... 1 "
Menthol ....0.05 "
Oil of neroli ....0.05 "
Oil of rose ....0.05 "

#6—Magnesium carbonate.. 20 gm.
Gum tragacanth ...... 40 "
Borax .... 30 "
Fuller's earth .... 10 "
Add witch-hazel to make a paste of the whole, the ingredients of which should be finely ground or sifted.

Liquid Face Powder

#1—Prepared chalk .... 2 lb.
English prec. chalk..... 2 "
Zinc oxide .... 8 oz.
Boracic acid .... 2 "

Mix thoroughly and then place in a kettle with half gallon water; boil for 10 minutes. Then pour off the water and add 1 pint glycerin, 2½ gal. water; perfume to suit; pour in bottles, being careful to stir con-stantly. For flesh color, use same for-mula; and color to suit.

#2—Zinc oxide .... 54 gm.
Bismuth oxychloride ... 54 "
Water ....807 cc.
Glycerin .... 67 "
Perfume to suit
Shake before using.

The preparation of good face pow-ders entails the use of snow white ingredients, finely sifted and bolted. If colored powders are to be made, then this requirement should not be adhered to as strictly as if the powder were to be white. The perfumes are added to small portions of the base, usually precipitated chalk or powdered talc (steatite powder), rubbed up and then mixed with the whole. Small amounts of ground violet root are also used in some face powders.

The following is recommended:

#1—Precipitated chalk ....3000 gm.
    Zinc white .... 200 "
    Wheat starch ....1000 "
    Talc powder .... 500 "
    Essence of rose .... 30 "
    Extract of jasmine.... 30 "
    Extract of orange flow-
      ers .... 30 "
    Extract cassia .... 30 "
    Tincture of musk..... 7½ "

#2—Talc powder .... 50 gm.
    Magnesium carbonate.. 50 "
    Zinc white .... 50 "
    Orris oil .... 30 drops
    Rose oil .... 20 "

Rose colored face powder: take 150 gm. of the above powder and tint with ½ gm. of powdered carmine.

#3—Talcum .... 3 oz.
    Powdered orris root.... 5 "
    Corn starch .... 30 "
    Sodium perborate .....2½ "

Tint and perfume if desired.

#4—Rice flour .... 16 oz.
    Talcum powder, finest.. 16 "
    Magnesium carbonate.. 2 "
    Oxide of zinc or per-
      oxide .... 2 "

Perfume with oil of rose or other scent.

#5—Prepared chalk .... 8 lb.
    English prec. chalk.... 7 "
    Carbonate magnesia....1½ "
    Boracic acid .... 4 oz.
    Oxide of zinc .... 1 lb.

Mix, and then add 16 oz. glycerin, then add a thin solution of gum traga-canth.

#6—Powdered talc .... 2 lb.
    Powdered carbonate mag-
      nesia .... 4 oz.
    Powdered boric acid...1½ "

#7—Precipitated chalk ..... 96 gm.
    Zinc oxide .... 76 "
    Talc powder .... 16 "
    Starch powder .... 32 "

The mixture is scented as desired.

Perhaps the simplest face powders are those composed only of rice starch, or merely talc powder, scented.

The following is a simple preparation:

#8—Powdered talc .... 20 gm.
    Magnesium carbonate... 8 "

#9—Starch .... 70 parts
    Talc powder .... 1 "
    Orris root .... 1 "

An inexpensive scent for this powder is rose oil.

Bath Salts

Some of the following compounds have been found satisfactory as bath salts: sal-soda, sodium chloride, epsom salts, trisodium phosphate, sodium carbonate, etc. Large crystals of the substances are generally used, and they are dyed in different colors and perfumed. Oil of paris rose is a common type of perfume for a bath salt. Trisodium phosphate (TSP), sal-soda, and sodium carbonate really have value, as they soften water and lessen the amount of soap needed to produce a lather or remove dirt and grime.

Bath Powders

Several of the bath powders or bath salts appearing on the market have been found by chemical analysis to be either purified table salt in large crystals, or epsom salts, to which perfume such as oil of paris rose, or oil of cedar, and coloring has been added.

The following are four formulas that have been elaborated a bit to produce certain desired effects, usually upon the water and not upon the bather. Use a small palm full to the bath.

#1—Powdered borax .... 1 lb.
    Ammonia muriat ...... 2 oz.
    Synthetic violet .... 2 dr.
    Synthetic heliotrope ... 2 "

#2—Epsom salt .... 20 parts
    Table salt .... 6 "
    Boracic acid .... 1 "
    Baking soda .... 1 "

#3—Effervescent:
    Baking soda .... 9 parts
    Tartaric acid .... 10 "
    Borax .... 6 "

#4—Boracic (boric) acid... 1 lb.
    Borax .... 1 "
    Salt .... 2 oz.
    Baking soda .... 1 lb.

Work the well sifted mixture up with oil of rose, or oil of pine. It is best to work up a small portion of the powder at a time.

Stainless Iodine Ointment

Iodine crystals .... ½ oz.
Oleic acid .... 1 "
Soft paraffin wax......... 11 "

Mix the iodine and oleic acid and heat gently with stirring until combination takes place. Then add the paraffin; stir, and allow the ointment to cool. Lanolin may be used as the basis if preferred. Use a low temperature in mixing.

Ointment for the Skin

#1—Boracic acid .... 8 gm.
    Carbolic acid .... 2 "
    Vaseline .... 1 lb.
    Perfume to suit

Melt the vaseline and then incorporate the boric acid and the carbolic acid crystals and then, as it is cooling, whip in the perfume.

#2—Vaseline .... 1 lb.
    Lanolin .... 4 oz.
    Paraffin wax .... 2 "
    Oil of mustard ....1½ dr.

Melt the paraffin with the vaseline; add the lanolin and mix well. Remove from fire and stir until nearly cold, then add oil of mustard and mix thoroughly. Perfume if desired.

Ointment for All Purposes

#1—White wax .... 4 oz.
    Lard .... 12 "
    Carbolic acid (crystals) ½ "
    Calomel .... ¼ "
    Camphor .... 1 dr.

#2—Oil of sassafras .... 1 oz.
    Oil of wintergreen ..... 1 "
    Oil of tar .... 1 "
    Carbolic acid .... ½ "
    Yellow wax .... 4 "
    Vaseline .... 24 "

Melt the wax, add the vaseline and mix with other ingredients.

#3—Petrolatum .... 12 oz.
    Carbolic acid .... ½ dr.
    Camphor .... 1 "
    Menthol .... 2 "

#4—Vaseline .... 5 lb.
    Oil juniper .... 2 oz.
    Thymol crystals .... 2 "
    Eucalyptol .... 2 "
    Camphor .... 2 "
    Oil wintergreen .... 1 "

#5—Petrolatum .... 1 lb.
    Yellow wax .... 1 oz.
    Camphor .... ½ "
    Solid extract arnica.... 2 dr.
    Menthol .... 10 gm.
    Carbolic acid .... 1 dr.
    Oil wintergreen .... 20 "

Mix.

#6—Petrolatum .... 70 oz.
    Paraffin wax .... 7 "
    Camphor .... 2 "
    Carbolic acid .... 3 "
    Oil wintergreen .... 2 dr.
Mix.

Excessive Perspiration Powder

#1—Salicylic acid .... 1 oz.
    Borax .... 1 "
    Boric acid .... 1 "
    Talcum powder .... 12 "

Mix. Wash the parts with soap and water often and dust well with powder.

#2—Stearic acid .... 30 gm.
    Carbonate of potassium. 2 "
    Glycerin .... 30 "
    Water ....150 "
    Boric acid .... 1 "
    Bicarbonate of soda ... 25 "

Mix gently the water and glycerin, and add the boric acid and stearic acid, and heat slowly, until the acid is completely melted. Boil, then remove from the fire and add to the mixture the carbonate of potassium and bicarbonate of soda dissolved in about ½ oz. of hot water. Add gradually and stir briskly.

#3—Salicylic acid, in fine
    powder .... 1 part
    Boric acid .... 4 "
    Starch .... 4 "
    Talc .... 14 "

Powder all. Mix. The powder may be perfumed.

#4—Salicylic acid .... 10 gm.
    Bismuth subnitrate .... 15 "
    Zinc oleate .... 10 "

This has been recommended against profuse or fetid perspiration.

#5—White wax .... 8 oz.
    Liquid petrolatum ..... 24 "
    Borax ....100 gm.
    Benzoic acid .... 20 "

    Salicylic acid ....400 gm.
    Hot water .... 16 oz.

Dissolve the wax in the heated oil, and then dissolve the borax, the benzoic acid, and the salicylic acid in the water. Mix all, while cooling. Beating vigorously produces a creamy product.

#6—Zinc chloride, chemically
    pure .... 2 gm.
    Water ....100 cc.

Perfume with rose water and color if desired.

Sachet Powder

#1—Powdered orris root.... 1 lb.
    Oil of violet .... 1 oz.

#2—Mix tea leaves, lavender flowers, rose petals, orange and lemon peelings. Add three times their weight of powdered orris root. Keep tightly stoppered.

#3—Powdered orris root ... 4 oz.
    Rose leaves .... 2 "
    Essence of heliotrope... ¼ "

#4—Red rose petals, ground 6 oz.
    Sandalwood, ground....1½ "
    Oil of rose .... ½ dr.
    Oil of rose geranium... ½ "

Nail Polishes

#1—Tin oxide .... 4 dr.
    Oil of rose .... 1 drop
    Carmine, powdered .... 2 gr.

#2—Talcum powder .... 5 dr.
    Tin oxide .... 3 "
    Gum tragacanth ...... 5 gr.
    Glycerin .... 1 dr.

Mix to a paste with the addition of rose water. Tint with carmine or eosine.

Nail Gloss

Amyl acetate .... 7 oz.
Photographic film (washed) ¾ "
    Perfume and color to suit.

Polishing Powder for Finger Nails

#1—Oxide of tin .... 10 oz.
  Prepared chalk .... 4 "
  Fine powdered orris root 1 "

#2—Putty powder (fine)... 4 dr.
  Carmine .... 2 gr.
  Oil of rose .... 1 drop

#3—Tin oxide .... 8 dr.
  Carmine .... ¼ "
  Oil of rose .... 6 drops
  Neroli oil .... 5 "

Nail Polishing Liquid

  Castile soap .... 1 part
  Hot water .... 16 "
  Zinc chloride solution, 10 per cent,
   quantity sufficient

Dissolve the soap in the water and to the solution add the zinc chloride solution until no further precipitation occurs. Let stand overnight; pour off the clear fluid, wash the precipitate well with water, and dry. Carmine may be added if desired to color.

Hand Cleanser

#1—White soap chips...... 1 lb.
  Household ammonia ... 1 oz.
  Turpentine .... 1 "
  Fine pumice stone .... 7 "
  Oil of sassafras...enough to suit

The pumice stone acts as a mild abrasive, and the soap as a colloid to carry away the dirt after it has been removed by the action of the turpentine and the ammonia, the latter saponifying any grease on the hands. Any odor other than that of the sassafras can be used. If finely ground stone dust or sand can be had, it can be used instead of pumice, although the product will then be somewhat harsher on the skin.

#2—Soap chips, 5 lb.; water, 5 gal. Dissolve by boiling, take off the fire and add 2 lb. soda ash and 5 lb. pum-ice stone powder and 1 oz. oil of citronella.

#3—Household ammonia.... 1 pt.
  Water ....,.... 1 "
  Turpentine .... 1 "

Lotion for Sweaty Hands

  This preparation consists of:
  Salicylic acid .... 4 gm.
  Borax .... 4 "
  Boric acid .... 1 "
  Glycerin .... 16 "
  Alcohol .... 16 "

Hand Cleaning Paste

#1—Fine sifted sand ...... 6 oz.
  Silicate of soda (water
   glass) .... 2 "
  Pumice powder .... 1 "
  China clay (kaolin).... 10 "

Mix the whole together and put up in Mason jars for use in the shop, or if to be carried about in the car, pour into tins. Water or even glycerin and water can be added if the paste is too stiff. Wood flour (finely divided wood) can be used as a substitute for the sand, as the sand will sometimes interfere with the proper operation of drainage from sewer systems.

#2—Three bars white soap dissolved in soft water, 1 gal. Slice the soap in fine pieces, and dissolve in the water by the aid of heat. When cool add: Powdered borax, 4 oz.; sodium carbonate, 2 oz.; ammonia water, 1 oz. A little oil of cinnamon, citronella, or sassafras, or a mixture of these, may be added. Stir in a little pumice stone before the paste cools and stir till cool.

Hand Lotion

Place the following in a gallon glass jug:

#1—Liquid petrolatum (par-
        affin oil) .... ½ pt.
     Oil of lavender .... 15 drops
     Oil of bergamot .... 15 "

Place the stopper in the bottle and
roll the mixture about inside of the
jug until the entire inner surface has
become coated. Now add:

     Sodium benzoate ...... 2 dr.
     Powdered gum traga-
        canth .... 1 oz.

Shake thoroughly and add a pint
of water at a time until the quantities make one half a gallon.

The following hand cream, which
contains lanolin, or wool fat, will be
found easy to make by amateurs:

#2—Anhydrous lanolin ..... 65 gm.
     Peach kernel oil .... 20 "
     Water .... 15 cc.

The lanolin is melted and removed
from the source of heat. The peach
kernel oil is then incorporated while
the lanolin is still liquid, and then the
water is added, beating the whole up
to an emulsion. It can be scented if
desired: Ionone, 1 or 2 drops, or the
synthetic ylang-ylang, 2 drops, improves the preparation.

#3—Quince seed .... 4 oz.
     Hot water .... 16 "
     Glycerin .... 32 "
     Witch-hazel ....128 "
     Boric acid .... 6 "
     Extract rose .... 2 "
     Extract violet .... 1 "

Macerate the quince seed in the
hot water; add the glycerin and witch-
hazel in which the boracic acid has
been dissolved. The mixture should
stand for 2 or 3 days, shaking occasionally. It is then strained.

#4—Gum tragacanth ...... 50 gm.
     Shaken up with:
     Alcohol ....100 gm.
     Glycerin ....200 "

The perfume is added at this point,
and with further shaking, 650 cc. of
water is added, the whole then appearing as an emulsion. This type of
lotion is more economical than the
lanolin types.

#5—Water .... 2 qt.
     Powdered gum traga-
        canth .... ⅓ oz.
     Tincture benzoin ...... 1 "

Dissolve the tragacanth in the
water. Pour in the benzoin, and shake.

#6—Glycerin .... 5 oz.
     Rose water .... 1 pt.
     Tincture of cochineal, enough to
        color. Mix.

Depilatories

Depilatories usually contain unslaked lime or an alkaline earth sulphide. The latter decompose when
water is added, yielding hydrogen sulphide gas. Other ingredients such as
orris root and starch act as retarders.
Emollients such as lanolin or other
creamy mixtures act to allay smarting.
The sulphides and the quicklime
should be fresh, otherwise the powders do not remove the hairs. They
should be mixed with water and the
paste applied.

#1—Quicklime .... 3 parts
     Sodium sulphide .... 6 "
     Corn starch .... 2 "
     Orris root powdered.... 1 "

For quicker action:

#2—Quicklime .... 1 part
     Sodium carbonate ..... 2 "
     Lard .... 6 "

Remove after three or four minutes
of application.

#3—Barium sulphide .... 2 oz.
     Zinc oxide .... 1 "
     Flour or starch .... 1 "

Mix and bottle tightly. When desired for use, make into a paste with

a little water and apply to the part from which the hair is to be removed and leave on for ten minutes. Usually one application is enough. If necessary repeat. Use fresh barium sulphide.

It should not be assumed that depilatories will prevent the return or regrowth of the hair it removes. Acting only in a mildly alkaline manner and destroying the hair, depilatories do not penetrate the skin and attack and destroy hair roots. It is for this reason that the hair will grow again, and hence the use of a depilatory is only equal to that of shaving. However, shaving has certain limitations, and a good blade even of the safety type cannot be used on all parts of the body with the ease with which it is applied to the face. Hence, depilatories are used by many.

Solid Hair Gloss

#1—Petrolatum (vaseline).. 8 parts
    Paraffin wax .... 2 "

Gently heat the vaseline and stir in the wax, beating thoroughly. As the mixture is cooling, add any perfume or flower essence as desired.

#2—White wax .... 8 parts
    Paraffin oil .... 7 "
    Vaseline .... 7 "

Perfume as desired.

#3—White petrolatum ..... 1 lb.
    White beeswax .... 1 oz.
    Castor oil .... 3 "
    Paraffin .... 1 "

Liquid Hair Gloss

#1—First soak gum tragacanth by placing a small amount of the gum in water and letting it stand 24 hrs. Vary the amount of water in order to get the consistency that you wish. Regulate amount to suit own consistency. To 1 gal. of this base add 6 oz. glycerin and 1 oz. of boric acid which

has first been dissolved in a small amount of warm water.

#2—Olive oil .... 4 parts
    Glycerin .... 3 "
    Alcohol .... 3 "

Perfume as desired.

#3—Melt 250 parts of lard and 25 parts of white wax at moderate heat; mix with 200 parts of vaseline, add 10 parts of quinine, 15 parts of bergamot oil, 3 parts of lavender oil. Benzoinated lard or lanolin may be added where a thicker preparation is desired for men's hair.

Paste for the Hair

#1—Make a mucilage with gum tragacanth, or flaxseed, or Irish moss, then add 1 oz. boracic acid and 6 oz. glycerin to gallon. Color and perfume to suit.

#2—Vaseline .... 16 oz.
    White wax .... 4 "
    Paraffin .... 4 "
    Borax .... 1 dr.
    Water .... 16 oz.

Melt the wax, paraffin and vaseline, on low fire, dissolve the borax in the water and add all together, continuing to heat until it "soaps up." If it is to be colored, add the color to the water before saponifying. Paraffin can be increased or decreased, according to stiffness desired. Perfume to suit.

Hair Dressings

#1—Water white paraffin oil 32 oz.
    Alkanet root .... ½ "
    Oil of bergamot....... 1 dr.
    Oil of rose.......... 2 drops

The alkanet root should be macerated with the paraffin oil at a low gentle heat, and then filtered or strained through fine cloth, and the perfume oils added afterward.

♯2—Cocoa butter .... 4 oz.
　　White vaseline .... 8 "
　　Lanolin .... 2 "
　　Oil of bergamot ...... 5 drops
　　Oil of rose............ 2 "

Melt all, except the oils, in a double boiler. When cooling, add the oils.

Bay Rum for the Hair

Oil of bay, soluble......... 4 dr.
Alcohol ♯40.......... 1 pint or more
Water .... 7 pt.

Let stand several days, after adding suitable coloring (Evergreen [γ] or R and F is suitable). Then add 1 dram of acetic ether.

To Keep Hair Curled

♯1—Borax .... 1 oz.
　　Gum arabic .... 30 gr.
　　Spirits of camphor..... 6 dr.
　　Water, warm .... 16 oz.

Dissolve. When cool, add the camphor. Wet the hair with above and roll on papers as usual, let dry, unroll, and form into ringlets.

♯2—Paste:
　　Gum arabic .... 1 dr.
　　Borax .... 3 oz.
　　Water .... 1 qt.
　　Spirits of camphor..... 3 oz.

Dissolve the borax and gum in hot water; when nearly cool, add the spirits of camphor. Wet the hair with the above liquid and roll in the usual curlers when retiring at night.

♯3—Liquid:
　　Gum arabic .... 1 oz.
　　Sugar .... 1 "
　　Sodium benzoate ...... 1 dr.
　　Boracic acid .... ½ oz.
　　Rose water .... 1 pt.

Use as above.

Hair Pomade

Vaseline .... 5 lb.
Yellow beeswax .... ½ "
Paraffin wax .... ½ oz.
Castor oil .... 2 "
Perfume to suit

Melt the waxes and castor oil over a low fire. Melt the vaseline in another pan over low fire. When both are liquid pour the first mixture into the second and stir well; add the perfume after removing from fire.

Dandruff Compounds

The usual dandruff compounds contain quinine salts, cantharides, etc. Here are two that are extremely simple to make:

♯1—Boracic acid .... 4 gm.
　　Resorcinol .... 8 "
　　Water .... 120 cc.

The substances are dissolved in water. If a cream is desired, the two chemicals can be mixed with lanolin, or cold cream, or liquid paraffin oil may be used, this also giving a gloss to the hair.

♯2—Resorcinol .... 40 gr.
　　Quinine sulphate ..... 30 "
　　Tincture cantharides... 4 dr.
　　Tincture cayenne ..... 3 "
　　Bay rum .... 4 oz.
　　Alcohol (♯40) .... 8 "
　　Water, preferably dis-
　　　tilled .... 2 qt.

First dissolve the quinine in the bay rum, adding then the resorcinol, tincture of cayenne and cantharides, and then add the alcohol, lastly the water. Oil of rose geranium can be used instead of the bay rum. It should be dissolved, using as much as is required to produce the desired odor, in the alcohol.

Hair Dyes

Black: Two solutions are used, the first consisting of 2.5 gm. of silver nitrate dissolved in about 100 cc. of water, to which is added enough pure ammonium hydroxide (not household ammonia) to cause the precipitate to dissolve, when the ammonia is added to it. This solution is applied to the hair after washing. The solution is allowed to dry on the hair and then a solution of 3 or 4 gm. of pyrogallic acid dissolved in 100 cc. of water is applied. A solution of potassium sulphide (liver of sulphur), 6 or 8 gm. dissolved in 100 cc. of water can also be used as the second solution.

Brown:

Silver nitrate	480 gr.
Copper nitrate	90 "
Distilled water	8 oz.
Ammonia water, sufficient to clear

Dissolve the two salts in the distilled water and add the ammonia water until the liquid becomes a clear fluid.

Walnut:

Silver nitrate	45 gr.
Pyrogallic acid	3 dr.
Distilled water	2 oz.
Glycerin	6 "

The following recipe is an old fashioned one using walnut shells:

Green walnut shells, crushed	45 gm.
Rose water	12 "
Powdered alum	3 "

The whole is mixed well, after chopping, and thirty parts of the whole are shaken with 100 parts of alcohol, rubbing alcohol being used. It is then left in a warm place for several days, and then filtered. Can be scented with oil of rose and oil of bergamot.

Another dye consists of:

Pyrogallic acid	4.0 parts
Citric acid	0.3 "
Boro-glycerin	19.0 "
Water	90 "

Chestnut:

Pyrogallic acid	1 dr.
Nitric acid	5 min.
Alcohol	½ oz.
Water enough to make.	4 "

Mix. Wash hair thoroughly, rinse well. When dry apply the dye with a small sponge dampened with the mixture. Repeat daily.

Eyebrow Pencils

Cocoa butter	30 gm.
Paraffin wax	40 "
White vaseline	10 "

Melt together and add enough lampblack to produce the required color. The amount of paraffin wax can be increased if the product is too soft. It can be poured into molds lined with tin metal foil. If a perfume is desired, oil of rose can be used, it being added after the lampblack is incorporated into the melted mix.

Rouge

Liquid petrolatum	389.0 gm.
White wax	278.0 "
Spermaceti	278.0 "
Carmine	55.5 "
Perfume to suit

Rub the carmine to a smooth paste with the liquid petrolatum, then add remainder of liquid petrolatum; melt the wax and spermaceti and add the carmine mixture.

Solid Rouge for Compact

#1—Talc powder	600 gm.
Gum arabic	50 "
Carmine powder	30 "

This simple mixture is thoroughly mixed by grinding in a mortar with a pestle, and then water is added carefully to form a paste. The paste is then packed into suitable containers. The gum arabic gives adherence to the mass, making it compact and solid.

#2—Carmine powder ..... 1 oz.
Fine talc .... 21 "
Gum acacia .... 2 "

Mix the three in a mortar, add ammonia and some water, and pound into a fine mass—adding more water, in small portions, so it forms a stiff paste, and pour into the molds.

Rouge Liquids

#1—Carmine powder ...... 4 parts
Strong ammonia water 4 "
Essence of rose....... 16 "
Rose water, to make... 500 "

#2—Powdered cochineal .... 4 oz.
Ammonia .... 4 "
Water .... 4 "

Cover and let simmer 3 or 4 hours in double boiler. It is ready for use when cool.

#3—Bring to a boil in an aluminum vessel 1 quart of water, to which add 1 ounce of the best pulverized cochineal. Stir in carefully 30 grains of alum. Continue boiling 5 minutes and then set aside to cool. Pour off the clear liquid from the top, and dry the sediment carefully.

Freckle Bleach

#1—Ammonium chloride .. 2 oz.
Sulphate of zinc...... 3 "
Epsom salt .... 6 "
Glycerin .... 4 "
Boracic acid .... 1 "
Rose water; enough for 1 gal.

#2—Borax .... 1 gm.
Potassium chlorate ... 1½ "
Peroxide of hydrogen.. 1 "
Glycerin .... 2 "
Rose water .... 1 pt.

#3—Use hydrogen peroxide (peroxide) several times daily.

#4—Precipitated sulphur .. 30 parts
Zinc oxide .... 15 "
Sweet almond oil...... 30 "
Lanolin .... 25 "

The whole should be mixed, using heat to liquefy the lanolin.

#5—Zinc oxide .... 4 dr.
Resorcin .... 2 "
Corn starch .... 3 "
Nujol or vaseline (white petrolatum) .... 1 oz.

Teeth Whitener

#1—To one pint of water add half an ounce of chemically pure hydrochloric acid. Of this mixture, take 6 ounces and dilute with one quart of water and half a pint of chemically pure glycerin. Flavor to suit the taste. It is used by pouring several drops upon the tooth brush and brushing the teeth with same.

#2—Use peroxide of hydrogen, the ordinary 3% solution.

#3—Sodium perborate made into a paste with water.

Tooth Paste

#1—Orris root .... 2 oz.
Cuttlefish bone .... 4 "
Precipitated chalk .... 12 "
Bicarbonate of soda .. ½ "
Essence of violet...... 1 dr.

Perfume and color as desired.

#2—Precipitated chalk .... 160 gm.
Soap powder .... 45 "
Wheat starch .... 45 "
Carmine coloring, powder .... 1 "
Oil of peppermint .... 30 drops
Oil of anise seed ..... 12 "
Oil of cloves .... 12 "
Oil of geranium ...... 30 "

The above is made into a paste with alcohol and glycerin in equal proportions.

#3—Precipitated chalk ..... 8 oz.
    Orris powder .... 8 "
    Shredded white castile
        soap .... 2 "
    Borax .... 2 "
    Myrrh .... 1 "

Glycerin and honey, enough to make a paste of the above. Sieve all.

#4—Honey .... ½ lb.
    Precipitated chalk .... ½ "
    Powdered orris root... ½ "
    Carmine .... 2 dr.
    Oil cloves .... ½ "
    Oil nutmeg .... ½ "
    Oil rose .... ½ "

Add enough water to make a paste.

#5—Precipitated chalk .... 1 lb.
    Shredded castile soap.. ¼ "
    Orris, powdered ...... ¼ "
    Sugar XXXX .... ¼ "
    Sodium salicylate ..... 80 gr.

Glycerin enough to form a paste.
Perfume if desired.

#6—Precipitated chalk .... 12 oz.
    Powdered myrrh ..... ½ "
    Powdered soap .... 1½ "
    Bicarbonate soda ..... 1½ "
    Oil lavender .... 10 dr.
    Oil lemon .... 10 "
    Oil bergamot .... 10 "
    Oil rose .... 10 "

Glycerin and honey, enough to make a paste.

Tooth Powder

#1—Precipitated chalk .... 20 gm.
    Fine calcium phosphate 20 "
    Magnesium carbonate.. 20 "
    Salol .... 4 "
    Sodium bicarbonate .. 15 "

Oil of peppermint is used as the scenting material, it being rubbed up with the magnesium carbonate, and then incorporated into the rest of the powders. It is finally sifted through a flour sifter, if made at home.

#2—Borax .... 50 oz.
    Chalk .... 100 "
    Myrrh .... 25 "
    Orris root .... 22 "

Perfume with oil of wintergreen if desired.

#3—Precipitated chalk .... 16 oz.
    Shredded castile soap.. 1 "
    Orris, powdered ...... 2 "
    Sugar .... 1 "
    Oil of wintergreen..... ¼ "

The oil of wintergreen is used as the flavoring material and it should be rubbed up with the chalk, using but a portion of the whole at first, then incorporating all, a bit at a time. The rest of the finely sifted ingredients are added, and then mixed, sifting again.

#4—Precipitated chalk .... 500 oz.
    Orris root .... 500 "
    Sugar .... 1 "
    Essence of rose........ 4 "
    Essence of neroli...... 4 "

Color with about 1 oz. of carmine powder.

#5—Precipitated chalk ..... 3 oz.
    Powdered orris root.... 1 "
    Sugar XXXX .... 2 "
    Prepared chalk .... 3 lb.
    Castile soap, shaved... ½ "
    Powdered orris root... ½ "
    Powdered sugar ...... ½ "
    Oil wintergreen .... ¼ dr.
    Oil peppermint .... 2 "

Mix all together thoroughly.

Shaving Cream

#1—Spermaceti .... 5 parts
    Borax .... 3 "
    Stearic acid .... 20 "
    Glycerin .... 20 "
    Water .... 80 "
    Toilet soap (shavings). 10 "
    Caustic soda solution
        (20 per cent)....... 2 "

#2—Stearic acid .... 10 parts
    Caustic potash (KOH) 1 "
    Glycerin .... 5 "
    Spermaceti .... 2 "
    Borax .... 2 "
    Water .... to 100 "

Perfume as needed.

It must be remembered that caustic potash (potassium hydroxide) is sold in stick or pellet form and absorbs water from the air, hence it must be weighed out rapidly and always protected from the air in well stoppered bottles. The caustic potash is first combined with the stearic acid to produce a soft soap. This should be done with gentle heating to prevent free caustic from being present in the finished product.

The following has been used with good results:

Toilet soap .... 5 gm.
Stearic acid .... 15 "
Glycerin .... 20 cc.
Potassium hydroxide ...... 2 gm.
Tragacanth mucilage ..... 5 cc.
Borax .... 2 gm.
Almond oil .... 5 cc.
Spermaceti .... 3 gm.
Water .... 80 cc.

The potassium hydroxide (do not handle with the fingers or leave it exposed to the air) is dissolved in practically all of the water and heated with the stearic acid and allowed to stand until cold. The borax is then dissolved in the remaining water and the toilet soap shaved and mixed in. Heat the latter gently and whip in the spermaceti, and add the other ingredients, followed by mixing with the stearic acid-potash mixture. Keep the whole fairly warm and whip or beat with an egg beater if more than the quantities given in the above formula are used.

Shaving Stick
Powdered castile soap...... 1 lb.
Rose water .... 1 pt.
Cocoa butter .... 2 oz.
Carbonate of soda......... 1 "

Heat all together for half an hour, then add 4 oz. glycerin and pour into molds.

Shaving Aid
Melt in a double boiler 1 lb. cocoa butter and add half oz. menthol crystals and when melted add 3 oz. of rose water, a little at a time; take off the fire and beat until cold.

Latherless Shaving Cream
Brushless or latherless shaving creams are made without heat, the ingredients being beaten together in a suitable container. A good formula is:

Ammonium stearate paste.. 10 oz.
White mineral oil .... 1 "

The cream can be perfumed to suit. It has the properties of a combined shaving cream, vanishing cream, and cold cream.

A latherless hair cleaner, somewhat similar to that of latherless shaving cream, water being substituted for the mineral oil, is made of:

Ammonium stearate paste.. 15 oz.
Water .... 1 "

The cleanser is made by mixing the above two substances until the mass has become homogeneous.

Shaving Lotion
#1—Menthol .... 1 dr.
    Boric acid .... 4 "
    Glycerin .... 4 oz.
    Rubbing alcohol ..... 1 pt.
    Witch-hazel, enough to
      make .... 1 gal.
Dissolve the menthol in the alcohol, add the glycerin and shake. Dissolve

the boric acid in the water or witch-hazel and mix all together. Allow to stand and filter.

#2—Boric acid .... 5 gr.
    Quince seed solution... 45 "
    Benzoic acid .... 5 "
    Glycerin .... 2 oz.
    Alcohol (rubbing) .... 3 "
    Oil of rose geranium... 1 dr.
    Oil of bitter almond... 30 min.
    Glycerite of starch.... 2 oz.
    Add witch-hazel to make 1 pt.

Dissolve the two acids in half a pint of the witch-hazel; macerate the quince seed in this solution for three hours; and strain. Beat up the glycerite with the glycerin, and gradually add with constant beating the quince seed solution. Finally beat in the oils dissolved in the alcohol, adding the solution slowly; then add enough witch-hazel to make the required volume.

#3—Quince seed .... 90 gr.
    Boric acid .... 30 "
    Salicylic acid .... 20 "
    Glycerin .... 1½ oz.
    Cologne water .... 4 "
    Boiling water .... 4 "
    Spirit of lemon to perfume

Triturate the quince seed with the boiling water, add the acids, and strain through muslin.

#4—Water or witch-hazel . 1 qt.
    Alum .... 1 oz.

Mix and dissolve, then add glycerin, 2 oz.; tincture benzoin, 1 dr.

#5—Boracic acid .... ½ oz.
    Glycerin .... 4 "
    Menthol .... 1 dr.
    Alcohol tax-free #40
    .... 4 oz. or more
    Nonalcoholic perfume to suit
    Boiled water .... 1 gal.

Rub the perfume with precipitated calcium phosphate, then add to the water. Dissolve the menthol in

the alcohol (denatured by formula #40) which has been colored if desired. Mix.

#6—Oil bergamot .... 2 cc.
    Oil lemon .... 1 "
    Oil spike-lavender .... 1 "
    Oil bay .... 2 "
    Sodium salicylate ..... 16 gm.
    Resorcin .... 10 "
    Water sufficient to make
    ....1000 cc.

Rub up the essential oils with the sodium salicylate and a little water, finally adding water sufficient to make a clear solution. Dissolve the resorcin in the remainder of the water, and mix the solutions. Allow to stand a week and perfume.

Simple Bay Rum

#1—Alcohol (den #40)..... 200 cc.
    Oil of bay leaves...... 1 gm.
    Oil of cloves.......... 4 "

Dissolve and then pour into 200 cc. of water. It is best to allow this to stand several days and filter to make a clear solution before using.

#2—Oil of bay leaves...... 1 dr.
    Alcohol .... 18 oz.
    Water .... 18 "

Mix and filter through magnesia.

#3—Oil of bay leaves...... 6 dr.
    Oil of orange......... ½ "
    Tincture of benzoin... 4 "
    Orris root powder..... 1 oz.
    Alcohol .... 2 qt.
    Water .... 2 "

Mix all, excepting water. Allow to stand several weeks, add water and filter.

Theatrical Grease Paints

The base for making a grease paint is usually two parts of lard and one of either white paraffin wax or petroleum jelly. Cocoa butter is an excellent base but is somewhat expensive.

Larger quantities of wax will produce a firmer cream. The substances should be melted to mix them.

Black:
#1—Lampblack .... 1 part
    Base (as above)....... 6 "

#2—Lampblack rubbed up with glycerin. This is quite easily washed off after using, as the glycerin is soluble in water.

Red:
Zinc white .... 15 dr.
Bismuth subnitrate .... 15 "

The above is mixed into a paste with almond oil. Color with 20 grains of carmine dissolved in about 80 minims of ammonia water. It may be perfumed with 12 minims oil of peppermint.

White: Mix 1 oz. each of zinc oxide and bismuth subnitrate into paste with 5 or 6 drams of almond oil.

Brown: To six parts of the base as described above, add about 1 part of burnt umber and when nearly cold add five drops of oil of neroli.

Yellow: Use equal parts of yellow ochre, precipitated chalk and zinc white (zinc oxide) with white vaseline.

When making theatrical face paints, the shade the cream will produce should be ascertained by rubbing a bit on the back of the hand. In this manner, the consistency of the paste under actual conditions is also observed, as the heat of the hand will have a tendency to keep the cream or paint softer than would be the case if the paint were judged in the mixing bowl.

Freckles are made by using burnt umber and a base.

Nose putty is made from paraffin wax 8 parts, bleached rosin 8 parts, and suet or mutton tallow 4 parts, the whole being incorporated by gentle heat. It should be colored to suit.

FAMILY MEDICINE CHEST

Homemade Liniments

These liquids, which are for external application, are not difficult to compound, usually the simple mixing of the ingredients producing the desired product:

#1—Oil of wintergreen (synthetic) .... ¼ oz.
    Oil of eucalyptus...... 1 "
    Oil of capsicum ...... 1 "
    Rubbing alcohol ...... 1 qt.

#2—Tincture of capsicum.. 1 oz.
    Tincture of myrrh.... ½ "
    Menthol .... 1 dr.
    Oil of sassafras....... ½ oz.
    Oil of origanum...... 1 "
    Camphor .... 1 "
    Rubbing alcohol ...... 1½ pt.

#3—Tincture arnica ...... 2 oz.
    Oil of origanum ...... 3 "
    Oil of sassafras .... 2 "
    Spirits of camphor.... 1 "
    Chloroform .... 1 "
    Rubbing alcohol ...... 2 qt.

#4—Oil of turpentine...... 9 oz.
    Tincture of capsicum.. 12 "
    Spirits of camphor.... 96 "
    Stronger ammonia water .... 9 "
    Alcohol (rubbing) .... 18 "
    Oil of sassafras .... ½ "

Dissolve the oils in the alcohol, add the stronger ammonia water and mix by shaking. The above has been called "Magnetic Liniment."

Antidotes for Poisons

In case of poisoning, first send for a physician. Then induce vomiting by tickling the throat with the finger, drinking hot water or strong mustard and water, or swallowing sweet oil or whites of eggs. See next page for poisons and antidotes. Acids are antidotes for alkalies, and alkalies for acids.

TABLE OF POISONS AND ANTIDOTES

Poisons	*Antidotes*
Hydrochloric, oxalic, acetic, sulphuric, and nitric acids	Soapsuds, magnesia, and limewater.
Prussic acid, potassium cyanide......	Dilute ammonium hydrate; dash water in the face; use solution of cobalt nitrate.
Carbolic acid......................	Flour and water; mucilaginous drinks.
Caustic potash, caustic soda, lye, ammonia	Vinegar, or lemon juice in water.
Arsenic, rat poison, fly poison, Paris green	Milk, raw eggs, sweet oil, limewater, flour and water, iron salts.
Lead, saltpeter, corrosive sublimate, sugar of lead, copper compounds..	White of eggs, or milk in large quantities.
Chloroform, chloral, ether..........	Artificial respiration; dash cold water on head and chest.
Sodium carbonate, cobalt, and iron compounds	Soapsuds and mucilaginous drinks.
Iodine, antimony, salts, tartar emetic.	Starch and water, strong tea, or any astringent infusions.
Mercury and its salts..............	White of eggs, mucilaginous milk drinks.
Opium, morphine, laudanum, paregoric, soothing powders, or syrups.	Strong coffee, hot baths, and keep person moving.
Silver compounds	Salt water.

For Home Medicine Chest

Aromatic Spirits of Ammonia—Two ounces. One-half teaspoonful in some water for faintness.

Boracic Acid—Four ounces. Dissolve 2½ teaspoons in a glass of hot water and use as an eye wash, in an eye cup.

Carbolated Vaseline—One tube. For external use, in treatment of burns.

Castor Oil—Eight ounces. Dose—one to two tablespoons.

Oil of Cloves—For toothache.

Tincture of Iodine—For wounds.

Syrup of Ipecac—Dose, one teaspoon, followed by a drink of warm water, to cause vomiting.

Camphor Ice

#1—Crushed camphor	2 gm.
Paraffin oil	2 "
Glycerin	2 "
White vaseline	8 "
White wax	5 "

Medicinal mineral oil can be used for the paraffin oil. The vaseline, oil, and wax are melted, using as little heat as possible, and the camphor dissolved in this heated mixture. The glycerin is incorporated last. The consistency may be changed as desired; using more wax produces a harder, firmer ice, and more vaseline or paraffin oil thins it.

♯2—Stearine	8 parts
Lard	10 "
White wax	5 "
Spermaceti wax	5 "
Camphor	2 "

♯3—Oil of almonds	16 parts
White wax	4 "
Spermaceti wax	4 "
Paraffin	8 "
Camphor	1 "

Treatment of Burns

Carron oil: This mixture can be made from limewater and linseed oil. Equal parts of the two are shaken together so an emulsion is formed. Half as much paraffin oil can also be used with the two liquids with equal success. The parts burned are smeared with the mixture.

Household ammonia: Household ammonia is efficacious in treating burns where the skin has not been broken or seared open. It is applied on a cloth. It has been said to neutralize the sarco-lactic acid which is produced.

Picric acid: A strong solution of picric acid crystals in water is often used on burns. Medicinal gauze can be saturated with the acid and allowed to dry. When desired for use, the cloths can be wetted and applied to the parts affected.

Toothache Powder

| Powdered alum | 1 oz. |
| Powdered cloves | 2 " |

Mix. Moisten a small piece of cotton and dip in powder. Apply to aching tooth.

Toothache Liquid

♯1—Oil of cloves. Apply.

| ♯2—Creosote | 1 part |
| Oil of cloves | 1 " |

♯3—Paraffin	8 oz.
Vaseline	3 "
Oil of cloves	3 dr.
Beechwood creosote	4 "

Melt the paraffin and the vaseline together over a low heat. When melted remove and stir until it has become cool but not yet congealed. Stir in the oil of cloves and then the beechwood creosote.

To Disguise Taste of Epsom Salts

Epsom salts	½ lb.
Saccharin	12 gr.
Extract of vanilla	1 oz.
Glycerin	2 "
Water	1 pt.

Filter if necessary. The dose is 1 tablespoon.

Cold Inhaler

♯1—Into a small, wide mouthed bottle place a small piece of camphor, then insert a piece of sponge or cotton batten, and drop thereon fifteen drops of the strongest ammonia and fifteen drops essential oil of mustard. Keep tightly corked when not in use. Inhale through the nostrils.

♯2—Oil of cinnamon	10 drops
Oil of eucalyptus	15 "
Oil of pine	90 "
Chloroform	90 "
Creosote	60 "

Mix oils in chloroform, then creosote. Sprinkle a few drops on handkerchief and inhale.

♯3—Melt 1 lb. white petrolatum in a double boiler and add 1 dram of menthol crystals and 1 dr. eucalyptol.

Chapped Hands

#1—White wax .... 4 dr.
    Spermaceti .... 18 gr.
    Olive oil .... 2 dr.

#2—Glycerin .... 4 oz.
    Rose water .... 4 "
    Witch-hazel .... 8 "
Dir.: Mix glycerin with rose water, then add the witch-hazel.

#3—White vaseline ....$1\frac{1}{2}$ oz.
    White wax .... $\frac{1}{2}$ "
    Spermaceti .... 40 gr.
Melt above by hot water-bath. This preparation is also good as a nail pomade.

#4—Melt together in a double boiler white wax and spermaceti each 1 oz.; camphor, 2 oz.; sweet almond oil, 1 lb.; then after mixing thoroughly add 1 lb. of rose water slowly. This is excellent for chapped lips and hands.

#5—Sweet almond oil...... 3 oz.
    Spermaceti .... 2 "
    Camphor .... 1 "
Melt in a double boiler.

Rheumatic Liniment

Menthol .... 15 gr.
Chloroform .... 1 oz.
Oil of wintergreen.......... 1 "
Camphorated oil .... 1 "
Dissolve the menthol in the chloroform, then add the wintergreen oil and then the camphorated oil.

Antiseptic Powders

The following do not contain permanganates which will stain the skin and clothing:

#1—Borax .... 3 oz.
    Dried alum .... 3 "
    Thymol .... 22 gm.
    Eucalyptol .... 20 dr.
    Menthol ....$1\frac{1}{2}$ gm.
    Phenol .... 15 "
    Oil of wintergreen ..... 4 dr.
Mix.

#2—Powdered alum .... 50 parts
    Powdered borax .... 50 "
    Carbolic acid crystals... 5 "
    Oil of eucalyptus....... 5 "
    Oil of wintergreen...... 5 "
    Menthol .... 5 "
    Thymol .... 5 "

#3—Boric acid .... 10 oz.
    Borax .... 4 "
    Alum .... 1 "
    Zinc sulphocarbolate ... 1 "

#4—Boric acid .... 70 parts
    Iodoform .... 25 "
    Salicylic acid .... 4 "
    Oil of eucalyptus....... 1 "

Sunburn Lotions

These well known remedies for sunburn can be prepared easily and from ingredients readily obtainable.

#1—Zinc sulphocarbolate ... 1 part
    Glycerin .... 20 "
    Rose water .... 75 "
    Alcohol (rubbing) ..... 8 "
    Spirits of camphor ..... 1 "

#2—Almonds, blanched .... 1 dr.
    Borax .... 20 gr.
    Tincture benzoin .... 50 min.
    Orange flower water....$3\frac{1}{2}$ oz.
    Hydrogen peroxide .... $\frac{1}{2}$ "
Bruise the almonds, dissolve the borax in the orange flower water, and triturate the almonds with successive portions of the latter. Strain through cloth, and add the tincture of benzoin and hydrogen peroxide.

#3—Bismuth subnitrate.....$1\frac{1}{2}$ dr.
    Precipitated chalk ..... 30 gr.
    Glycerin .... 2 dr.
    Rose water ....$1\frac{1}{2}$ oz.
Rub up the powders with the glycerin, then add the rose water.

#4—Borax .... 4 parts
    Potassium chlorate .... 2 "
    Glycerin .... 10 "
    Alcohol (rubbing) .... 4 "
    Rose water to make... 90 "

#5—Liquid paraffin oil..... 1 oz.
Peach kernel oil .... 1 "
Lanolin .... ½ "
Limewater .... 3 "
Borax .... ½ dr.
Tincture of benzoin.... 2 "

To Relieve Mosquito Bites

Common yellow soap rubbed on mosquito bites will allay itching. Dilute household ammonia or the usual 40% solution of formaldehyde will also produce a marked lessening of the sting.

Lotion for Poison Ivy

#1—Iron chloride .... 5 gm.
Glycerin .... 45 cc.
Water .... 50 "

Mix together, apply to the skin and allow to dry thereon. The iron combines with the irritating substance of the ivy, relieving the irritation.

A 5% solution of potassium permanganate applied to the inflamed area also relieves itching, the brown discoloration produced being easily removed later with a weak solution of oxalic acid which is washed from the skin after the coloration disappears.

#2—When benzoyl peroxide powder is dusted well over the spots affected by poison ivy, and kept in place by a light bandage, the itching disappears in about fifteen or twenty minutes and does not return for eight or ten hours after a single application. It is not a certain cure in all cases, but it relieves the itching and prevents further spread.

#3—Apply a strong solution of sodium hyposulphite (hypo).

To Remove Warts

#1—Use sodium bisulphite solution as a treatment for the removal of warts, the solution being applied in two baths, for fifteen minutes each daily. It is said that young warts will disappear in eight days. Old growths should be exfoliated and scraped before applying the solution.

#2—Smear vaseline around the wart, upon the live skin, and then with a toothpick or glass rod apply strong nitric acid to the wart. Allow to remain for about ten minutes. The vaseline prevents the acid from burning the live healthy tissue around the wart, in the event that the acid rolls off the wart.

#3—Chromic acid (chromic anhydride) dissolved in water can also be used.

#4—Salicylic acid .... 2 gm.
Acetic acid dilute...... 30 cc.

Warts may be removed by the application of a 40% solution of formaldehyde, commonly sold as formalin.

In removing a wart with acid a film of vaseline is brushed on the live skin around the wart, before any of the acid is placed on the wart. This precaution should always be observed with the utmost care, as the vaseline film protects the skin from acid which might accidentally roll off the wart.

Potassium dichromate solution, as strong as can be made, has also been recommended for removal of warts.

Powder for Babies

Zinc stearate is used "as is" for many dusting powders. Its fluffiness has been found a detriment, as it is easily carried by air currents and so may be breathed into the lungs. Replacing the zinc metal in the zinc stearate by magnesium gives magnesium stearate, which can be tolerated by the human system much more readily than the metal zinc. Thus the second formula herewith is given.

#1—French chalk, bolted, and rice starch, equal parts. Mix by sifting through cheese cloth.

#2—Magnesium stearate in
fine powder .... 1 part
French chalk .... 7 "
Magnesium carbonate
(powder) .... 3 "

Sore Throat Gargle

The glyceride of tannic acid has been found to be effective for sore throat. It is readily made by allowing about twenty grams of tannic acid (C. P. or U. S. P. grades) to dissolve in about eighty cubic centimeters of glycerin. The crystals of the tannic acid can be suspended in a cloth bag while solution is taking place, if the liquid cannot be stirred from time to time. Do not heat to a very high temperature as the glycerin will decompose, thus ruining the product. The resulting thick liquid is of a brownish color and about a half a teaspoonful should be dissolved in a cup of water and used as a gargle. Despite its somewhat astringent character, this gargle is effective and cheap to make. Use strong or thick glycerin in its preparation.

Soda-salt Gargle. A teaspoonful each of salt and baking soda dissolved in a glass of warm water makes a good gargle for throat irritations.

Chlorate of Potash. Dissolve 1 dr. potassium chlorate in one pt. water.

Mouth Washes

#1—Boracic acid .... 2 parts
Oil wintergreen .... 1 "
Glycerin .... 11 "
Alcohol #40 .... 15 "
Distilled water enough
to make .... 60 "

#2—Acid tannic .... 3 oz.
Oil wintergreen .... 3 dr.
Powdered orris root.... 12 oz.
Alcohol and water, each 12 "

Color to suit. Stand for 8 days and filter.

#3—Thymol .... 1 part
Benzoic acid .... 12 "
Tincture of eucalyptus.. 60 "
Alcohol ....400 "
Oil of peppermint ..... 3 "

Cuticle Remover

Use a strong solution of salicylic acid in water to which has been added rose water for perfume.

Smelling Salts

#1—Ammonium carbonate. 360 gm.
Camphor .... 120 "
Phenol .... 480 "
Oil of eucalyptus...... 1 dr.
Oil of lavender....... 1 "
Strong ammonia ...... 2 oz.

Mix.

#2—Ammonium carbonate. 1 lb.
Strong ammonia ..... 2 oz.
Oil of eucalyptus...... 4 "
Oil of lavender....... 1 dr.
Oil of peppermint.... 2 "

#3—In a bottle, place ammonium carbonate
cubes and cover with
tincture of orris.... 1 oz.
Extract of violet...... 3 dr.
Ammonia water ...... 1 "

#4—Put carbonate of ammonia into a bottle with a glass stopper; add any desired perfume, as 8 parts of carbonate of ammonia to 1 part of oil of lavender.

#5—Tincture of orris....... 5 min.
Oil of lavender........ 10 "
Extract of violet....... 30 "
Ammonia water ...... 2 oz.

Tasteless Castor Oil

#1—Glycerin .... 12 parts
     Castor oil .... 12 "
     Tincture of orange peel. 4 "
     Tincture of senega..... 1 "
     Cinnamon water ...... 20 "

Mix by shaking, thus forming an emulsion. Normal dosage is 1 tablespoonful.

#2—Castor oil and maple syrup, or molasses, equal parts by volume of each, is more palatable than the oil alone.

Foot Powders

These mixtures are easily prepared, usually by simply sifting the ingredients together.

#1—Talc .... 12 oz.
     Boric acid .... 10 "
     Zinc oleate .... 1 "
     Salicylic acid .... 1 "
     Oil of eucalyptus ...... 2 dr.

#2—Burnt alum .... 5 gm.
     Salicylic acid ....2½ "
     Powdered starch ...... 15 "
     Talcum .... 50 "

#3—Boric acid .... 2 oz.
     Zinc oleate .... 1 "
     Talcum .... 3 "

Zinc stearate can be used instead of zinc oleate.

#4—Salicylic acid .... 6 dr.
     Boric acid .... 3 oz.
     Talcum .... 36 "
     Slippery elm bark ..... 1 "
     Orris root .... 1 "

#5—Salicylic acid .... 100 gr.
     Boric acid .... 300 "
     Powdered alum .... 60 "
     Powdered talcum ..... 8 oz.

Mix by sifting.

#6—Zinc stearate .... ½ part
     Boracic acid .... 1 "
     Precipitated chalk .... 4 "
     Cornstarch .... 2 "

#7—Zinc stearate .... 1 oz.
     Boric acid, powdered.. 2 "
     Precipitated chalk .... 3 "

The many foot powders are composed principally of some such base as talc and starch, together with boric or salicylic acid. A modification is as follows:

#8—Salicylic acid .... 6 dr.
     Boric acid .... 3 oz.
     Powdered elm bark ... 1 "
     Powdered orris root ... 1 "
     Talcum powder ...... 36 "

Oxygen-liberating powders are used also. A typical formula is:

#9—Sodium perborate .... 3 oz.
     Zinc peroxide .... 2 "
     Talc .... 15 "

#10—Salicylic acid .... 1 oz.
     Boric acid .... 3 "
     Zinc oxide .... 2 "

Mix and divide into powders of 1 dr. each. Shake one powder into each shoe once a day.

Deodorizers

Deodorizers consist of substances that usually give off a characteristic odor which masks the objectionable odor.

Napthalene (moth balls), paradichlorbenzene, camphor, and other substances have been used with success. One method is to use paradichlorbenzene in which has been impregnated some suitable flower odor such as violet, rose, or lilac. This can be accomplished by mixing the odor, which may be in the form of an essence or extract, with crystals of paradichlorbenzene, and placing the mixture in a tightly closed bottle such as a preserve jar. If allowed to remain for several days or a week, the chemical will absorb a large quantity of the flower odor, and if placed where it is to be used, such as the sick room, the combination of the flower and the dichlorbenzene odor will be found to blend nicely.

To Disguise Cod Liver Oil

For each ounce of cod liver oil, add 2 or 3 drops of oil of eucalyptus.

FIREWORKS

On the Safe Side

The formulas given in this section give satisfactory results, the most of them being of the safe type. By safe is meant the tendency for the mixtures not to explode by percussion, and to this end, potassium chlorate and sulphur will be found not to occur together in the formulas. It is well known that mixtures of sulphur and potassium chlorate or many mixtures containing both of these will explode by percussion. Various gums, such as shellac, gum kauri and rosin, or metals, will be found to take the place of sulphur in a formula in which potassium chlorate is used, and where sulphur is included, potassium chlorate will be absent, either potassium nitrate or potassium perchlorate being substituted for the chlorate. This observation will eliminate this one hazard of the home manufacture of fireworks. Of course, any combustible mixture when confined, as when contained in a tight case, will form a device of the cracker or bomb type which may prove dangerous. When the various colored light mixtures, smokes, etc., are packed in cardboard or paper tubes and fired by lighting a fuse inserted in the top of the mixture, very little danger is present, for the gases produced in the combustion are not confined and an explosion will not result.

In making or mixing any of the following pyrotechnical items purchase the ingredients already pulverized or powdered if possible, otherwise grind each substance separately, cleaning the mortar and pestle thoroughly after each grinding.

Mixing is best performed on paper with a wooden knife or spatula. All of the parts are, of course, by weight. A small photographer's balance is suitable for weighing the mixtures for home use.

The simplest firework mixtures are the colored fires. The most popular is a red fire. The following formula will be found to produce an excellent red fire:

#1—Strontium nitrate	66 parts
Potassium chlorate ...	25 "
Powdered orange shellac	9 "

#2—Strontium carbonate ..	16 parts
Potassium chlorate	72 "
Orange shellac powdered	12 "

#3—Potassium chlorate ...	37 parts
Strontium nitrate	50 "
Shellac	13 "

It is best to purchase the shellac already powdered as this substance is very difficult to pulverize.

#4—Strontium nitrate	8 oz.
Sugar	4 "
Potassium chlorate ...	1 "

#5—Potassium perchlorate..	15 oz.
Strontium nitrate	80 "
Flowers of sulphur....	20 "
Wood charcoal (powdered)	1 "
Gum kauri (red gum) .	2 "
Vaseline-sawdust mixture	10 "

The sawdust and vaseline mixture is made by rubbing 8 oz. of sawdust with 6 oz. of melted vaseline.

#6—Potassium perchlorate. 4½ oz.
Strontium nitrate ..... 20 "
Sulphur .... 5½ "
Rosin .... ½ "
Sugar .... ½ "
Antimony, powdered... ¼ "
Vaseline-sawdust mix-
ture .... 10 "

#7—Perchlorate potash ....12½ parts
Nitrate strontia pow-
dered .... 50 "
Powdered charcoal .... 1 "
Powdered sugar ...... 4 "
Red gum .... 15 "

#8—Potassium chlorate ... 6 parts
Strontium nitrate ..... 2 "
Strontium carbonate .. 1½ "
Gum kauri (red gum). 2½ "

Green Fire Composition

#1—Barium chlorate ...... 90 gm.
Powdered orange shellac 10 "

This mixture is made by mixing
the above two ingredients together.

#2—Barium chlorate ...... 23 parts
Barium nitrate .... 59 "
Potassium chlorate .... 6 "
Orange shellac .... 11 "
Stearic acid .... 1 "

The stearic acid should be grated
and mixed very thoroughly with the
rest of the chemicals.

#3—Barium chlorate ...... 55 parts
Barium nitrate .... 33 "
Shellac .... 12 "

#4—Barium nitrate .... 6 parts
Potassium nitrate ..... 3 "
Sulphur .... 2 "

#5—Barium nitrate .... 18 parts
Shellac .... 4 "
Mercurous chloride ... 4 "
Potassium chlorate .... 2 "

#6—Barium nitrate .... 3 parts
Potassium chlorate .... 4 "
Gum kauri (red gum). 1¼ "

Blue Fire Composition

#1—Potassium chlorate .... 6 parts
Ammonio-sulphate of
copper .... 8 "
Shellac .... 1 "
Willow charcoal ...... 2 "

#2—Potassium chlorate ... 40 parts
Copper sulphate ...... 8 "
Rosin .... 6 "

This composition can be moistened
with alcohol and the resulting paste
smeared upon objects. When dry,
the powder adheres to the support
and can be easily lighted. This property is useful in making the blue fire
climb poles.

White Fire Compositions

#1—Potassium nitrate ..... 24 parts
Sulphur .... 7 "
Charcoal (wood) ..... 1 "

This is Mohr's white fire and is an
exceptionally simple one. The white
light produced is very beautiful. The
powder mixture burns softly and
slowly.

#2—Potassium nitrate .... 7 parts
Sulphur .... 2 "
Powdered antimony ... 1 "

This is an excellent white fire, burning softly and slow. Although the
antimony is not inexpensive, the mixture is economical owing to the small
amount used. Antimony sulphide can
be substituted for the antimony.

#3—Potassium perchlorate. 3½ oz.
Barium nitrate .... 17 "
Powdered sulphur .... 3½ "
Finely powdered alumi-
num .... 5 "

#4—Potassium perchlorate.. 7 oz.
Barium nitrate .... 34 "
Flowers of sulphur .... 7 "
Aluminum bronze (dust) 2 "
Aluminum flakes ..... 7 "

#5—Potassium perchlorate. 3½ oz.
Potassium chlorate ... 2 "
Barium nitrate .... 5 "
Powdered magnesium
metal .... 4 "

This is suitable for flashlight photography. It is very fast and powerfully actinic.

#6—Barium nitrate .... 75 parts
Aluminum powder .... 21 "
Sulphur .... 4 "

The sulphur produces a characteristic flame of its own which is somewhat different from the white color desired. The barium nitrate decomposes, and produces a greenish tinge which neutralizes the off-white color produced by the sulphur.

Fuse for Fireworks

Fuse for igniting the colored fire or smoke compositions, etc., are easily made. The following formula has produced good results:

Potassium perchlorate .... 9 parts
Wood charcoal .... 2 "
Sulphur .... 2 "

The whole mixture is sifted through a sieve and made into a paste with a gum solution. The gum solution can be made by rubbing dextrine up with water (1 oz. dextrine to 1 pt. of water) to make a thin paste. A thin mucilage water can also be used. The mixture is then rubbed upon soft cotton string, coating the string well, and allowed to dry by hanging in a warm place. It will be found that extemporaneous gum solutions such as shellac will not prove satisfactory in mixing the above preparation to form a paste for coating upon string.
Another mixture for fuses is:

Potassum nitrate .... 62 parts
Sulphur .... 14 "
Charcoal .... 20 "
Starch .... 4 "

This is made with water, coated upon soft cotton string and suspended until dry. Fuse is used by inserting about half an inch into the colored fire composition, which is packed into cardboard or stiff paper cases or tubes. The free end, which should be about three or four inches long, is then held in an upright position while a thickness or two of tissue paper is pasted about the top portion of the paper case so that the upper edge of the paper protrudes about an inch and a half above the upper edge or rim of the case. The tissue paper is then twisted about the fuse, and the twist tied with light thread. This holds the fuse in position and at the same time acts as a cover to keep the composition from falling from the case. The case can be of a color to correspond with the mixture within.
Another fuse consists of:

Potassium nitrate .... 6 oz.
Lead nitrate .... 2 "

Dissolve in one pint boiling water. Soak cotton cord or paper in the liquid and let dry. To waterproof, when thoroughly dry, dip in *thin* solution of shellac.

Powder for Fireworks

A simple gunpowder formula consists of:

Potassium nitrate .... 1 lb.
Sulphur .... 3 oz.
Charcoal .... 2 "

A particularly good mixture which deviates from the usual gunpowder formula is:

Potassium perchlorate .... 9 parts
Sulphur .... 2 "
Charcoal .... 2 "

Use finely pulverized wood charcoal. Animal charcoal should not be used as it leaves an ash when burned. The potassium perchlorate is the oxidizer and by its use the mixture becomes fast burning. It is also easily fired. It is particularly suited for small cannons for use in celebrations. The ingredients are mixed by sifting through a fine copper screen.

Meal Powder

Potassium nitrate	56 parts
Sulphur	13 "
Wood charcoal	31 "

The powder is first mixed, then dampened with water and rolled into a cake. It is then dried and afterward crushed to a powder and finally sifted. It is used for driving rockets, expelling signals, fuse, and can be used as a simple burning composition.

Showers of Fire

#1—Potassium nitrate	18 parts
Sulphur	8 "
Lampblack	5 "

This composition burns with a yellowish color, throwing out streamers of golden sparks, due to the lampblack which is used. The mixture burns slowly and is suitable for filling paper tubes.

#2—Potassium nitrate	10 parts
Sulphur	2 "
Charcoal	2 "
Iron filings (fine).....	7 "

For loading into ordinary paper cases.

#3—Potassium nitrate	36 parts
Sulphur	2 "
Charcoal (wood)	10 "

For loading into paper cases.

Light Sticks

#1—Fill thin paper tubes of about ⅜″ outside diameter and 1′ long with the colored fire compositions, alternating. One end of the tube should be closed tightly to a depth of 3″ with clay or sand. Fill with powder of the desired color and close end by pasting a piece of tissue paper around it, after inserting a fuse.

#2—Boil a handful of sawdust or wood shavings in a cup of water containing a teaspoonful of potassium nitrate. When dry, it will burn with a whitish yellow flame, sizzling as it burns. Add ½ teaspoon of strontium nitrate to the water before boiling the sawdust in it. When the sawdust is then immersed and dried it will burn with a red flame. Barium nitrate will make the flame green; copper sulphate, blue.

Homemade Sparklers

White potassium chlorate..	10 oz.
Granulated aluminum	2 "
Charcoal	1⁄16 "

Mix to consistency of thick cream with a solution of 2 oz. of dextrine in a pint of water and coat upon wires or slender wooden sticks.

For red sparkler add 1½ oz. powdered strontium nitrate.

For green sparkler add 2 oz. powdered barium nitrate.

Smoke Composition

White: Powdered potassium nitrate	4 oz.
Powdered soft coal	5 "
Sulphur	10 "
Fine sawdust	3 "
Red: Potassium chlorate..	15 parts
Paranitraniline red	65 "
Lactose (powdered)	20 "
Green: Synthetic indigo...	26 "
Auramine yellow O	15 "
Potassium chlorate	33 "
Lactose (powdered)	26 "
Yellow: Precipitated red arsenic sulphide	55 "
Powdered sulphur	15 "
Potassium nitrate	30 "

Black:

#1—Magnesium powder . 18.6 parts
  Hexachlorethane .... 60.5 "
  Powdered napthalene. 20.9 "

The napthalene can be obtained by powdering moth balls.

#2—Powdered potassium ni-
  trate .... 6 oz.
  Flowers sulphur ...... 6 "
  Powdered asphalt .... 1¼ "

#3—Pitch (low melting)... 29 parts
  Potassium nitrate .... 47 "
  Borax .... 10 "
  Chalk dust .... 5 "
  Sand .... 5 "
  Sulphur .... 4 "

Simple smoke producing mixture:

Potassium chlorate .... 22 parts
Gum kauri .... 1½ "
Charcoal .... 1 "

Pharaoh's Eggs

Mix together 6 parts of potassium bichromate, 3 parts of potassium nitrate, and 6 parts of sugar, all finely powdered. Add a small amount of alcohol and press into cones and dry. When ignited they produce a long snake-like ash.

Black Rain Fire for Daylight

Potassium chlorate .... 3 parts
Napthalene .... 1 "
Charcoal .... ½ "
Sulphur .... 2 "

Powdered moth balls can be used as napthalene, as they are nearly pure napthalene.

Miscellaneous Formulas

Perchlorate potash .... 16 oz.
Flower sulphur .... 8 "
Lampblack or charcoal.... 3 "

This can be mixed without any danger of explosion by friction. Put in tubes, apply blasting fuse with cap. Do not use chlorate of potash!

A sensitive detonating mixture is made of potassium chlorate 10 parts, black antimony sulphide 5 parts and red phosphorus 1 part. Mix without friction and at some distance from the operator's face. It is quite sensitive to blows, very unlike the potassium chlorate-sulphur mix.

A match composition contains black antimony sulphide 23 parts, potassium chlorate 46, and strontium carbonate, 31 parts. Mix, using a liquid of 1 oz. gum arabic in ½ pint of water. Mold into a disc and dry. For the striker, use 4 parts powdered glass and 1 of red phosphorus using gum arabic water as before. Dry in form of disc. These latter discs rubbed across the first antimony composition discs cause ignition of the former. This match is used as a substitute for fuses.

Igniting compositions are used to communicate the fire of the fuse to the colored fire composition, and usually consist of 6 parts of potassium nitrate, 4 of sulphur and 1 of charcoal, all powdered, measured by weight, of course, and mixed.

FOR THE HANDY MAN

Waterproofing Concrete

Concrete walls, storage tanks, or building blocks are porous, and allow water to pass through them to some extent, making them damp. "N" Brand water-glass (sodium silicate), properly applied, will usually reduce or prevent this dampness. It is important to have the water-glass absorbed as fully as possible into the concrete. This treatment should penetrate the concrete up to about a half inch. The quantity needed is about one gallon per 1000 square feet for each coat. It should be understood that this treatment serves to fill the pores of the concrete, but it does not fill or caulk cracks.

Cement Patches

In patching or resurfacing concrete, water-glass or sodium silicate can be used to insure a good bond between the old and new cement. To refill a hole it should be chipped out clean and somewhat under-cut. The fresh surface should then be painted with the silicate full strength. Neat cement should then be dusted over the surface and worked in with a broom or stiff brush. The new concrete can then be applied in the usual manner.

For resurfacing, the concrete should be roughened with a pick, all loose particles removed and the floor wet thoroughly with water overnight. Immediately before the new surface is applied the old one should be washed with a freshly prepared mixture of 10 pounds of neat cement with one quart of water-glass in fourteen quarts of water. This mixture should be brushed in well and followed at once with the surface layer.

Crack Fillers

If the cracks are large and upon such items as construction work where only a rough patch up job is required, cement can be used to advantage. However, this is objectionable because the cement will pull away from the inner surfaces.

#1—The following formula will produce a substance that can be rammed home with a hammer and blunt cold chisel, and effectively seal the crack.

Flour	1 lb.
Borax	1 tablespoon
Alum	1 "
Glue	1 oz.
Water	3 qt.

Soak the glue in the water and when it has dissolved, add the other ingredients to the warmed solution. Stir in shredded newspapers to pro-duce a puttylike mass and ram the mass into the cracks.

#2—The following can be used for mahogany finished furniture:

Melt 4 oz. of beeswax and add 1 oz. of red lead and enough yellow ochre to produce tint required.

Rust-Proofing Metals

This Parkerizing process is especially adapted for the treatment of tools, typewriters, ordnance and motor parts, where rust should be prevented and an attractive finish is desired. In the operation of the process the articles are freed from oil and grease by immersion for about 20 minutes in a solution of caustic soda, maintained at over 200° F., and then are thoroughly rinsed in hot or boiling water, to dissolve any soaps formed in the cleaner. When free from caustic they are washed with a 5% sulphuric acid pickle in which 1 oz. of sodium bisulphite per gallon of acid has been dissolved and kept below 150° F. When clean, after 20 minutes, the work is again thoroughly rinsed in boiling water, to remove all acid and iron sulphates, then dried, sand tumbled, or rubbed, and passed into the phosphate tank where it remains for from 1 to 2 hours at 212° F., until the evolution of hydrogen ceases. The work then is dried, dipped in a paraffin oil mixture and dried.

The processing solution is made by mixing the phosphoric acid-iron phosphate mixture and manganese dioxide in the proportion of 4 pints acid and 2 lbs. of manganese dioxide to each gallon of water, mixing and boiling. Prolonged boiling for 12 hours is necessary when the solution is first made. Continuous circulation of the solution is effected by proper construction of the tank, which should be provided with side heating coils and deflection vanes. Sludge forming from manganese dioxide (pyrolusite) after the tank has been in use for some time is prevented from coming in contact with the work by baffle plates placed a certain distance from the bottom of the tank.—L. E. Eckelmann in *Chem. & Met. Eng.*

Vaseline either smeared upon the tools or dissolved in benzene, or toluene is well suited for this purpose.

Preserving wax dissolved in gasoline or benzene also makes a good material for painting machinery parts which are to be laid away for a period of time.

Antimony trichloride, 9 parts; crystallized iron chloride, 9 parts; tannic acid 4 parts, in 18 parts of water. Apply with a cloth, let it dry, and apply again, if necessary. This mixture forms a brown coating on the article. When dry, wash with water. Dry, then polish with linseed oil.

Removing Rusted Machine Screw

First, put a little oil on the screw. Then heat a long iron wire to a red heat and hold it on the screw head for a minute or two. Let the screw cool, adding more oil if all has evaporated. When cold, the screw usually can be removed with ease. If it still refuses to loosen, heat again and apply more oil.

Filling Cracks in Plaster Walls

Cracked plaster walls can be repaired with plaster of Paris mixed with thin glue size and with a small amount of hydrated lime added. Mix only a small quantity at a time.

If plaster walls are to be painted with oil paints, the cracks may be filled with thick white lead to which either precipitated chalk or plaster of Paris has been added. If the walls have already been painted, the crack filler may be colored until it matches.

Filling Cracks in Wood

Cracks in furniture, toys and other woodwork, if not too extensive, can be filled with wood sawdust or file dust mixed with thin liquid or carpenter's glue. Mix a few drops of the glue and a little wood dust until a thick paste is formed, and apply with a knife. Let the mixture harden slightly and then rub the wood with fine sandpaper. This covers the crack with fine dust, which is held by the soft glue and conceals the defect.

Cleaning Oilstone

To remove old oil from an oilstone that will no longer cut, heat the oilstone slightly and apply a paste of whiting (precipitated chalk) and water. When the paste has absorbed the oil, scratch off the whiting, reheat the stone, and apply a fresh batch of whiting. Repeat until no more oil is absorbed by the chalk.

Cleaning Mortar from Bricks

Hydrochloric acid may be used for cleaning mortar or cement from face brick and brick fireplaces. The acid is applied and another brick used to rub the excess mortar from the face of the brick.

To Make Tight Pipe Joints

#1—White-lead or red-lead paste, just as it comes in the tin or keg, is excellent for making pipe joints gastight, water-tight and air-tight. Good plumbers and gas-fitters white-lead or red-lead all joints.

#2—Shellac produces a good gastight joint when applied to the threads.

#3—Water-glass solution, talc and fine asbestos fibers.

To Trace Underground Water

The sodium salt of fluorescein has been found useful in determining the course of underground waters. Its use in ascertaining the direct pollution of wells or determining the drainage of an area has proved highly successful.

The chemical, called also fluorescein sodium salt, which is a dye, is dissolved in water and then mixed with the water, the course of which it is desired to trace. Search in the vicinity will soon reveal the point where the water reappears, because the water will be a brilliant green, due to the dye. The color is visible to the naked eye in a concentration of one part in forty million of water, or if a long clear glass tube is used, through which the water is viewed, the dye can be detected in one part in about ten billion parts of water.

Hectograph

Powdered whiting .... 1 lb.
Glycerin .... 4 oz.

Mix 8 oz. whiting with the glycerin and beat it up thoroughly: let stand 12 hours, then mix in rest of whiting and knead like dough. It will knead stiff so set it aside for the glycerin to work through. Knead well and then put in a shallow pan and flatten out. Make perfect surface on it with a straightedge.

If, on standing, the glycerin appears on the surface sprinkle on some dry whiting and knead the mixture. Don't wipe off the glycerin. The mixture should be just moist to work best. Add glycerin or whiting to secure this consistency.

Write what you wish on glazed paper with following ink. When writing is just dry lay the paper face down on the mixture and smooth flat with roller or hand. Let it remain 3 or 4 minutes, then remove. Put on blank paper: let first one remain just an instant, remove and apply another, which let remain a little longer and

so on. Many fine copies can be made. Wash off with damp rag to erase writing.

Ink—Dissolve a copying pencil or egg dye in water; add a little glycerin and some gum arabic and oil of cloves or, better, carbolic acid. Hectograph inks are sold at stationery supply stores.

Other formulas as follows can be used for the pad.

#1—Gelatin .... 10 oz.
    Water .... 40 "
    Glycerin .... 120 "

Whiting enough to making stiff paste.

#2—Gelatin .... 10 parts
    Kaolin (china clay)... 5 "
    Glycerin .... 38 "
    Water .... 38 "

#3—Dextrine .... 1½ oz.
    Sugar .... 2 "
    Gelatin .... 15 "
    Glycerin .... 15 "
    Zinc white .... 1½ "
    Water .... 10 "

#4—Glycerin .... 10 parts
    Gelatin .... 1 "
    Dextrose .... 1 "

Ground heavy spar enough to give desired consistency.

#5—Glycerin .... 12 oz.
    Gelatin .... 2 "
    Water .... 7½ "
    Sugar .... 2 "

#6—Water .... 10 oz.
    Dextrine .... 1½ "
    Sugar .... 2 "
    Gelatin .... 15 "
    Glycerin .... 15 "
    Zinc oxide .... 1½ "

#7—Glue .... 10 oz.
    Water .... 40 "
    Glycerin .... 120 "
    Barium sulphate ...... 8 "

Use of Carbon Tetrachloride

This liquid can be used as a fire extinguisher and also as a clothes cleaner. Its heavy gas promptly blankets a fire, shutting out the oxygen. Its non-electrical conductivity makes it useful in extinguishing fires where high tension electric wires are present. Being a good solvent for many waxes, greases and oils, the substance is widely used as a garment cleaner in the rightly called dry cleaning processes. On a large commercial scale, the garments are treated with the hot tetrachloride, tumbled, and the excess liquid freed from suspended dirt and distilled, thereby recovering the carbon tetrachloride to be used in treating other batches of clothing.

Preserving Anatomical Specimens

Jares-Klotz method.
Fix for one or more weeks in

(1)—Modified Carlsbad salts
(see below) .... 300 gm.
Hydrated chloral ..... 300 "
Formaldehyde solution. 300 "
Water ....9,600 cc.

(2)—Wash (one to two hours) in running water.

(3)—Preserve in the following:

Modified Carlsbad salts 250 gm.
Hydrated chloral ..... 100 "
Formaldehyde solution. 50 "
Water ....9,600 cc.

The modified Carlsbad salts has the following composition:

Potassium sulphite ... 2 gm.
Potassium nitrate .... 38 "
Sodium chloride ...... 18 "
Sodium bicarbonate ... 20 "
Sodium sulphite ...... 22 "

Preservative mixture for mounting skins:

White arsenic .... 2 dr.
Corrosive sublimate .. 2 "
Nutgalls .... 1 oz.
Capsicum, in powder.. ½ "
Sal ammoniac .... ½ "
Camphor, in powder.. 6 dr.

Mix together.

FOR THE HOUSEHOLD

Furniture Polish

Furniture and automobile polishes may, in most cases, be used interchangeably, for similar finishes are encountered in both lines of application. These finishes are either enamel, varnish, lacquer, or baked enamel. A good type of furniture or automobile polish is composed of an emulsifier (sodium oleate), carnauba wax (lustering agent), and steam-distilled pine oil (dirt and grime remover). The soap-pine oil combination insures the removal of dirt and grime from the surface, while the carnauba wax imparts the desired luster to the thoroughly cleansed surface.

A typical formula follows:

Red oil (oleic acid) soap.. 7.5 gal.
Water .... 67.5 "
Pine oil .... 15.0 "
Carnauba wax .... 10.0 "

Polishes of this nature do not contain inflammable or poisonous ingredients; they are permanently stable emulsions and therefore need not be shaken before using.

A simple furniture polish can be made by using the following formula and directions:

Potassium carbonate ..... 1 gm.
Beeswax .... 100 "
Turpentine .... 180 "
Water .... 350 cc.

Dissolve the potassium carbonate in about 100 cc. of water and add to the beeswax, which should be shredded. Heat the mixture to boiling and continue to boil until the wax saponifies at the expense of the small amount of carbonate present. Stir until cold, adding at this time any water that has been lost by evaporation. Add the turpentine, which will dissolve the saponified beeswax which the carbonate has formed, and the free beeswax which is unchanged. Stir until the whole is of the same consistency throughout, which will result in the formation of a creamy emulsion. Now add the remaining water and shake or stir. The polish is now complete, but a small amount of oil of cedar, oil of citronella, oil of pine, or other odorant may be added to produce a scent. The polish is applied to surfaces with a soft cloth, rubbing the surface briskly after applying to bring out the luster of the thin wax film.

Wabeck's polishing wax. Melt 4 parts of yellow wax and 1 of rosin; stir the mass vigorously, and when it is cooling, stir in 2 parts of turpentine.

Other desirable polishes are:

#1—Cedar oil .... 1 lb.
    Turpentine .... 1 pt.
    Ammonia water ...... 1 "

Dissolve the oil in the turpentine and then add the water, followed by a small piece of soap which tends to keep the liquids in the form of an emulsion.

#2—Acetic acid .... 1 oz.
    Raw linseed oil .... 1 "
    Alcohol, 188 proof .... 2 "
    Turpentine .... 2 "

Shake well before using. If desired this polish may be colored by adding a little anilin brown. If made in large quantities keep well stirred while bottling.

#3—Melt 1 oz. beeswax. Remove safe distance from fire and add 4 oz. warm turpentine. Next 1 pt. gasoline. To this add 1 pt. light paraffin oil and 1 teaspoonful of household ammonia. Shake well before bottling and shake well before using. A small piece of soap will tend to keep it from separating.

#4—Yellow wax .... 4 lb.
    Beeswax .... 2 "
    Linseed oil .... 4 gal.
    Turpentine .... 1 "
    Paraffin oil .... 1 "
    Water .... 7 "
    Carbonate of potash .. 3 oz.
    Soap chips .... 1 lb.

#5—Paraffin oil .... 1 pt.
    Kerosene .... 1 "
    Acetic acid .... 8 oz.

Mix by shaking. Shake before using. Dries quickly and does not coat wood.

#6—Yellow wax .... ½ lb.
    Oil turpentine .... 9 oz.

Melt the wax and add the turpentine.

#7—Beeswax .... ½ oz.
    Castile soap .... ½ "
    White wax .... ½ "
    Cover with:
    Warm water .... ½ pt.
    Turpentine .... ½ "

Shred together and allow to dissolve.

#8—Yellow wax .... 1 lb.
    Raw linseed oil ...... 4 oz.
    Oil turpentine .... 4 "

Mix the oil and yellow wax, and heat gently. Remove from heat and add the turpentine.

#9—Shellac .... 1 oz.
    Rosin .... 1 "
    Alcohol .... 8 "
    Oil turpentine .... 2 "
    Raw linseed oil ...... 8 "

#10—Linseed oil .... ½ gal.
    Butter of antimony.. 4 oz.
    Alcoholic shellac .... 1 pt.
    Turpentine .... 8 "

#11—Shellac .... 3 oz.
    Gum sandarac ...... 2 "
    Denatured alcohol ... 3 pt.

#12—Acetic acid .... 3 oz.
    Linseed oil .... 1 pt.
    Butter of antimony... 2 oz.
    Rosin .... ¼ "

Dissolve rosin in the oil, then add rest. Shake well.

#13—Stearine .... 10 parts
    Yellow wax .... 3 "
    Caustic potash ...... 6 "
    Yellow laundry soap. 1 "

Dissolve the potash in a small amount of water and add to other substances which have been melted over a low fire.

#14—Beeswax .... 1 lb.
    Shaved soap .... 4 oz.
    Potassium carbonate.. 2 "
    Water .... 1 gal.

Boil with stirring and cool. Color with alkanet root if desired.

Polishing Cloths

These cloths are usually made in two grades—one for cleaning the baser metals, or objects upon which considerable scouring must be done in order to clean them, and the second grade for the noble metals such as gold or silver.

The first step in making polishing cloths is the same for either of the two grades, and consists of impregnating flannel cloths cut to the desired size with a fixing medium to which the polishing powder adheres. Such a fixative is made from:

Oleic acid .... 4 oz.
Ammonia water .... 4 "
Water .... 1 gal.

The oleic acid should be mixed well with the ammonia water and the water added afterward. Soak the cloth in water and wring out, then immerse the cloths in the prepared solution and work the solution into the cloths using a hot solution. Wring the cloths dry and while still damp sprinkle with fine emery powder for the first grade or first type of cloth, and fine tripoli powder for the second grade or second type of cloth. Dry and brush off the loose powder which has not adhered to the material. Repeat this operation on the other side of the cloth.

Other formulas for the initial soaking mixture, or adherent, are:

Liquid paraffin (oil)....... 3 qt.
Cottonseed oil .... 1 "
Paraffin wax .... 3 oz.

Heat to mix and use about one part of the mixture dissolved in about six or seven parts of straight gasoline.

Another: Equal parts yellow dextrine and oxalic acid dissolved in warm water to make a thin cream. Soak the cloths in this paste and then sift the polishing powder on them.

The polishing powders can be sifted on with a flour sifter or a large salt shaker.

Different colored cloths can be used, one to receive the emery flour for coarse cleaning, and another color of flannel cloth, say white, to clean and polish fine tableware, and upon which the tripoli powder is to be sprinkled. Infusorial earth (diatomaceous earth) or fossil flour can also be used. A powder which has good polishing powers is also sold under the name of Silex, and the finest of this (air floated), or even the water floated variety, may be used.

#1—Liquid paraffin .... 3 qt.
    Cottonseed oil .... 1 "
    Gum benzoin .... 3 oz.

Heat the whole, making sure that the gum benzoin melts and mixes with the oils.

#2—Paraffin oil .... 1 oz.
    Oil of cedar .... 1 "
    Gasoline (straight) ... 1 qt.

Place cloths of any size in the above mixture and then hang up and allow to dry, thus causing the gasoline to evaporate. The remaining paraffin oil on the cloth will then cause dust particles to adhere to the cloth. The oil of cedar is merely used to give the cloth a pleasing odor. If the above cloths are to be manufactured for profit, a dark colored cloth should be selected. Package in waxed paper bags or cellophane.

Two other mixtures for the polishing cloths are:

Make a paste from oleic acid and whiting. Saturate flannel cloths with the mixture.

Dissolve 4 oz. soap in 30 oz. hot water. Add 2 oz. pumice powder. Saturate cloths with the mixture and wring dry.

Some of the chemically prepared dust cloths which have a wide sale on the market today contain mixtures of a vegetable oil and a mineral oil, with or without a gum or plastic. A good cloth which retains the dust as one uses it can be made by immersing any desired cloth in a solution of about one part of gum benzoin dissolved in a warm mixture of 15 parts of cottonseed or rapeseed oil and 50 parts of mineral oil such as light paraffin oil. One may use 1 ounce of the gum in a mixture of 4 pints of mineral oil and one pint of the vegetable oil.

Fumigating Incense

The following is made into a paste with the alcohol and formed into cones.

#1—Gum olibanum .... 2 oz.
    Gum storax .... 1 "
    Gum benzoin .... 6 dr.
    Peruvian balsam ...... ½ oz.
    Tolu balsam .... 3 dr.

Alcohol, sufficient quantity.

#2—Powdered gum arabic. ¼ oz.
    Powdered cascarilla bark ½ "
    Powdered benzoin .... 4 "
    Potassium nitrate .... ½ "
    Powdered charcoal ... 7 "
    Oil of eucalyptus...... 25 drops
    Oil of cloves .... 25 "

Water, enough to make a paste.

Dissolve the nitrate in the water and use it to make a paste with the other ingredients.

Removing Match Scratches

Match scratches on woodwork often can be removed by rubbing them with a slice of a lemon, then with whiting, and finally with a moist, soapy cloth. Shellac stains can be removed with washing soda. Borax also will dissolve shellac.

Removing Rain Spots

Rain spots on the ceiling can be removed with a little unslaked lime dissolved in alcohol (denatured alcohol can be used). The lime is thoroughly shaken up with the alcohol until it crumbles into a fine powder. This mixture is then brushed over the spots. When dry, the ceiling can be painted in the usual way.

Removing Stopper from Bottle

When the stopper of a cut glass bottle becomes so tightly stuck that it cannot be removed, it can be loosened by placing on the joint a mixture of 5 parts glycerin, 10 parts chloral hydrate, 3 parts 25 percent hydrochloric acid, and 5 parts water.

Removing Ink Spots from Wood

Ink spots usually can be removed from woodwork with a strong solution of oxalic acid. Prepare the solution by dissolving oxalic acid crystals in water until no more will dissolve. If several applications do not cause the stains to disappear, apply the acid once more and immediately add some chlorinated lime. Should this fail, try repeated treatments with phosphoric acid of fifty percent strength. Be sure to remove all traces of the chemicals from the surface with water and allow the wood to dry before attempting to refinish it.

Wax Dressing for Floors

Yellow wax (ceresine or beeswax)	10 parts
Potassium carbonate	5 "
Water	70 "
Soap	½ cu. in.

In making this inexpensive and easily applied emulsion, the potassium carbonate is dissolved in a small quantity of the water and the soap added and shaken to make complete solution. Place the remaining water and wax in a vessel and heat to melt the wax, then add the soap-carbonate solution cautiously and stir until an emulsion is produced. It can be colored any desired shade with water soluble anilin dye.

Bare wooden floors can be preserved by the application of the following mixture of drying and non-drying oils:

Linseed oil	1 part
Light lubricating oil	1 "
Cottonseed oil	1 "

The cottonseed oil may be omitted if desired, and the linseed oil can be used alone. The lubricating oil tends to prevent the floor from becoming dull and matte. The whole mixture is used on floors that have not been painted, and is useful for the porches, sun houses, garage floors, outside stairways, etc., where it is not desired to protect with paint. The liquid mixture can be applied with a whitewash brush.

Preparations for Dance Floors

For waxing dance floors, the following have been found to be useful:

#1—Paraffin wax	1 lb.
Boracic acid (technical).	5 "

Oil of lavender or oil of Paris rose, enough to perfume.

The paraffin is melted and the boracic acid sifted in, beating until it is thoroughly incorporated. While the mixture is cooling, add the scenting oil and whip again. When cold, the whole stiff mixture is worked through a sieve made of fly screen. It is broadcast upon the floor.

#2—Yellow wax	5 oz.
Stearine	1 lb.
Oil of turpentine	3 "

Heat the turpentine with caution so it will not ignite and melt the wax in it, take off the fire and stir until nearly cold, then pour into cans.

Destroying Smoke Odors

Odors of smoke in clothing or in rooms can be removed by exposure to the fumes of formaldehyde. If only a few garments are to be deodorized, place them alone in a closet on the floor of which is placed a solution of 4 oz. of formalin (40% formaldehyde solution) in a quart of water. Close the door tightly and allow the garments to be exposed to the fumes for 24 hours. Remove and air the clothing. If the odor of formaldehyde persists, expose the clothing to the fumes of ammonia.

Rooms or buildings, that have been subjected to smoke can be deodorized by the same formaldehyde treatment, using about a quart of the strong formaldehyde to a room.

Bottle-capping Compounds

The bottles are inserted, top first, into the melted mixtures. The compounds can also be used as cements or sealing waxes.

#1—Rosin .... 4 lb.
    Tallow .... 1 "
    Red lead .... 1 "

Mix with heat. For black color, use lampblack. For green, use chromic oxide in place of the red lead.

#2—Shellac .... 3 oz.
    Venice turpentine ..... 1½ "
    Boric acid .... 72 gr.
    Powdered talcum ..... 3 oz.
    Ether .... 6 dr.
    Alcohol .... 12½ oz.

#3—Gelatin .... 1 oz.
    Starch .... 1 "
    Gum arabic .... 1 "
    Salicylic acid .... 20 gr.
    Water .... 1 pt.

Dissolve, with aid of heat, the gelatin, salicylic acid, and gum arabic in half of the water, and if a scum forms, strain through cloth. Mix the starch (corn starch) with the other half of the water, and stir this into the heated gelatin mixture. Easter egg dye may be added to color.

#4—Rosin .... 100 parts
    Tallow .... 20 "
    Prepared chalk ...... 2 "
    Cottonseed oil .... 6 "

Heat to mix. Do not overheat. Dip bottle in while hot.

#5—Rosin .... 12 parts
    Turpentine .... 7 "
    Tallow .... 6 "
    Whiting .... 8 "
    Litharge .... 6 "

Use hot.

To Clean Glass Windows

Mix one ounce of pulverized whiting, one ounce of alcohol, one ounce of ammonia and one pint of water and apply to the outside of the window with a soft cloth. After the mixture has dried, rub it off with another soft cloth. The glass will shine brightly for a long time.

Disinfectants

These disinfectants consist of pine oil and rosin soap, emulsified with water. A simple method of preparing such an emulsion is to use

#1—Pine oil (steam distilled) .... 1,000 gm.
    Rosin .... 400 "
    25 per cent sodium hydroxid solution .... 200 "

The oil and rosin are heated together in a covered porcelain vessel until all the rosin dissolves. The mixture is cooled to 80° C., the sodium hydroxid solution added, and the liquid violently stirred for at least 10 minutes. Sufficient water is added to make the mixture to the original weight, and the preparation cooled. The emulsion can be used by diluting one part with 40 parts of water, for general purposes, although weaker dilutions are also effective on some types of bacteria. For the bathtub, wash basin, tile floor or toilet, a 1:10 dilution may be made. In dog kennels, poultry houses, and in garbage receptacles, 1:10 or a 1 to 12 dilution of the emulsion with water is satisfactory.

#2—Lye: Use a 2% solution in water (1 lb. lye in 5½ gallons water).

#3—Chlorinated lime: Use 6 oz. dissolved in 1 gallon of water. Has an odor.

♯4—Lime: Use 1 part slaked lime to 4 of water. Has no odor.

To Prevent Flies Hatching

♯1—Use of borax: Apply in the proportion of 10 ounces of borax to 10 cubic feet of manure immediately on its removal from the barn. Apply the borax particularly around the outer edges of the pile with a flour sifter or any fine sieve, and sprinkle two or three gallons of water over the borax-treated manure.

In addition to the application of borax to horse manure to kill fly larvae, it may be applied in the same proportion to other manures as well as to refuse and garbage. In the case of garbage, use two ounces of borax to the can.

Borax may also be applied to floors and crevices in barns, stables, markets, etc., as well as to street sweepings, and water should be added as in the treatment of horse manure.

♯2—Hellebore as a germicidal agent: For the treatment of manure a water extract of the hellebore may be prepared by adding ½ pound of the powder to 10 gallons of water, and after stirring, allow to stand 24 hours. The mixture thus prepared is sprinkled over the manure at the rate of 10 gallons to every 8 bushels (10 cubic feet) of manure. From the result of 12 experiments with manure piles treated under natural conditions, it appears that such treatment results in the destruction of from 88 to 99 per cent of the fly larvae.

Trisodium Phosphate

This substance is finding wide use as a detergent in cleaning many items. It is inexpensive, and is stocked by many smaller retail chemical supply houses, or drug stores. It is appearing on the market packaged by itself under various trade names.

Trisodium phosphate (TSP) is a neutral salt in the dry state, but when dissolved in water, hydrolysis takes place, forming a little sodium hydroxide and disodium phosphate. The percentage of sodium hydroxide formed is about 6% of the amount of the trisodium phosphate used. In other words, if 100 pounds of trisodium phosphate is dissolved in distilled water, there results 6 pounds of sodium hydroxide and 94 pounds of disodium phosphate.

In many cleaning compounds which are either modified sodas or soda ash, while such compounds are neutral in the dry state, they are, however, slightly alkaline when put into solution. The hydrolysis taking place in both modified soda and soda ash is so much greater that the quantities of sodium hydroxide liberated is present in sufficient quantities to injure fabric, destroy linoleum, rubber, varnish and painted surfaces.

Trisodium phosphate does not contain caustic, grease, soap or acid.

For home use, the trisodium phosphate is simply dissolved in water. To wash clothes put 1 or 2 teaspoons in the tub overnight. For washing dishes, use a teaspoon to the dish pan. Precipitating lime as it does, half an ounce of TSP in ten gallons of water for the bath will result in a soft water. For washing woodwork, floors, use 1 ounce in a pail of water. The same solution is useful in cleaning motors, engines, and mechanical parts of grease and dirt. For washing the hands, use four ounces of the chemical dissolved in a gallon of water and use the solution like liquid soap. As TSP is an antiseptic, it aids in healing cuts and abrasions of the skin. It is also used as a boiler compound, a minimum of about four pounds per 1000 gallons of water being required. When used in boilers, the alkalinity of the treated water should be at least P_h8.

General Cleaning Preparations

This preparation can be used for painted walls, or a hand cleanser, one part of the following being added to about 15 parts of water (one ounce taken and diluted to one pint).

Household ammonia	1 part
Water-glass	12 "
Borax	2 "

Filling Cracks in Floors

It frequently happens that floor boards shrink badly, particularly pine floors, showing wide and unsightly cracks. These should be filled in before refinishing. Of course, they are always filled with dirt which must be carefully removed and the cracks dusted out. Do not attempt to fill in these wide cracks with ordinary putty because it will dry up and shrink in a short time and jar out of the floor. Use the following formula.

Soak white blotting paper in water and squeeze out the excess water. Knead whiting and glue size into this soft paper until it forms a putty, after which it may be colored to suit with dry colors. Wet the cracks with water and press this putty firmly into them, smoothing out as evenly as possible. When dry, sandpaper flush with the surface of the floor.

Another excellent filler is ordinary cornstarch mixed with equal parts of linseed oil and turpentine with sufficient japan drier to set it quickly. Mix this to putty-like consistency and wet the cracks with linseed oil before applying.

To Keep Pipes from Sweating

The sweating of pipes is caused by their carrying cold liquids which cool the pipes and the surrounding air to such an extent that the water in the air is condensed or liquefied upon the surface of pipes. One manner in which this condensation, which is often accompanied by dripping, is counteracted, is to clean the pipe of rust or oil and then painting with red lead or a white lead paint. While the paint is still wet, pulverized cork is applied until no more will adhere. A method of coating the pipe with the cork is to hold a screen or shield in back of the pipe and scatter the pulverized cork against the pipe. The excess cork is kept from scattering by the back-up shield. When the paint dries, the cork will be found firmly imbedded in it, the cork layer acting as a heat insulator, preventing the cooler pipe from coming into contact with the surrounding air. The cork layer is afterwards painted a suitable color which further binds the particles together.

To Remove Mildew from Canvas

Mildew can be removed from canvas or other cloth by sponging with a weak solution of calcium hypochlorite, or bleaching powder. The bleaching powder solution should be well washed out afterward.

To Prevent Mildew on Canvas

Saturate the canvas in a hot solution of $\frac{1}{4}$ pound of soap in a gallon of water. Wring out and while still moist immerse for twelve hours in a solution of $\frac{1}{2}$ pound of alum in a gallon of water.

To Bleach Beeswax

Yellow beeswax is bleached by shredding and exposing it to the sun and air for a period of a month or two. It is occasionally watered, if the morning dews are not heavy enough to moisten the wax at frequent intervals. Tests are frequently made upon the wax to determine if the wax on the interior of the shredded pieces have been bleached, and if conditions warrant, they may be gathered, melted, shredded and again exposed to the atmosphere.

Re-inking Typewriter Ribbons

A solution for re-inking typewriter ribbons consists of the lead of an indelible pencil dissolved in a solution of equal parts of pure grain alcohol and glycerin. Apply to the ribbon with a semi-stiff brush.

To Keep Down Outdoor Dust

Dust may be kept down on roads, private driveways, tennis courts, or playgrounds by sprinkling with water as is well known, but this gives only temporary relief.

The modern method of dust control now used by officials of states, counties, cities and villages from coast to coast is to put clean moisture into road surfaces and keep it there. This modern method has the same effect as a good rain. It makes the road as moist as though it had been thoroughly sprinkled with a hose and regulates the supply of moisture in the road—keeping it there for weeks.

This necessary moisture is easily obtained by applying calcium chloride to the road surfaces. A preparation specially prepared for this purpose can now be purchased.

The chloride flake is prepared by driving off the natural supply of moisture in huge dryers, and the product is then processed into thin flakes and sealed up in moisture-tight containers. The dry flakes, like small pieces of shell, can be spread about on the road easily. Within a few hours the flakes dissolve themselves in the moisture they absorb. Wherever the flakes have been applied the earth is moist—not only the day after it is put on—but all through the dusty season.

Two hundred pounds of this substance, modified calcium chloride, will produce about 600 to 1,000 pounds of water. Two lbs. is used to each sq. yard of road surface.

Dustless Coal and Coke

The process for treating coal and coke to control dust is comparatively simple. A solution of a deliquescent chemical is atomized and distributed over the coal's surface, thereby rendering it permanently dustless. Dustless coal and coke have been on the market for several years and the results obtained through actual consumer use have been so satisfactory that the treatment has been adopted as standard practice by thousands of mine operators, shippers and coal merchants in all parts of the United States and Canada.

For many years it was the general practice to dampen coal with water to lay the dust. While this offered temporary relief, the moisture soon evaporated under the influence of drying winds, low humidity, and warm basements, and the coal became as dusty as ever.

The calcium chloride treatment eliminates the biggest objection to coal—dust and dirt. The coal merchants can now supply the public with clean, dustless coal. The process of dust-proofing coal is extremely simple and consists merely of spraying the fuel as thoroughly as possible with the correct amount of calcium chloride solution.

Under ordinary conditions fuel may be best treated either during the process of unloading the cars or of loading the delivery trucks. Preference should be given to the placing of spray nozzles at some point in the handling operation where the coal is passing over a chute or conveyor in a comparatively thin layer. This allows more complete coverage of the coal or coke.

The use of a mist-like spray of the correct strength solution is the most economical and satisfactory way to treat coal. A finely atomized spray concentrated on the coal or coke will eliminate the use of excess solution and at the same time will give complete coverage. A comparatively small quantity of solution is required, from one to three and a quarter gallons per ton, depending upon the amount of slack or fines present in the fuel.

Coal properly treated should show no drippage nor should it show any dust when a shovelful is thrown into the air.

There are on the market at the present time a number of satisfactory spray equipments.

For ordinary applications, the following table will give the strength of solution and the quantity in gallons required per ton of coal to produce a permanently dustless fuel:

	Pounds calcium chloride per gallon solution	Gallons of solution per ton fuel
Semi-bituminous (including pocahontas) prepared sizes	3-3½	2¾-3
High volatile bituminous prepared sizes	3-3½	2¼-2¾
Anthracite prepared sizes	3-3½	1 gallon
Anthracite buckwheat for stoker use	3½	¾ gallon
Coke (household grades and sizes)	3	2-2½

For home use, the calcium chloride solution can be sprayed upon the coal with a whitewash sprayer before the coal is laid away. The solution is especially suitable when small quantities, such as hodfuls are to be carried into living rooms to replenish fires.—Courtesy Dow Chemical Co.

Silver Polish

To 4 pounds best grade whiting add ¼ pound cream tartar and 3 ozs. calcined magnesia. Mix thoroughly.

Linoleum Polish, or Wax

Yellow ceresine wax	......	4 oz.
Hard paraffin wax	....	2½ "
Boiled linseed oil	....	1½ "
Turpentine	....	16 "

Oil of mirbane to give odor. Dissolve with the aid of gentle heat.

Paste Metal Polish

Iron oxide finely ground...		5 oz.
Pumice stone	....	16 "

Oleic acid enough to make pasty.

To Clean Brass

If there is any oily substance on the brass, boil it in a solution of strong lye. Mix equal quantities of nitric and sulphuric acids in a stone or earthen vessel. Dip the brass in the solution, but take it out immediately and rinse it in soft water, and wipe it in sawdust till it is dry.

Mosquito Repellents

#1—Oil of citronella .... 1 dr.
   Oil of pennyroyal ..... 1 "
   Kerosene, enough to make 6 ounces.

A small quantity of oil of lavender might be added to improve the scent. Used in spray guns.

#2—Oil of cedar .... 2 dr.
   Oil of citronella .... 4 "
   Spirits of camphor .... 1 oz.

For skin applications.

#3—Oil of citronella is one of the most widely used mosquito repellents. It may be used pure or mixed with mineral oil, vaseline, or lanolin in the proportion of one part to five. Almost any oily preparation on the skin repels mosquitoes to some extent.

Another move against the mosquitoes is spraying with a kerosene pyrethrum mixture. This will destroy those struck by the spray and also acts as a repellent.

There is no cure for mosquito bites, but one method of relief consists in rubbing the punctures gently with a moist piece of toilet soap.

#4—Oil pennyroyal .... 1 oz.
    Oil of anise .... 1 dr.
    Spirits of camphor..... 3 "
    Rubbing alcohol ...... 8 oz.

#5—Castor oil .... 1 oz.
    Alcohol .... 1 "
    Oil of lavender .... 1 "

This mixture avoids the odor of the oil of citronella.

Heating Bottles

The various bottles that give out warmth when placed in hot water or the oven, or when water is added to them, operate upon well known physical or chemical principles.

One of the simplest bottles is made by slowly slaking lime in a suitable container, the reaction producing heat. However, in practical operation the chemical reactions used are usually of an oxidizing type.

Several such compositions consist of iron borings and an electrolyte such as salt, or copper sulphate, to which water is added; or they consist of aluminum metal and an alkali which, on the addition of water, produces heat.

A composition producing mild heat when water is added is:

#1—Iron filings .... 40 parts
    Manganese dioxide ... 5 "
    Salt .... 3 "

Another, containing iron:

#2—Iron filings .... 4 parts
    Sodium chloride ...... 1 "
    Calcium chloride ..... 2 "
    Sulphur .... 1 "

The above will also produce heat on the addition of water. It is well to use degreased iron filings or borings. They can be freed from grease by washing with benzol, or if very greasy, with gasoline.

#3—Iron filings .... 12 oz.
    Copper chloride ...... 5 "
    Sal ammoniac .... ½ "

Mix the above and add about half a pint of water. Heat will be liberated.

#4—Sodium hyposulphite.. 9 parts
    Sodium acetate .... 1 "

The above mixture, if placed in a suitable container and allowed to melt by placing the container in hot water, will when removed give off heat for several hours. The chemicals dissolve in their own water of crystallization, so it is not necessary to add water.

#5—Sodium acetate can be incorporated in a bottle heater, however, if water is to be added, by mixing the sodium acetate with calcium chloride.

Cleaning Bottles

Grease or gum can be removed from bottles by a solvent such as gasoline, carbon tetrachloride, alcohol, toluene, etc. Shot, sand, or even soil, shaken about in the bottle with water, will mechanically remove dirt, scums, and dried yeast. A bottle brush and a scouring powder will prove helpful.

Solidified linseed oil, gasoline dregs or the gums formed by gasoline on long standing, are easily removed by a chromic acid solution, or even strong sulphuric acid. The chromic acid solution can be made by dissolving powdered potassium bichromate in sulphuric acid to which has been added an equal part of water, or the water may be omitted. This acid is easily washed out of the bottle after being left in contact with the substance to be removed.

Moth Repellent

#1—Carbon tetrachloride . 2 gal.
    Straight gasoline ..... ½ "
    Gum camphor .... 4 oz.
    Oil cedar leaf ....6 to 8 "

The above is mixed thoroughly, then sprayed on both clothes and inside of trunk, box or other container.

Poultry Tonic

Epsom salts .... 1 lb.
Magnesium oxide .... 1 oz.
Ferrous sulphate (copperas) 4 "
Ground ginger .... 2 "
Flowers of sulphur .... 6 "
Mustard .... 2 "

Mix. One tablespoonful in moist mash for twelve birds each morning for three mornings. Discontinue for two weeks and repeat.

Removing Spots from Polished Tables

Cover the spot with several soft paper napkins, cut the same size as the spot. Apply a hot iron to the paper, regulating the heat so that the paper does not scorch. Remove the napkins and the iron and apply a cloth on which are several drops of mineral oil. Then rub briskly, allowing no time for the spot to become cool. Polish with a dry cloth, and repeat the process if necessary.

Sweeping Compounds

There are many sweeping compounds on the market made of sawdust, sand oil, coloring matter and disinfectants. Usually fine hardwood sawdust, moistened with water at the time of use, will prove satisfactory for this purpose. Some sweeping compounds contain sand and oil while in others sawdust is the important ingredient

The following makes a good sweeping compound:

Fine sawdust .... 3½ parts
Sand .... 10 "
Salt .... 1½ "
Paraffin oil .... 1 "

Another compound consists of a uniform mixture of finely ground sawdust and clean fine sand properly impregnated with a refined heavy mineral oil and water. Such a preparation must show an analysis not more than 20% of water, not more than 50% of clean sand, not less than 5% of refined heavy mineral oil, and the remainder finely ground sawdust.

In some commercial sweeping compounds, coloring matter is added, such as iron oxide or other pigments. Naphthalene flakes or various disinfectants are also added.

Essential oils, such as oil of eucalyptus or oil of sassafras are frequently added to impart a pleasant odor or to suppress unpleasant odors that may be due to the ingredients.

Disinfectants of various types may be employed. Pine oils, or small amounts of creosote oil, or "dead oils" might answer the purpose.

Three other sweeping compounds that will prove satisfactory are:

#1—100 lb. of sifted sawdust and 60 lb. sifted sand. In a bucket place 1½ gal. paraffin oil, some oil soluble green color, 2 oz. creosote and ½ oz. oil of cedar. Mix thoroughly, add to the sawdust and sand and work in until thoroughly mixed.

#2—Sawdust (sifted) ..... 2 pk.
    Salt .... 2 lb.
    Flake naphthalene ..... ¼ "
    Carbolic acid .... 2 oz.

Mix well, then add enough paraffin oil slightly to moisten the powder.

This is sprinkled on the floor before sweeping.

#3—To every hundred pounds of sawdust add 1 pt. of paraffin oil and mix well. If colored compound is desired add an oil soluble anilin dye to the oil and also a little oil of cedar or oil of sassafras.

Fly Paper

The paper used should first be sized around the edges to prevent the sticky material from spreading, but if large sheets are taken and only the center of the sheets are smeared with the glue, this may be omitted. It will be best, however, to lay the sticky prepared sheet on uncoated sheets to avoid penetration.

#1—Venice turpentine ..... 2 oz.
    Rosin .... 8 "
    Castor oil .... 2 "
    Sugar .... 2 "

Dissolve in double boiler and apply with a brush while it is warm.

#2—Lard oil .... 4 oz.
    Rosin .... 1 lb.

Boil together, spread thinly on Manilla paper.

#3—Castor oil .... 12 oz.
    Rosin .... 27 "

Melt. Size or varnish paper with a mixture of glue, 12 oz.; water, 4 pt. When dry apply the oil and rosin mixture.

#4—Rosin .... 9 parts
    Rapeseed oil .... 3 "
    Honey .... 1 "

The rosin and oil should be melted together and then add the honey. Spread upon sheets of paper cut to convenient size.

Another type of paper, of a poisonous nature, is prepared by dipping unsized paper into a solution of the following ingredients:

Quassia chip liquor .... 5 parts
Cobalt chloride .... 1 "
Water .... 20 "

The quassia chip liquor may be made by boiling quassia chips in water until the volume of boiling water has been reduced about one-half.

Repellents for Fleas

#1—Oil of pennyroyal is a good repellent for fleas.

#2—On animals: Derris powder, an insecticide consisting of the finely ground roots of the tropical plant known as derris, is effective in killing fleas on cats and dogs. Scattering a teaspoon of the powder along the back of the animal is the method suggested. Fresh pyrethrum powder answers the same purpose. Neither is poisonous to humans or animals.

#3—The thorough washing of infested animals in kerosene emulsion is a cheap and satisfactory method of destroying fleas. Five gallons of this emulsion may be made by dissolving 2 oz. of washing soap in 1 quart of hot water and when brought to a boil removing it from the fire and adding 2½ pints of kerosene. The mixture should be agitated violently with an egg beater or something of the sort. This should result in a milky mass from which the oil does not separate. Water is then added to make 5 gallons. Free kerosene will burn animals, and if any separates out the mixture should be reheated, care being taken to avoid spilling it on the fire or boiling it over, and then it should be beaten again. The skin of cats is much more easily injured with chemicals than that of dogs; hence, any preparation used should be weaker for cats than dogs.

Mosquito Repellents

Cold cream, or lanolin, serving as a base for oil of pennyroyal, will be found an effective mosquito repellent. Melt the cold cream or the lanolin by placing it in a vessel of water and heating. This simple water bath will cause the cream to melt without decomposition. When melted, remove from the fire and allow to cool, whipping, and at the same time introducing oil of pennyroyal. This will thoroughly incorporate the repellent with the cream and when cool the cream is ready for use.

Equal parts of creosote and oil of eucalyptus, or even oil of eucalyptus alone, will be found to repel mosquitoes.

Oil of lavender has been claimed by some to be a good repellent. Other preparations are:

#1—Oil of citronella ...... 1 oz.
Spirits of camphor ... 1 "
Oil of cedar .... ½ "

#2—Oil of eucalyptus ...... 2 oz.
Alcohol .... 8 "
Glycerin .... 8 "

Dissolve the oil in the alcohol, then add the glycerin. Apply to the exposed parts of the body and wash off in the morning.

Pyrethrum powders, known to the trade as Dalmatian insect powder, Persian insect powder, buhach, and otherwise, are very effective when fresh and pure. Pyrethrum powders are usually used dry, and are puffed or blown into crevices frequented by insects, or puffed or blown into the air of a room in which there are mosquitoes. The burning of the powder in a room at night is common practice.

The following, when molded into cones, produce a smoke and odor that act as mosquito repellents:

#1—Powdered wood charcoal 14 oz.
Potassium nitrate ..... 2 "
Carbolic acid ....1½ "
Dalmatian insect powder 8 "
Gum arabic or tragacanth mucilage, enough to form a paste.

#2—Powdered charcoal .... 14 oz.
Nitrate of potassium... 2 "
Benzoin .... 4 "
Hard tolu balsam .... 2 "
Insect powder (Dalmatian) .... 4 "
Tragacanth mucilage, a sufficient quantity
Powder the solids, and make into cones with water.

#3—Thyme .... 2 oz.
Lavender, flowers ..... 2 "
Insect powder .... 2 "
Potassium nitrate, powdered .... 2 "
Tragacanth, powdered.. 3 dr.
Mix thoroughly, make into a mass with water, form into cones and dry. The lavender flowers and the thyme should be powdered.

Repelling Roaches

#1—One of the most common methods of killing the roach is with ordinary borax, 1 part of borax to 3 parts of finely pulverized chocolate, sprinkled freely about the places frequented by roaches. Or it may be mixed with any food that seems to attract the roaches.

#2—Sodium fluoride mixed with starch, corn meal or flour and sifted about their runways will repel roaches.

Mineral Licks for Cattle

Salt .... 187 lb.
Phosphate rock .... 62 "
Sulphur .... 14 "
Copperas .... 9 "
Epsom salts .... 7 "
Manganese sulphate ...... 4 oz.
Potassium iodide .... 4 "
Mix and press into cake. Ninety-

three lb. of bone meal can be used instead of the ground phosphate rock.

Runs in Silk Hosiery

Aluminum ammonium sulphate (ammonia alum) has been used to prevent runs in silk hosiery. The dry stockings are soaked in:

Aluminum ammonium sul-
  phate .... 1 oz.
Water .... 1 qt.

About thirty minutes should be allowed, the stockings then removed, rinsed and washed with soapy water.

Hard Wood Floor Polish

A good polish for hard wood floors is made as follows:—Melt together in a bowl set in hot water, half a pint of turpentine, two and a half ounces of powdered resin, and three-quarters of a pound of beeswax. Do not let these ingredients come in contact with fire while being melted, as they are inflammable. When melted apply with a soft cloth and polish with a brush.

Despite the fact that modern houses are built with hardwood floors, many floors are oiled. For floor oil, the following will be found to be suitable:

♯1—Potassium carbonate... ¼ lb.
  Beeswax, shredded ... ½ "
  Water .... 3½ pt.

Dissolve the potassium carbonate in a pint of the water and melt the remaining water and the beeswax together. Then mix the two solutions and boil the whole until emulsification takes place as judged by a creamy-like formation.

♯2—Kerosene .... 1 pt.
  Limewater .... 1 "
  Light paraffin oil ..... 1 gal.

Mix and shake before using.

Flower Jar Potpourri

♯1—Dried lavender ...... 1 lb.
  Whole rose leaves... 1 "
  Crushed orris root... ½ "
  Broken cloves, cinna-
    mon, allspice ..... 2 oz. each
  Table salt .... 1 lb.

♯2—Put ½-inch layers of flowers in a glass jar with layers of fine salt between, screw the top on jar tightly and place in some dark, cool place. Let stand for two months, then strain and press the liquid through a cloth and put in a glass bottle.

FOR THE KITCHEN

Flavoring Paste

For a base, gum tragacanth is used and the flavoring oils incorporated in this gum, which is made into a jelly-like mass by soaking the gum in water. Take 8 ounces of gum tragacanth and soak it in several quarts of water until it swells and becomes thoroughly softened. This will require about a week, and half of the gum will dissolve in the water. Use cleaned gum to start with and much trouble will be avoided in freeing the mass from foreign particles. The resulting paste should now be mixed with about ten ounces of glycerin, using heat to make a good blend, but do not burn. When cool, add to the resulting mass, two ounces each of the following oils to produce the desired flavor: Oil of wintergreen, peppermint, lemon, orange, clove, cinnamon. If an almond flavor is desired, add half a liquid ounce of chemically pure benzaldehyde.

Homemade Candies

Chocolate Fudge—Cook 2 cups sugar, ½ cup milk, ⅔ cup water, 2 squares unsweetened chocolate, stirring constantly until soft ball is formed when dropped in water. Add 1 tablespoon butter and remove from stove. Let stand till nearly cold; then add ½ teaspoon vanilla, beating hard till it begins to thicken. Spread on buttered pan till cool and cut in squares. Vary by adding nuts or cocoanut.

Turkish Paste:

Gelatin	2 tablespoons
Cold water	½ pt.
Sugar XXXX	1 lb.
Orange juice	1 gill
Lemon juice	2 teaspoons

Sprinkle gelatin into one-half of water, then cover and stand two hours. Bring the remainder of water and sugar to boiling point, add gelatin, bring to boiling point again and simmer twenty minutes. Remove from fire, add grated rind of one orange, stir in orange and lemon juices. Pour into a cold pan and set in a cool place to harden. Cut in cubes and roll in sifted confectioners' sugar.

Common Twist Candy—Boil three pounds of common sugar and one pint of water over a slow fire for half an hour, without skimming. Rub the hands with butter and pull when cool until it is white.

Butter Scotch—Take 5 tablespoons molasses, 4 tablespoons sugar, 2 tablespoons butter, 4 tablespoons water; boil till brittle when dropped in cold water; before removing from the stove, put in a pinch of soda, then pour out on buttered tins and mark in squares when cool.

Cream Candy—Take 1 pound of white sugar, 1 cup of water, ½ teaspoon cream of tartar, 2 teaspoons vinegar, 2 teaspoons vanilla, butter the size of an egg; boil until it hardens when dropped into water. Pour upon a buttered platter and when nearly cold, pull.

Chocolate Caramels—Take one cup each of grated chocolate, sugar, milk, molasses, and butter the size of an egg; boil it until it drops hard; then pour it out on a buttered dish and mark it in squares before it cools.

Maple Candy—Take a pound of maple sugar and a pint of rich milk, or thin cream; cook it until a soft ball is formed when it is dropped in water; flavor with vanilla, add a cup of pecans, or other nuts, and pour it out on a greased pan to cool; mark it off in squares before it becomes too firm.

French Creams—Take 2 cups granulated sugar, add to it ½ cup milk. Bring slowly to a boil and boil for 5 minutes; take off the fire and set in a pan of cold water; stir rapidly until it creams; shape into balls with the hands. Place nuts on top of the creams, or it can be arranged in layers and figs or dates placed between; then cut into squares. Fine chocolate creams can be made of this mixture by dipping the balls into melted chocolate, and placing on buttered tins.

Inexpensive Fudge—To two cups sugar add one cup water, three tablespoons cocoa, and a small pinch of salt; boil until it makes a soft ball in water. Then add a tablespoon of butter and cool it in a bowl of water. Add ½ teaspoon vanilla, stir until creamy and pour on buttered dish.

Vanilla Extract Powder

Color 4 ounces of granulated sugar very dark by using anilin brown in liquid form. In another vessel mix 15 drams vanillin and 2 drams coumarin with 2 ounces powdered sugar. Now mix the colored sugar and the powdered sugar containing the flavor with 1½ pounds of granulated sugar, stirring until the batch takes on an even brown tint. Use 2 ounces to ½ pint of warm water to make a good strong extract.

Baking Powders

The formulas for baking powders are controlled first by the amount of available gas the baking powder must contain, and second, by the capacity of the acid-acting material to decompose and liberate the gas from the bicarbonate of soda. This capacity is known as "neutralizing strength."

The Federal Government requires a minimum of 12% available carbon dioxide in baking powder sold in interstate commerce. Most state laws specify the same minimum, although some states have a minimum of 10%.

Most baking powders are made up to contain approximately 28% bicarbonate of soda. This will yield 14½% of carbon dioxide when the baking powder is fresh and provides a margin of safety to compensate for any loss of strength if the powder is held for a long period in storage or on the grocers' shelves, as frequently happens.

The amount of acid-acting materials required are calculated from the amount of soda and the neutralizing strength of the acid. For instance, cream of tartar has a neutralizing strength of 44.6%, which means that 100 pounds of cream of tartar are necessary to react completely with 44.6 pounds of bicarbonate of soda. Thus a baking powder containing 28% soda would have to contain 62.7% cream of tartar and the remainder would be starch.

The high grade mono calcium phosphate of commerce is guaranteed to have a neutralizing strength of 80%. From this we figure the formula for pure phosphate baking powder to be:

     28% Soda
     35% Phosphate
     37% Starch

The so-called phosphate alum baking powders contain mixtures of mono calcium phosphate and sodium alumi-

num sulphate as the acid acting ingredients. A common formula for baking powder of this type is as follows:

     28% Soda
     19% Sodium aluminum sulphate
     12% Mono calcium phosphate
     41% Starch

The above data in private communication from Victor Chemical Works.

Following are simple formulas for making baking powder:

#1—Cream of tartar....... 2 parts
     Baking soda .... 1 "
     Cornstarch .... 1 "

The cornstarch coats each particle of the two reacting substances, and prevents the moisture of the air from acting upon the substances until it is used.

#2—Sodium acid phosphate. 4 parts
     Calcium acid phosphate 4 "
     Sodium bicarbonate ... 5 "
     Starch .... 7 "

#3—Cream of tartar...... 3 lb.
     Baking soda .... 1½ "
     Cornstarch .... 1¼ "
     Powdered tartaric acid. 1 oz.
Sift all together several times.

Preserving Eggs

The Philadelphia Quartz Company recommends the following process of preserving eggs, which may be purchased when the prices are low, holding them over for use at any later time:

The preserving solution is a dilute solution of silicate of soda (waterglass). The silicate as purchased is a syrupy liquid, mostly clear or sometimes a little cloudy in appearance, clean and odorless, and with an alkaline taste. Dilution by adding nine measures of water to one of silicate is recommended by the Bulletin of the U. S. Dept. of Agriculture on the subject. Our experience has been that solutions more dilute than this will serve, and that as much as twelve measures of water can be used.

If the water is hard or otherwise not entirely pure it should be boiled. When cooled, the proper amount is measured out and the silicate stirred in.

Stone or earthenware crocks, wooden kegs, glass jars, tin or iron vessels, or galvanized iron cans may be used —practically any convenient water-tight vessel that can be kept covered. Galvanized iron ash or garbage cans are convenient. The silicate in time dissolves off the galvanizing, but it will not rust the iron. The containers should be cleaned and scalded before using.

The vessels containing the eggs should be kept covered to prevent evaporation. If they have no regular covers, waxed paper tied around will serve, or layers of newspaper held down by weighted boards, or any other convenient cover. It is not necessary to seal the covers tight, but only to keep the solution from drying out.

The eggs used should be strictly fresh. The silicate solution will not make bad eggs good. Non-fertile eggs are to be preferred. The eggs should not be washed before putting into the solution, as this removes some of the natural preservative in the shells. Spots of dirt on the shells should be picked off, though badly soiled eggs had better not be used at all. Eggs with cracked shells should not be put in the solution, as they will spoil.

A five-gallon container will usually hold fifteen dozen eggs. To cover these properly will take about ten quarts of the diluted preserving solution; that is, about one quart of silicate of soda diluted with nine to twelve quarts of water. These figures will serve as a guide in estimating for other quantities.

Have about two inches of the preserving solution clear above the eggs so that there will be no danger of drying down and exposing the eggs. Inspect the vessels occasionally to be sure that the eggs are well covered.

If necessary to add more solution because of evaporation, make up a fresh quantity of twelve-to-one solution and pour in. Do not simply fill up with water.

The preserving solution in the course of time may thicken up like a whitish mush. This has no effect upon its preserving qualities, and the eggs will keep in it perfectly well.

Use fresh solution each year. Unused silicate either full strength or diluted will keep over from year to year if in a tight can or jar, but a solution that has been used for keeping eggs should not be used a second season.

If an egg should break in the solution it will spoil, but the effect of the spoiled egg will not penetrate the other eggs, as they are tightly sealed by the silicate.

Boiled eggs that have been preserved in silicate are not very satisfactory, as the eggs are sealed so tightly that they crack. Making a pinhole into the air chamber in the large end helps somewhat. The eggs do not keep very long after being taken out of the water-glass solution.

Cleaning Aluminum

#1—Aluminum is usually cleaned in the household by means of steel wool. Care should be taken in cleaning aluminum because it dissolves, or is eaten away by caustics such as lye water, at the same time yielding hydrogen gas.

#2—To clean, the objects are dipped in kerosene or some other solvent, and the kerosene is then dried by the use of sawdust. In the case of tubing and cooking utensils this drying is accomplished by hand. A large box of sawdust is conveniently located near the kerosene and the utensil is partially buried in the sawdust. With several quick turns the sawdust is exposed to the entire surface of the object and the kerosene or other solvent is quickly absorbed.

Artificial Vinegar

Water	25 gal.
Acetic acid 80%...........	½ "
Acetic ether	2 oz.

Caramel coloring to suit.

A New Condiment

An interesting condiment, devised and marketed by Japanese chemists several years ago, has come into wide usage throughout China and Japan, and is now making friends in this country. Chemically, the material is sodium glutamate. It is made from the gluten or protein part of wheat by acid hydrolysis, followed by bleaching, neutralization, and crystallization. It is thus of vegetable origin and does not violate the food prescriptions of any race or religion.

Aji-no-moto is a white powder, looking like bicarbonate of soda, of such character that it keeps well and may be dispensed from a salt shaker. It has a faint but definite odor of rather strong cheese. The taste, however, is that of the red juice from roast beef: salty, meaty, and appetizing. This condiment is the making of chop suey and other Chinese dishes. It goes especially well with spaghetti and other vegetarian dishes.

Cleaning Linoleum

Beeswax	5 oz.
Oil of turpentine...........	11 "
Varnish	5 "

Melt the wax over a slow fire, take off the fire and add the turpentine, a little at a time, then add the varnish and mix well. To use: Clean the linoleum with soap and water, or, still better, with milk and water; and after wiping dry, apply the above cleanser with a soft cloth and polish with a clean cloth.

To Remove Stains from Porcelain

♯1—Use a strong solution of oxalic acid, scrubbing with a brush or small mop. Oxalic acid solution will not burn the hands, but is poisonous.

♯2—Sodium acid sulphate solution, as strong as possible, is a good cleaner for porcelain or stoneware. It hydrolyzes and forms sulphuric acid, which is the real cleaner. It must be borne in mind that rubbing is necessary in almost all cases where these chemical cleaners are used, as the cleaners are somewhat slow in action.

♯3—Brown stains on porcelain bathroom fixtures or sinks may be removed by letting concentrated hydrochloric acid trickle (by means of a medicine dropper if the stain is small) on the stain until it is removed. Then wash thoroughly with water to remove all trace of acid.

Stove Polishes

♯1—Lampblack	1 oz.	
Powdered graphite	1 "	
Iron sulphate	4 "	
Soap, shredded	½ cu in.	
Water, enough to form a paste		

♯2—Graphite, in fine powder	1 lb.	
Lampblack	1 oz.	
Rosin	4 oz.	
Turpentine	1 gal.	
Oil of cedar, enough to perfume		

Dissolve the rosin in the turpentine and stir the whole mixture after adding the lampblack and graphite. Shake well before using.

#3—Soap, chips .... 4 oz.
     Boiling water .... 1 pt.

Graphite, enough to make a paste with the above soap water.

#4—This formula is flammable:

Rosin .... 1 oz.
Graphite (powdered) ...... 4 "
Benzol (or gasoline)........ 1 qt.

#5—Asphaltum .... 1 lb.
     Linseed oil .... ¾ pt.
     Turpentine .... 3 "

Dissolve asphaltum in heated oil, and add turpentine when cooling.

FOR THE LAUNDRY

Making Soap at Home

In making soaps, various oils and fatty acids are used, among the most common being palm oil, red oil (oleic acid), cottonseed oil, cocoanut oil, olive oil, tallow, and to a lesser extent, peanut oil and linseed oil. These could be called glyceryl salts of oleic, palmitic, or stearic acids, and when saponified, or acted upon with an alkali, such as lye, there is usually formed sodium oleate, sodium palitate, or sodium stearate, which are the chemical names for the three typical kinds of soaps.

The usual method in making soap is to boil the fats or oils together with the alkali or lye, which forms the soap. This is called saponification, and results in the mass in the vessel becoming more pasty or creamy. Usually, common salt is then added (called "opening"), which causes the soap to rise to the top of the vessel where it is gathered off. The salt water and the lye solution which has not reacted during the process is drained from the bottom, and in many instances, the glycerin which is also formed during the formation of the soap is reclaimed from the salt water which is drawn off. As the reclama-

tion of glycerin is a highly technical process, it is not attempted when soaps are manufactured at home.

Home manufacture of soaps, especially toilet soaps, however, may not be profitable to many, but the few formulas and working methods given here show how the process is carried out and their intelligent use will result in good products. Some of the formulas here are for producing modified or special soaps which are not so easily purchased but quite easily prepared. These are liquid soaps, cocoanut oil soap shampoo, carbolic acid soap, dry cleaner's soap, hexalin soap, and silicate soaps.

Water-Glass or Silicate Soap

The raw soap is made in the usual way, by boiling with weak lye, graining with brine and settling, boiling up with strong lye, graining with additional strong lye, and settling. Rosin can be included if desired.

The details of the formulae used and of the process of handling vary greatly according to the stocks that are available and the results desired. The following gives one formula and process, which can be taken as typical:

Tallow .... 100 parts
Cottonseed oil .... 30 "

Boil with weak lye (8° to 10° Baumé) until the stock will not take up any more. Open with salt or brine. Settle and run off the settlings to be worked for glycerin. If rosin is to be used, next run in lye of 18° to 20° Baumé and boil up, adding the rosin and additional lye as may be required. Open with brine and run off the lye.

After the rosin change is run off, or, if no rosin is used, after the stock change, add lye for the strengthening change, at 13° to 14° Baumé if closed steam is used, or 20° to 22° if open steam. Boil, adding fresh lye as required. A head or foam will rise on the surface of the soap; continue boiling until the foam disappears and the soap settles to a smaller space in the kettle. The soap should be in a pea grain, and lye thrown up by the boil should settle down quickly through it. When the soap reaches this point it has taken all the strength that it will combine with. Add water and boil with open steam; the soap will thin out. Boil until the soap is of uniform consistency, adding water gradually. When it reaches the point that the soap is thin and the lye will separate on a paddle, it is done. Settle over night and run off the lye under the soap into a tank for future use. Finish the soap in the usual way, taking care to leave enough free alkali to combine with the amount of silicate that is to be added. The soap at this stage should contain about 31% water.

The soap at a temperature of 185° to 200° F. is run into the crutchers. While crutching, from 20 to 25 pounds of silicate per 100 pounds of this raw soap usually can be mixed in. Larger amounts can sometimes be used. The silicate should be at a temperature of about 85° to 110° F. The soap is run from the crutchers to the frames at about 140° F. Frames are usually stripped after about forty-eight hours and the soap allowed to stand three days before cutting.

As previously mentioned, this is only one method of making boiled soap. Various factors, such as the kinds of fats and oils used, the conditions under which the caustic is added to and allowed to react with the silicate, the temperature of the soap from the kettle, the temperature of the silicate, and other details, affect the amount of silicate that can be incorporated in the soap. By careful manipulation, the maximum amount is much higher than the above-mentioned figures.

Cold Process Soap

In the cold process of soap making, instead of prolonged boiling of the fats with weak lye, settling, reboiling, etc., as already outlined, the whole process is carried out in a crutcher, in a single operation and in a very short time. The exact quantities of fats, strong lye and other ingredients required are carefully weighed or measured out, and everything that goes into the crutcher remains in the soap. There is no spent lye to drain off and the glycerin is retained in the soap. The equipment required for the cold process is much less than for boiling, as no kettles are needed and no steam. It is hard to make a good, uniform soap by the cold process. Unless the mixing is very thorough, there will be spots containing excess alkali and others containing excess fats or oils.

Many formulae are in regular use, but the following is typical:

#1—Tallow	75	lb.
Cocoanut oil	25	"
Caustic soda lye, 35.5° Baumé made of 76% caustic	75	"
Silicate of soda	125	"
Pearl ash lye, 36° Baumé	20	"
#2—Tallow	75	lb.
Cocoanut oil	25	"
Caustic soda lye, 35.5° Baumé made of 76% caustic	70	"
Silicate of soda	100	"
Pearl ash lye, 36° Baumé	17	"

Refined cottonseed oil up to 30% to 50% can be substituted for an equal weight of tallow, if the tallow is hard. If the tallow is soft or mixed with grease, use less oil. The soap will not be quite so hard and will take longer to harden, but it will be a good washing soap. In these formulas the amounts of caustic are calculated so as to include the proper excess for the silicate to take up.

Three weighing tanks are usually arranged; one to supply the exact amount of grease stock, another for the exact amount of lye and the third for the silicate. With the silicate is mixed the pearl ash lye.

The whole amount of grease stock is first run into the crutcher. Its temperature should be about 145° to 150° F. in cold weather and 125° to 130° F. in summer. The crutcher is started and then the whole amount of the lye is quickly run into the grease and the mixture stirred rapidly until it begins to thicken up. This marks the beginning of the reaction between the fat and the alkali, and is accompanied by considerable heat. The whole amount of the mixed silicate and pearl ash lye is then run in rapidly. As this mixes with the soap the whole will thin out. The crutching (stirring) is continued and in a few minutes the whole mass will gradually turn creamy. The whole process is a quick one, taking from ten to fifteen minutes. When the soap is thick enough for a mark made on it to remain, it is quickly dropped into a frame and the frame moved immediately to the spot where it is to stand to cool. The formation of the soap goes on to some extent in the frame while standing, and it is particularly important that the frame should not be moved or shaken until the soap is cold.

Semi-boiled Process

This is another method by which soaps can be made. It is similar to the cold process just described, except that in this process, a higher temperature is reached. The various ingredients may be run into the mixer or crutcher at around 140° F. and the reactions will cause the temperature to rise nearly or quite to the boiling point. Or a steam-jacketed crutcher (stirring machine) may be used. The ingredients are run in at the same temperature as for cold soaps, but when the reactions begin the temperature is raised by means of steam to about the boiling point and kept there until the soap is uniform.

This process has many of the advantages of the cold process and makes a better soap. The fats are more completely saponified, and the soap is more uniform. The time of operation is longer than for the cold soap. A typical formula would be as follows:

Tallow	315 lb.
Cocoanut oil	55 "
Soda lye, 35° Baumé......	280 "
Silicate of soda..........	185 "
Pearl ash lye, 32° Baumé..	30 "

Warm the stock to 140° F. and mix in the other ingredients as described for cold process soaps. The mixture is then allowed to stand for one to one and a half hours, until it is observed to become heated. The crutching (stirring) machine is then started slowly. When the materials have combined into a homogeneous mass, the soap is run into the frame. It should then be crutched or stirred by hand for fifteen to twenty minutes to avoid the formation of streaks.

Soaps from Fatty Acids

These are made by essentially the same processes as the other soaps. In making boiled soap from fatty acids, there is no separation of glycerin, as the glycerin has already been removed. But otherwise, the process is similar to that already described. Soda ash may be used instead of caustic soda lye, though care must then be taken to guard against excessive foaming from the carbon dioxide of the soda ash.

—From "Silicates of Soda in Soap Making," by Philadelphia Quartz Company.

Soap for General Use

The following will produce a good soap for general use:

Oleic acid	35	parts
Sodium hydroxide solution 40° Baumé	14	"
Sal soda	7	"
Water	28	"

The mixture is heated slightly and left to saponify, which produces a clear paste. It is then boiled, and removed from the source of heat. The soda is then stirred (crutched) in and agitated until the whole mass is cold. If the soap is to be scented the perfume material is added just before the mixture becomes cold. When cold, the product will be in the form of a hard mass. It can be powdered and used as soap powder.

The following soap is made in the same manner and is less expensive than that given above:

Palm kernel oil	13.5	parts
Palm oil	2	"
Sodium hydroxide, 40° Baumé solution	10	"
Water	80	"

After mixing, 105 parts of sal soda are added to produce the soap paste.

Liquid Soaps

#1—Dissolve any good soap in hot water making a thick paste. To each quart of this add the following clarifying and liquefying agent, 1 pint warm water and ½ pint alcohol. More water may be added if a thinner soap is desired. This liquid is also a good shampoo.

#2—Cottonseed oil or olive oil	4	parts
Potassium hydroxide	1	"

The potassium hydroxide (caustic potash) should be dissolved in enough water, using as little as possible. Warm the oil and then stir in the potassium hydroxide solution, which will form the soap. If oily globules of the cottonseed oil are seen upon the surface, it is an indication that saponification is not complete and more of the caustic solution should be added. The soft soap produced will then separate and come together. The spent lye solution with the glycerin should be drawn off, and the soap then dissolved in denatured alcohol, using, preferably, alcohol denatured by formula #40. It can be filtered to make a clear solution. This will make a soft soap that can be tinted and perfumed if desired.

Carbolic Acid Soap

Palm oil	20	lb.
Starch	1	"
Carbolic acid in crystals	1	oz.
Oil of lavender	2	"
Oil of cloves	1	"

The carbolic acid is added and thoroughly incorporated.

Soap Using T.S.P.

Dissolve 5 lb. soap or soap chips in one gallon hot water. In this dissolve 3 lb. trisodium phosphate and 1 lb. borax. Add 1 gallon household ammonia and mix thoroughly.

Textile Soaps

Certain special textile soaps contain as high as 20% of carbon tetrachloride in a clear solution of linseed or castor oil soap. These soaps find use in textile work for removing spinner oil and for taking machine oil spots out of textile. They have also found use in the household, for removing grease spots and other stains from clothing.

Carpet Soap

Fuller's earth	4 oz.
Spirits of turpentine	1 "
Pearlash	8 "

Rub smooth and make into a stiff paste with a sufficiency of soft soap.

Sal Soda Soap Paste

Take two pounds of sal soda, two pounds of yellow bar soap, and ten quarts of water. Cut the soap in thin slices and boil together for two hours; strain.

Transparent Glycerin Soap

Cocoanut oil	140 parts
Tallow	140 "
Castor oil	100 "
Glycerin	125 "
Sugar	60 "
Water	20 "
Lye solution 40° Baumé	170 "
Alcohol	70 "

To Make Simple Soap

Tallow	37.5 lb.
Melt and add a solution of	
Lye	5 "
Dissolve lye in 9 qts. of water.	

Slowly pour the lye water into the melted tallow and with a wooden paddle stir for at least a quarter of an hour, adding the lye solution during the entire length of time. When the mass has thickened, pour into molds or pans.

Soap Powders

The great number of powdered soaps now on the market makes it unprofitable to make powdered soaps. However, the following formulas produce a shredded soap that has a bit more energetic action than those commercially available.

#1—Powdered soap	7 parts
Soda wash	3 "
Borax	1 "
Mix all together.	

#2—Yellow soap	6 parts
Soda crystals	3 "
Potassium carbonate, pearl ash	1½ "
Sulphate soda	1½ "
Palm oil	1 "

#3—Powdered soap	4 parts
Sal soda	3 "
Silicate soda	2 "

Soap Jelly for Flannel

To make soap jelly for washing flannels and delicate fabrics, first shave quite thinly half a pound of soap into a saucepan and pour over it one quart of boiling water. Boil until the soap is melted, pour into a bowl or tin, and when cold it will be found to be a stiff jelly, which will readily dissolve in warm water. It is preferable to ordinary soap in washing flannels and delicate fabrics, where it is undesirable to rub the soap directly on the garment itself. The soft soap can be scented if desired. Suitable scents are oil of pine, or pine oil, oil of wintergreen, oil of cloves, etc.

Perfumes for Soap

#1—Oil of lavender	100 parts
Oil of caraway	75 "
Oil of rosemary	50 "
Oil of lemon grass	40 "
Oil of thyme	25 "

#2—Oil of citronella	1 part
Oil of cloves	1 "
Oil of bitter almonds	2 "

#3—Oil of caraway	2 parts
Oil of cloves	3 "
Oil of cinnamon	3 "
Oil of bergamot	2 "
Oil of sassafras	1 "
Oil of orange flowers	2 "

#4—Oil of thyme	2 parts
Oil of sage	4 "
Oil of rosemary	3 "
Oil of lemon	5 "
Oil of peppermint	4 "
Oil of lavender	4 "
#5—Oil of bergamot	4 oz.
Oil of citronella	1 "
Oil of lavender	4 "

Washing Powder

An excellent washing powder can be made by mixing sodium carbonate (soda ash) 60%, and trisodium phosphate, 40%. A simple mix is, therefore, soda ash, 6 lb., and trisodium phosphate (TSP), 4 lb. It has a total alkali content of 58%. It is best to use the substances dissolved in warm water. This mixture is a particularly good cleaner for dairy use, or for washing milk cans, as the phosphate has an appreciable effect upon the casein. It is easily rinsed, thus reducing the number of wash waters necessary after its use.

Starch for Laundry Use

#1—Potatoes and rice cooked at home may furnish starch for laundering purposes. The water remaining after cooking one-half cup of rice in two quarts of water can be diluted to one quart by pouring boiling water over the rice. It contains sufficient starch to stiffen several small garments slightly. This method of cooking serves another purpose; it not only frees more of the starch, but leaves a more individual and flaky grain of rice for food than is obtained in the double-boiler method of cooking. Likewise the water from boiled potatoes may be used.

#2—Melt 2½ pounds of the best paraffin wax over a slow fire. When liquefied remove from the fire to stir in 100 drops of oil of citronella, oil of pine, etc., and pour the melted paraffin wax into pie tins. Cut or stamp out with a tin cutter into small cakes about the size of candy mints. Two of these cakes added to each pint of starch will cause the smoothing iron to impart the finest possible finish to muslin or linen, besides perfuming the clothes.

#3—Because of the great variety of materials to be starched and the different methods used, an exact recipe can not be given for making starch suitable for all purposes. The following is a good general one, and this paste can be thinned with hot water until it gives the stiffness desired for the fabric:

Two to six tablespoons corn starch
One-third cup cold water
One-half teaspoon lard, paraffin, or any white wax
One quart of boiling water

Mix the starch and part of the cold water, and stir into the boiling water in a double boiler. Use the remaining water to rinse out the adhering starch. Add the lard or white wax, and cook for fifteen to twenty minutes. Strain if lumps have formed. However, if care is taken there should be no lumps.

Home Manufactured Starches

Special finishes are often used on certain fabrics, such as voiles, organdies, batistes, and many silks, to restore their crisp, new appearance. Dilute solutions of gelatin, gum arabic, and gum tragacanth are all good for this purpose. Avoid using too much of any one of them, since an excess will cause a sticky feeling. The following table gives the approximate quantity of each of these substances to be used with a pint of water in making the stock solution, and the quantity of hot water with which to dilute it at the time of use. A little

Substance	Quantity Used	Water	Dilution to Be Made
	Ounce	Pint	
Gelatin	1	1	1 part solution to 8 to 15 parts hot water
Gum arabic	1	1	1 part solution to 5 to 10 parts hot water
Gum tragacanth..	⅙	1	1 part solution to 8 to 12 parts hot water

borax added to the solution when first made helps to preserve it.

Add the cold water to the gelatin or gum and heat until it has dissolved. Dilute with hot water, the quantity depending on the kind of material and the stiffness desired.

However, since these starches are all more expensive and difficult to obtain than the corn starch, it is impractical to consider their use for the regular family wash. Moreover, the ordinary corn starch gives almost any of the desired effects when one or more of such softeners as paraffin, lard, beeswax, spermaceti, Japan wax, soap, tallow, and glycerin, and other foreign substances such as borax, alum, gelatin, and glue are mixed with it in the correct proportions.

All natural starches are insoluble in cold water, but when mixed with water and heated the starch grains swell, finally burst, and partially dissolve.

The so-called soluble starches are usually formed by treating ordinary starch with acid or alkali. The extent to which they dissolve depends largely upon the length of time of treatment and the quantity of acid or alkali used. Many of the starches sold in packages under various trade names are corn starch that has received modified treatment to make it partially soluble and thin boiling. They generally also contain one or more of the foreign substances.

Soap for Mechanics

#1—Soft soap .... 16 oz.
    Ammonia water ...... 1 "
    Turpentine, enough
    Fine pumice stone..... 6 "

This is made by first mixing the soap and ammonia water, incorporating the solvent and then adding the pumice stone.

#2—In 4 gallons of hot water dissolve 6 lb. of soap or soap flakes, 8 lb. silicate of soda and 1 lb. borax. While still hot add 1 pint linseed oil (raw). This mass can be thickened with any or all of the following: Powdered pumice stone, bran, corn meal, whiting, kieselghur, sawdust, etc.

#3—The following is a powder:
Soap chips .... 10 lb.
Borax .... 1 "
Soda ash .... 1 "
Powdered pumice stone.... ½ "

Mix together the materials, which should be dry and finely powdered.

To Make Hard Water Soft

For moderately hard water 1 lb. of soda ash or 1¼ lb. of sal soda should be completely dissolved in a quart of water and 2 tablespoons of this used for each gallon of water. All of the soda should be carefully dissolved.

for if solid particles are left they may adhere to the clothes and make holes in them. Lime is sometimes used in addition to washing soda, the process being spoken of as the lime-soda method. However, a slight excess of lime causes extra difficulty and this method is not successful in household practice. Lye is cheaper than washing soda and is often substituted for it, but it is so excessively alkaline that it can not be safely used for this purpose.

T.S.P. (trisodium phosphate), borax, and ammonia solution can be used also for softening water. Ammonia is a gas which is bought dissolved in water. So-called household ammonia is often a weak solution, and a high price is paid for the water and the bottle. It is sometimes more economical to buy concentrated ammonia solution of a druggist and dilute it according to need. This should be done carefully and out of doors, however, as strong ammonia solutions are unpleasant to handle.

Liquid Cleaner

Washing soda .... 2½ lb.
Lime .... 2 "
Household borax .... 2 oz.
Water .... 2 gal.

The above should be mixed, using hot water and the whole allowed to settle, and the clear solution above syphoned off.

To Remove Iron Stains on the Hands

Workers in chemical laboratories where iron compounds are used daily can remove the stains from the hands by washing the hands in muriatic acid. Raw or open cuts or sores should be absent. The acid will not burn or irritate healthy skin.

To Remove Iodine Stains

Soak the stained garment in a strong solution of sodium thiosulphate (hypo, or photographer's hypo), until whitened and then wash in clear running water to remove the hypo.

Detergents

A good cleaning substance is trisodium phosphate, sometimes called TSP. It can be purchased at any chemical supply house and at some druggists. It is a simple inexpensive white crystalline chemical which is dissolved in water as follows:

One oz. (tablespoonful) dissolved in pail warm or cold water for severe cleansing.

One-half oz. (teaspoonful) dissolved in pail warm or cold water for ordinary cleansing.

One pound dissolved in 70 to 100 gal. water according to use to replace soap, soda, etc.

Bleacheries, wool scourers, knitting and woolen mills, use TSP in connection with red-oil, soapstock, etc.

For rug or carpet cleansing, and fabrics, use TSP for cleansing and to brighten or bring out the colors.

Use about one tablespoonful of TSP to a pail of water when cleaning tile, marble, linoleum, or wood floors. Makes nonslip floor surfaces.

TSP is a germ killer, and quickly eliminates dirt, making it a wonderful cleanser and a useful disinfectant. It is harmless for milk dairy products, meats and food of all kinds.

It is harmless to the hands and rinses off freely.

One-half teaspoonful of TSP will remove the grease from any kind of pan, and is an absolute cleanser when used in washing dishes.

One-half cup of TSP to 50 gal. boiler of water will remove the dirt and grease from all clothes, cotton, wool, silk, linens, etc.

FUN WITH CHEMISTRY

Chemical Amusements

Hold a bright sheet of copper in Bunsen flame. A very beautiful display of colors will appear.

Throw a drop of water on a very hot plate heated by a Bunsen burner. It will roll up, assume the spheroidal state of water, the drop never touching the hot plate.

Illuminating gas contains about 4 per cent carbon dioxide. You can test the gas for this substance by bubbling some of it through limewater. A white precipitate, or cloud, will be formed. It is calcium carbonate, chemically the same as marble.

Into a wide mouthed bottle place enough acetic acid or vinegar to nearly fill the bottle and add enough sodium bicarbonate (baking soda) freely to generate a gas. Place a moth ball in the mixture. The ball will fall down through the liquid, then come up, supported by gas bubbles, which it releases upon reaching the surface, only to go down again. The ball will then repeat the process.

Lead nitrate crystals (white) ground with potassium iodide crystals (white) will produce yellow lead iodide.

A lighted Bunsen burner can be extinguished by placing the finger directly over the stack, in the flame. You will not be burned.

Strong sulphuric acid dropped into strong sugar syrup (or white molasses) will carbonize the sugar and cause black carbonaceous substances to flow out of the container.

Heat about 20 gm. of sulphur in a large test tube. A clear yellow liquid results. On further heating a black mass results, which upon being heated still further becomes fluid again. If the liquid sulphur is now poured into cold water, it will be found to be elastic and plastic.

Glass dissolves in water! This little-known fact can be proved by grinding some glass in a clean mortar and then adding several drops of distilled water to the glass powder, grinding some more, and then adding a drop or two of phenolphthalein solution. A reddish-pink color indicates that the glass has dissolved in the water. This is due to the fact that glass is usually alkaline in content and will give the typical alkaline reaction as indicated.

Write a crazy question on the upper half of a piece of paper using sodium ferrocyanide and ferric ammonium sulphate both dissolved together in water. On bottom half write a funny answer using phenolphthalein solution. Use quill or gold pen point. Brush the paper with water-glass solution after drying it, and the question will disappear and the answer will appear.

Strong sulphuric acid placed on moist potassium permanganate crystals will give off brown particles of manganese dioxide, and ozone. If a pinch of sulphur is added, it will burst into flames.

If alcohol is used instead of sulphur, in the previous experiment, the combustion is almost explosive. Illuminating gas led in by a tube can be ignited.

The following experiments illustrating the spreading of surface-active soluble substances on water are described. Particles of crystal-violet thrown on to a perfectly pure water surface show a lively movement analogous to that of camphor, and leave colored, spiral trails behind them. Eventually the whole surface becomes colored. If at this stage a drop of oleic acid be added, the colored layer is driven to the sides of the containing vessel and there sinks to the bottom. If a pure water surface is first touched with a drop of oleic acid and powdered crystal-violet is then added, the particles of the latter show no movement but send out colored streamers below the surface of the water. A particle of crystal-violet added to a water surface previously "spread" with tetraiodofluorescein splits the latter by itself, forming a cross-like pattern. Antipyrine can also be used for camphor in a camphor-water experiment.

To change paper into starch, immerse a sheet of filter paper in STRONG sulphuric acid for five minutes. Remove and wash. Touch it with a drop of WEAK tincture of iodine (diluted with water). A dark bluish coloration proves that the paper has been changed partially into starch.

Heat some powdered potassium dichromate in a test tube. The crystals will melt. Allow to cool. A crackling noise will be produced as the crystals form, and soon the test tube bursts into many pieces, due to the growth of the crystals.

Prepare three glasses as follows: Fill the first glass with water, and dissolve in it a little ferric ammonium sulphate; in the second glass, put a few crystals of tannic acid and stir; and in the third, a few crystals of oxalic acid. Pour the first glass into the second; the liquid will assume the color of black ink. If you pour this ink-colored fluid into the third glass, it will change back to the color of water.

Water, milk, port wine and champagne can be poured from one bottle in the following manner: Fill a one pint brown glass bottle with a solution of sulphate of iron made by putting one teaspoonful into a pint of warm water, and dissolving, adding six drops of sulphuric acid. The trickery is with the wine glasses. In the first glass put nothing. In the second for milk, put a solution of chloride of calcium made by dissolving several lumps in a few drops of water. The

third class contains wine, made by putting one-half a measure of potassium permanganate in the glass. The fourth glass contains champagne, made by dissolving four measures of sodium bicarbonate in a few drops of water. If the action is not quick enough, add more iron sulphate and several more drops of acid to the bottle.

Mix a saturated strong solution of calcium chloride, with a saturated solution of potassium carbonate, and a solid transparent mass will form.

Fairy Flames for Fireplace

Copper chloride, when sprinkled upon burning coals or wood, colors the flame a beautiful bluish green color. The copper chloride can be introduced into the fire by wrapping about half an ounce of the chemical in cellophane or tin foil, twisting together at the top, tying with string or ribbon, and throwing on the fire. These articles are sold at novelty and stationery stores, under the name of Fairy Fires.

Zinc chloride crystals, or even zinc metal, can be used to produce a delightful coloration.

Ammonium copper chloride produces a beautiful soft blue-green flame when thrown on burning logs or coals.

Compounds That Flame

Substances that take fire when exposed to the air are easily made and amusing to experiment with. They are not dangerous, in the sense that great quantities of heat or explosions are developed. They are similar to the Fourth of July sparklers.

Lead citrate, oxalate or tartrate, when heated to redness in a test tube, decomposes to form metallic lead in such a fine state of subdivision that, when poured out into the air, spontaneous combustion takes place with the evolution of light. The lead tartrate can be made by adding tartaric acid solution to a solution of lead nitrate or acetate, when lead tartrate will be precipitated. This should be filtered off and washed with water, dried, and heated in a test tube in a Bunsen burner flame until fumes are no longer given off. The tube should be tightly stoppered while still warm and the contents shaken out into the air when cold.

Heating lead oxalate and paraffin at a temperature of about 300° F. for an hour will also produce finely divided, or pyrophoric lead, to the extent of about 30% free lead. Lead formate also gives the same behavior.

Copper phosphide, made by heating *red* phosphorus in a solution of copper sulphate, is also spontaneously pyrophoric. The copper phosphide should be filtered from the copper sulphate solution, washed, and dried in the air.

Homberg's pyrophorus is made by heating a mixture of alum, flour, and starch in a tube. When no more vapors are produced, the powder within is shaken out into the air, where it will take fire by rapid oxidation.

Chemical Trees

These chemical oddities are easily made, and if carefully protected from outside influences such as jars, knocks, etc., can be kept for a considerable length of time.

A tree of lead can be made by dissolving four ounces of lead acetate (sugar of lead) in a quart of water. The solution is placed in a bottle, and a zinc rod or strip inserted through the stopper so that it extends down into the liquid. The zinc will replace the lead of the solution, the lead crystallizing out upon the zinc rod or strip in the form of beautiful spangles, slowly growing until the bottom of the bottle has been reached. The lead acetate solution will be turbid when made, but as the crystallization proceeds, this clears up, and the spangles are seen through a clear solution of zinc sulphate.

If several grams of mercury are placed inside a little linen bag with fine meshes and the bag immersed in a silver nitrate solution, metallic silver will be deposited on the bag and down into the solution, forming what has been called a "silver tree."

A "tin tree" is made by immersing a zinc rod or zinc strip in a rather strong solution of tin chloride. The metal replaces the tin from the solution, forming metallic tin which crystallizes out upon the zinc in beautiful silvery spangles.

Filling Toy Balloons

Toy balloons can be filled with hydrogen gas or illuminating gas to cause them to rise. As most rubber balloons can only be inflated to their maximum capacity by the use of illuminating gas under quite a strong pressure, the balloon will not be inflated to such an extent as to cause it to rise when filled with gas from the usual gas connection. Rubber balloons can be filled, however, by first allowing the gas partially to fill another balloon, or bladder, such as a football bladder. The bladder is then connected to the balloon, already partially filled, and the bladder compressed. This will inflate the rubber balloon. The bladder is removed, again filled with gas, attached to the rubber balloon and once more compressed with the hands. In this manner the rubber balloon can be filled to its maximum capacity.

Hydrogen gas is the lightest gas that can be used to cause rubber balloons to rise. It can be made or generated by allowing either muriatic acid or sulphuric acid, diluted to about three or four parts with water, to act upon iron filings or zinc scraps. The gas which is generated should be passed through quick lime or dry calcium chloride to remove the water vapor. The hydrogen will fill the balloon by its own pressure. To minimize weight, the balloon should be tied at its mouth with very light thread. Filling with noninflammable helium gas is impractical at home.

Model Airplane Dope

Anilin dyes have been found useful in coloring model airplane dopes. An ounce of the dye will color about four gallons, therefore only a small amount is needed. This is added to nitrate dope thinner or acetone, which can be bought in any drug store or model supply shop. An ounce bottle will hold all that is necessary of each color to keep on hand for ordinary use. A toothpick will be found useful in adding the dye to the thinner. In this way light and dark shades of the same color can be prepared easily to suit specific needs.

Luminescent Zinc Sulphide

This curious substance produces a shower of golden scintillations when rubbed with the finger nail or other stiff object. It is made by heating:

Zinc oxide .... 10 gm.
Flowers of sulphur........ 10 "
Manganese dioxide, enough just slightly to darken the above mixture when rubbed intimately with it.

The amount of manganese dioxide used is not critical, but a small amount is absolutely necessary. The mixture is heated in a closed porcelain crucible over a Bunsen, Mekker or Fisher burner for half an hour. The crucible is cooled and the powder removed. It is sprinkled upon a card coated with a clear spirit (alcoholic) lacquer or varnish, such as dammar varnish. When dry, the adhering powder will show flashes of light when it is stroked with a rather stiff object.

GARDENING

Spray for Trees

#1—The self-boiled lime-sulphur mixture has come into general use as a fungicide for the control of peach scab and brown rot. It is made up as follows:

Lump quicklime .... 8 lb.
Sulphur (commercial ground
or flowers) .... 8 "
Water to make 50 gal.

The lime is placed in a barrel and enough water poured on to cover it. As soon as the lime begins to slake the sulphur is added. The sulphur should first be run through a sieve to break up or remove lumps. The mixture is stirred constantly and water added as needed to form a thick paste and then gradually a thin paste. The lime should supply enough heat to boil the mixture several minutes. As soon as it is well slaked, cold water should be added to cool the mixture and prevent further cooking. If the mixture is allowed to remain hot too long (15 or 20 minutes) after the slaking is completed, the sulphur goes into solution, combining with the lime to form compounds which are injurious to the foliage. It is therefore important, especially with a hot lime, to cool the mixture quickly by adding cold water as soon as the lumps of lime have slaked down. The product should consist chiefly of the mechanical mixture of the lime and sulphur. The stage at which cold water should be added to stop the cooking will vary with the different limes. The mixture should be strained to take out any coarse particles of lime and diluted to the concentration indicated by the formula above.— Courtesy of National Lime Association.

#2—This material, sometimes called Villedieu's mixture, is prepared of the following:

Quicklime or ⎰ .... 12 lb.
Hydrated lime ⎱ .... 16 "
Aluminum sulphate .... 3 "
 Water to make 25 gal.

The lime is carefully slaked, or the hydrate is mixed with water, and the volume brought to 18 gallons. The aluminum sulphate is dissolved in 7 gallons of water and the two solutions mixed while stirring.

Kerosene Emulsion

Kerosene emulsion has long served as a standard spray for the control of soft-bodied sucking insects. If well made and properly diluted, kerosene emulsion will give satisfactory results. *It should never be combined with lime-sulphur.*

A good stock solution of kerosene emulsion containing 66 per cent of oil may be made as follows:

Kerosene (coal oil) .... 2 gal.
Fish-oil or laundry soap (1
 quart soft soap)......... ½ lb.
Water .... 1 gal.

First dissolve the soap in boiling water; then remove the vessel from the fire. Immediately add the kerosene, and thoroughly agitate the mixture until a creamy solution results. The stock solution may be more conveniently made by pouring the mixture into the tank of a spray pump and pumping the liquid through the nozzle back into the tank for some minutes. The stock solution, if properly made, should last for some time, but it is better to make it up as needed. Do not dilute until ready to use. To make a 10 per cent spray (the strength for trees in foliage) add, for each gallon of the stock solution, about 5⅔ gallons of water. For 20 and 25 per cent emulsions (for use on dormant trees and plants) use, respectively, about 2⅓ and 1⅔ gallons of water for each gallon of stock solu-

tion.—From Farmers' Bulletin 908, U. S. Dept. of Agriculture.

Tree-banding Materials

Bands of sticky material, 4 to 5 inches wide, applied around tree trunks sometimes may be used to advantage to prevent caterpillars, climbing cutworms, and certain other insects from injuring trees. These bands are also used to prevent nonflying and wingless moths, such as the gipsy moth, cankerworm moths, tussock moths, etc., from ascending trees to deposit their eggs. Cotton batting and wire screen also are used in making protective bands.

Rosin-castor Oil Mixture

This may be made according to the following formula:

Rosin .... 5 lb.
Castor oil .... 3 pt.

Place the rosin and castor oil in a pot and heat slowly until the rosin is melted. Add more oil if too thick. —Farmers' Bulletin 908, U. S. Dept. of Agriculture.

How to Get Rid of Borers

Dissolve ¼ lb. of flake or granulated glue in about 1 qt. of water. Dissolve 2 lb. of salt in about 1 gal. of water. To this solution add the glue and ¼ lb. of arsenate of lead (powder), together with 2 oz. of 40% nicotine sulphate. Make a thick cream by carefully slaking 8 lb. of fresh quicklime. Add the lime to the mixture previously prepared and add sufficient water to bring the mixture to the consistency of thick paint.

Remove the soil from the bases of the trees to a depth of three or four inches. Allow the crown to dry and then, with a stiff brush, remove all adhering soil particles from the crown and trunk. Apply the wash by means of a whitewash brush, coating the trunk to the height of fourteen to sixteen inches. Replace the soil about the tree.

The first application should be made in connection with worming in the spring. It should be as immediately preceding July 1 as possible.

Another application about mid-August is advisable for best results.—From Oregon Agric. College Exp. Sta. Tests.

Protection for Trees

The following formula will be found effective against animals that gnaw the bark of trees and also against borers.

Resin	5 parts
Beeswax	1 "
Linseed oil	¼ "
Lampblack	½ "
Strychnine	½ "

Melt the resin, add the beeswax and then add the linseed oil. Mix the lampblack and strychnine and stir in as the mixture cools. When ready to use, apply with a paint brush. Keep the wax warm enough to run easily, but not hot, and paint the trunks of the trees to be protected. The charcoal decreases the tendency of the mixture to flow. The wax is somewhat elastic and adjusts itself to changed conditions, such as expansion of the trunk.

It is, of course, a poison, and should be applied in the fall to the base of trees.

Much damage is done in the winter by rabbits, mice and other rodents gnawing the bark from the base of valuable trees. The following preparation is much better than whitewash.

The mixture is prepared by heating linseed oil until it is smoking hot—about 470 degrees F. It should then be set outdoors and flowers of sulphur added, one part to nine parts of oil by weight, making a ten per cent solution. It is best to sift the sulphur slowly into the hot oil and stir. The mixture will become hotter until all the sulphur is dissolved. When it cools it will be ready for use; but if it is to be sprayed on the tree trunks, thinning with turpentine may be necessary to put it through the spray pump.

Tree and Shrub Spray

#1—Copper sulphate (bluestone)	4 lb.
Fresh stone lime	4 "
(Or hydrated lime).....	6 "

A spray of this strength is referred to as a 4—4—50 mixture, the first figure referring to the number of pounds of copper sulphate, the second to the number of pounds of stone lime, and the third to the number of gallons of water. Dissolve each chemical separately in half of the water and then mix the two solutions.

#2—Finely ground sulphur..	8 lb.
Hydrated lime	4 "
Calcium caseinate	½ "

Insect Spray

The basis of the material used in insect sprays is usually a pyrethrum extract, obtained from a species of chrysanthemum. *Chrysanthemum cinerariaefolium* grows wild in Dalmatia and is known as "Dalmatian Insect Powder," this and *C. coccineum* are the probable botanical species used in the sprays. The latter grows wild in California and is known as buhach. Persian insect powder is another name for these flower heads from which the active ingredient is extracted.

The extract is usually diluted with gasoline or kerosene, or a mixture of both, to act as a carrier for the material. Various scents such as pine oil, methyl salicylate, oil of citronella, and oil of pennyroyal are used with the mixture. Oil of citronella acts in itself as a repellent for insects, and pine oil, having germicidal value, would seem to serve as something more than merely an odorant. Some typical formulas are:

#1—Pyrethrum extract .... 1 qt.
  Gasoline-kerosene ...... 5 "
  Paradichlorbenzene .... 8 oz.
  Pine oil .... 6 "
  Oil of citronella .... 1 "

#2—Pyrethrum extract ..... 1 qt.
  Gasoline and kerosene.. 6 "
  Paradichlorbenzene .... 4 oz.
  Oil of cedar wood .... 3 "
  Oil of pine .... 3 "
  Methyl salicylate ..... 2 "

Pine oil with the dilutant, either gasoline or kerosene or both, will serve as a good insect repellent, although the combination of the other ingredients acts as a more nearly universal repellent, one that is effective against a large variety of insect life.

The following spray formulas have also been used, but their cost is somewhat high.

#3—Methyl salicylate ..... 18 oz.
  Oil of citronella ...... 8 "
  Oil of lemon .... 1 "
  Pine oil .... 4 "

#4—Cedarwood oil .... 16 oz.
  Safrol .... 4 "
  Pine oil .... 8 "
  Oil of citronella....... 4 "

#5—Paradichlorbenzene .... 100 gm.
  Methyl salicylate ..... 20 cc.
  Kerosene ....1000 "

The paradichlorbenzene (also called dichlorbenzene) should be dissolved in the kerosene, the latter should be water-white and unmixed with oils as is frequently the case when purchased from gasoline filling stations. The methyl salicylate is added to give

it an oil of wintergreen odor, but oil of cedar or oil of pine may be used.

#6—The following is a product that is very toxic and inexpensive to make. It is used in a spray gun.

Pyrethrum flowers .... 1 lb.
Water-white kerosene ..... 1 gal.

Pyrethrum flowers can be purchased from dealers in spices, herbs, or drugs. To obtain the greatest quantity of the active principal from the flower heads shake the entire pound of flowers in a gallon jug with half a gallon of the water-white kerosene. One or more weeks should be given the kerosene to dissolve the active ingredient from the dried flowers. The jug should be shaken from time to time. The kerosene is then decanted off and the remaining fresh quantity of kerosene added to the flowers, the extraction process continuing for another week. The kerosene is then decanted off, mixed with the first half-portion, and the whole strained through cheese cloth and filtered through paper. If not filtered, the small particles are liable to plug the holes of the spray gun.

The extract can be perfumed by the addition of oil of cedar, pine oil, or a cologne. The addition of several ounces of paradichlorbenzene, allowing complete solution, will make the liquid more efficient in exterminating insects.

Insecticide Dust

Hellebore is useful as the active ingredient in dusts that are used to kill many harmful insects. The powder is dusted upon the plant, by means of a mechanical duster, or it can be introduced into the small bellows type bug dusters sold for the purpose. In the garden, the dust is best applied in the morning while the plants are still wet from dew.

Hellebore is the powdered roots of

the white hellebore plant (*Veratrum album*). It contains alkaloids which are poisonous to insects, but which in the quantities properly used for insecticides, do not seriously affect people. For this reason it may be used to protect fruit that is about to ripen, from injury by chewing insects. This material, however, is used only for small-scale operations, as it can not profitably be employed where many plants are to be treated.

A liquid application of hellebore is made from:

Hellebore	1 oz.
Water	1 gal.

A dusting powder contains: Hellebore 1 oz.; flour or air slaked lime, 5 to 10 oz.

Chemical Fertilizers for Garden

Substance	Amt. per sq. yd.
Sodium nitrate	1 oz.
Ammonium sulphate	1 "
Potassium sulphate	2 "
Wood ashes	4 "
Acid phosphate	4 "
Bone meal	3 to 4 "
Dried blood	2 "
Urea	½ "

Fertilizers for Potted Plants

#1—Urea is being widely used as a fertilizer by milady. It is a clean odorless substance. On *potted plants* it is used preferably in solution. *Use not more than one level teaspoonful in a gallon of water.* On plants of the palm family use one-tenth this strength and on roses one-half this strength. Apply the solution every eight to fourteen days, the same way as you would plain water. Do not wet the foliage. The solution will keep its strength for a long time, but it should be stirred after standing a while.

#2—

Ammonium nitrate ...	40	parts
Ammonium phosphate.	20	"
Potassium nitrate	25	"
Ammonium chloride ..	5	"
Calcium sulphate	6	"
Ferrous sulphate	4	"

Dissolve 1 part in 1000 parts water, and water the flowers with it 2 or 3 times weekly.

#3—

Ammonium phosphate.	80	gm.
Potassium phosphate..	21	"
Magnesium sulphate ..	1	"
Calcium nitrate	1	"
Water to make	1	gal.

Use one tablespoon weekly.

How to Make Plants Flourish

Plants grown in boxes for window or veranda decoration can be made to flourish much more vigorously than ordinarily by a little judicious feeding. For the purpose of feeding house plants, use either of the following mixtures:

#1—

Sodium nitrate	1½ lb.
Dry sodium phosphate (or 3 lb. of acid phosphate)	1 "
Potassium sulphate ..	1 "

#2—

Sodium nitrate	1 lb.
Acid phosphate	1 "
Bone-flour	2 "
Potassium sulphate ..	1 "

House-plant Mixture No. 1 is used in the following manner: A round tablespoonful is dissolved in 4 quarts of water; warm water can be used if one wishes it to dissolve quickly. About one-fourth of a pint of this solution is used once a week or once in two weeks on a plant in a 6-inch flower-pot and in corresponding proportions for smaller and larger areas. The solution is poured onto the soil and not on the foliage of the plant. If the mixture has stood for any length of time, it should be stirred from the bottom before dipping out to put on the soil. The surface of the soil is kept loosened by occasional stirring. Mixture No. 2, if preferred to No. 1, can be applied in the powdered form at the rate of half a teaspoonful to a 6-inch pot and then carefully mixed into the surface of the soil, for which purpose an ordinary kitchen fork makes a good cultivator.—From "Fertilizers and Crops." L. L. Van Slyke.

Humus for Garden

Stack carefully, with a fork, layers of weeds, grass cuttings, leaves, vegetable residues such as dead tops of plants, alternating regularly with layers of dirt. Such compost, after it rots down, is a fine substitute for manure. Plants which are diseased or harbor insects or which are noxious weeds should not be allowed in the compost pile. Burn them.

In making a compost pile, natural decomposition is a rather slow process, if unaided. Certain chemicals can be added that will materially increase the rate of decomposition and make it quickly available for adding to the soil. Forking over a compost pile two or three times a season and thoroughly wetting with water in dry weather also aids decomposition. To avoid the unsightliness of a compost pile on a small place, the compost can be made in old barrels or oil and paint drums with heads cut out with a cold chisel and with holes cut in the bottom for drainage.

A suitable chemical composition for use in making humus is:

Ammonium sulphate	60 parts
Superphosphate	30 "
Potassium chloride	25 "
Ground limestone	50 "

The limestone prevents the mass from becoming too acid.

The Missouri Experiment Station used a mixture composed of 45 lb. ammonium sulphate, 15 lb. rock phosphate, 35 lb. limestone, 2½ lb. magnesium sulphate, and 2½ lb. salt per 100 lb. Acid phosphate was later used successfully in place of the rock phosphate.

Each material was used at the rate of 150 lb. to a ton of dry straw or leaves. In the first tests, the materials and water were applied in layers. Later, satisfactory results were obtained when the home-made mixture was mixed with the straw and was piled in flat-topped piles. Good results were later obtained when the mixture without water was simply spread over flat-topped piles of straw. However, the two seasons in which this was done were wet ones. The rotting proceeded rapidly in all cases and a product resembling animal manure was obtained. It compared favorably with the animal manure in appearance, analysis, and results from field tests. About three tons of manure were had from each ton of straw, and the yield was about 85 cents a ton.

Equal parts of ammonium sulphate, precipitated chalk, and bone meal can also be sprinkled upon the straw or lawn clippings.

To Kill Earthworms

From the standpoint of economy and efficiency, corrosive sublimate is without question the best substance to use to rid turf of earthworms. Furthermore, it is exceedingly efficient if properly used . . . there are many who have injured their turf by applying it improperly. Corrosive sublimate may be applied either in a water solution or mixed with sand or similar inert matter. The liquid form of earthworm destroyer is regarded by many as preferable.

Two or not to exceed 3 oz. of corrosive sublimate dissolved in 50 gal. of water are sufficient for 1,000 square feet of green. After the solution is applied it should be followed with at least twice the quantity of water to wash it thoroughly into the soil. If it is desired to apply the corrosive sublimate dry, it should be mixed at the rate of 2 or 3 oz. to 2 cubic feet of dry sand, and the mixture scattered evenly over 1,000 square feet of green. Liberal watering should follow. When corrosive sublimate is applied in the way and at the rates suggested, especially if water is used freely afterward, no injury to the turf should result. In very hot, dry times applications as suggested may cause a very slight burning of the turf; and furthermore, it is rarely that earthworms are in action at such times. The effect of burning from the suggested rates, however, will not be of a lasting or serious nature.

In the case of comparatively small areas of grass an ordinary sprinkling pot may be used to apply the poison solution. As corrosive sublimate rapidly corrodes metals, the solution should not be allowed to stand in a metal container, and immediate washing is advised in case a sprinkling pot is utilized for this purpose. After the application of the solution the worms usually begin to come to the surface within a very few minutes, and they should be gathered up and disposed of immediately. There is a possibility that if they are permitted to remain, some birds might be killed or injured by the poison left on the bodies of the worms.

CAUTION: Where corrosive sublimate is used it should be remembered that it is a dangerously poisonous substance and great care should be observed in handling it. All packages of the poison should be plainly labeled and all vessels in which mixtures are made should be most scrupulously cleansed by washing after use.

Poisonous Bait for Birds

There is often a demand and need for the local control of birds that have become so numerous as to be a nuisance. Where intelligent elimination can be effected, and where poisoning is not prohibited by law, poisoned baits may be used effectively in reducing the number of birds. In the case of English sparrows, it has been shown that strychnine is the most effective and safest poison. Wheat has been found to be an excellent carrier for this poison.

The coating for a quart of wheat bait may be prepared by mixing one-eighth of an ounce of pulverized strychnine alkaloid with $1\frac{1}{2}$ teaspoons of starch or wheat flour and moistening with sufficient cold water to make a paste of the consistency of thick cream; three-fourths of a gill of boiling water should then be added and the mixture stirred well to form a smooth paste. The whole is then shaken with one quart of wheat in a half gallon jar. It can then be removed and dried.

Rodent Paste

The usual procedure in making a death paste for rodents is to mix an active poison with the bait. Three successful formulas involving this method are:

#1—Lard	1 lb.
Flour	1 "
White arsenic	2 oz.
Oil of anise seed	10 drops

The paste may be made by melting the lard in a tin can, adding the flour while molten and stirring in the white arsenic (arsenic trioxide), and then adding the anise seed oil.

#2—Strychnine sulphur ... 1 oz.
Sugar milk .... 1 "
Prussian blue .... 15 gr.
Arsenic .... 2¼ oz.
Corn meal .... 12 "

Mix well. To use moisten with some water and roll in balls. Allow to dry.

#3—Barium carbonate..... 3 oz.
White arsenic .... 1 "
Powdered squill ...... 1½ "
Grated cheese .... 1 lb.

Mix.

Non-poisonous to human beings:

#1—Barium carbonate .... 4 oz.
Sugar .... 1 "
Bread crumbs .... 16 "

Mix well, add water, and make into pellets.

#2—Barium carbonate .... 10 oz.
Ultramarine blue ..... 1 "
Flour .... 3 "
Star-anise powder .... 1 "

Mix into paste with water and molasses.

Chemical for Killing Dandelions

Iron sulphate, technically called copperas, can be used in solution form to kill dandelions. The solution is made by dissolving about a pound or a pound and a half of copperas in a gallon of water. It can be applied with a sprinkling can, one gallon to every 375 square feet. After applying, the grass seems burned, but in several days takes on its usual green appearance, but the dandelions are killed. Repeat if necessary.

Weed Killers

The following substances can be used to eradicate weeds or other vegetation where growth is not desired. It will be seen that the substances are easy to procure, are inexpensive, and are non-poisonous:

Calcium chloride; sodium chloride (common salt such as ice cream salt); sodium chlorate; copper sulphate; iron sulphate; magnesium sulphate; spent crankcase oil; gasoline.

All but the last two are soluble in water and they therefore can be sprinkled on with suitable appliances.

To Control Weeds

In case of certain weeds infesting small-grain crops it has been found profitable to spray with a solution of copper sulphate, iron sulphate, or salt. If this treatment does not kill the weeds, it at least prevents them from going to seed. Such treatment, if well done, does not permanently injure the grass and is effective against the weeds. This method seems to be of most use against the wild mustard.

The spray solutions are made by dissolving either 12 pounds of copper sulphate, 100 pounds of iron sulphate, or 125 pounds of common salt in 50 gallons of water. This quantity of solution is sufficient to spray about one acre. Any machine that throws a fine mist-like spray may be used. Where areas of considerable size are to be treated, a traction sprayer with a boom twelve to twenty feet long is the most economical. In the case of wild mustard the best time to spray is when the most advanced of the mustard plants are just starting to bud.

Garden Labels

Wooden labels which are sold for the purpose of labelling perennial and annual plants and shrubs can be written upon with India or drawing ink. The ink should be allowed to dry before being thrust into the ground next the plant, or wired to it. The lower end of the wooden label, if imbedded in the ground to mark the plant, will soon rot unless it is protected with a suitable varnish. Immersing the lower half or the pointed end of wooden labels in melted paraffin wax will preserve them for a year at least, if care is taken to obtain an immersion of about a quarter of an hour, which expels all air bubbles. Spar varnish is also a good protective agent.

Zinc labels or galvanized iron labels will last several years. However, a special ink is needed to write upon them. A good ink can be made by using copper chloride dissolved in water. When this is used to write upon the zinced surface, copper is deposited. The writing is legible for several years. A darker script can be placed upon zinced labels by using an iron nail as the pen, and the copper chloride solution as the ink.

The following ink for zinc, iron, steel or tin labels has also been used:

Copper sulphate .... 1 oz.
Sal ammoniac .... ½ "
Vinegar .... 1 gill
Lampblack, enough to color.

The whole mixture is shaken before using.

Aluminum tags, which can be self stamped, and are dispensed at many penny amusement places, make the best garden labels that can be procured. They should be affixed to the plant with copper wire, leaving enough slack to allow the plant growth for several years.

Mounting Herbarium Material

For ordinary purposes in herbarium practice the best and simplest medium so far found is water-glass. Sodium silicate can be used direct with either boiled or fresh material both in the field and in the laboratory. Because it solidifies quickly it is essential that the cover glass be added without delay. The prepared slides are permanent, dry, easy to use and there is comparatively little shrinkage.

Grafting Wax

#1—Grafting wax to apply with the hands may be made by melting together 4 parts of resin, 2 parts of tallow or linseed oil, and 1 part of beeswax. While hot the liquid mixture is poured into a vessel of cold water and when hardened sufficiently to handle it is taken out and pulled and worked until it has a light-yellow color. It may be kept in convenient form for use by wrapping in oiled paper. While applying it the hands should be kept greased with vaseline or tallow. The wax may be applied with a brush if kept in a semiliquid state by heating. Care must be taken, however, that it is not applied hot enough to injure the tissues. It is frequently used for waxing the twine used for wrapping grafts.

#2—Grafting wax regarded as more durable than that described above is made with 5 lb. of resin and 1 lb. of beeswax. When these ingredients are melted, one-fourth pint of linseed oil is stirred into it, and the mixture is then removed from the fire, after which one-half pound of lampblack or powdered charcoal is worked into it a little at a time. Adding the ingredients separately lessens the danger of fire, which would be likely to occur if the mixture boiled over. This wax is intended to be applied with a brush while kept soft by heating. Cover the entire exposed cut area.

#3—A good grafting wax may be made of resin, 4 parts; beeswax, 2 parts; tallow or linseed oil, 1 part— by weight. If a harder wax is needed, 5 parts of resin and 2½ of beeswax may be used with 1 part of tallow.

The resin and beeswax should be broken up fine and melted together with the tallow. When thoroughly melted the liquid should be poured into a vessel of cold water. As soon as it becomes hard enough to handle it should be taken out and pulled and worked until it becomes tough and has the color of very light-colored manila paper. If the wax is applied by hand, the hands should be well greased.

HINTS FOR THE MECHANIC

To Make Cup Grease

Cup grease usually is made from a lubricating stock to which has been added a soap. The use of aluminum stearate as a soap in the making of cup greases from lubricating oil has been found to produce better results than by using the common soaps. Some of the advantages are:

Aluminum stearate gun grease contains 6% more oil than the ordinary grease, which makes it a better lubricant.

Aluminum stearate greases are not destroyed by excessive heat; in fact, this grease has a tendency to thicken, up to a certain point, insuring proper lubrication at high temperature. Moreover, when normal temperature is again reached it is practically of the same consistency as when originally introduced into the grease connection of the machine.

Aluminum stearate greases do not dry or form crusts that clog up grease connections.

In making the grease, #3 cup grease, ten parts by weight of aluminum stearate with 90 parts oil gives very satisfactory results. The viscosity of oil may be varied according to the type of grease required but 200 viscosity at 100° F. seems to be the best grade for #3 cup grease.

Sift the aluminum stearate slowly into about one-third of the oil, beating with a paddle, or by using an agitator,

being sure that the powder is thoroughly dispersed before adding balance of the oil. Thoroughly agitate until the batch is homogeneous, taking at least an hour for this stirring. Then gradually raise the temperature to about 350° F. with continued stirring, holding at this heat until the aluminum stearate is completely dissolved.

Allow the mass to cool by radiation only, still agitating until the grease becomes thick at about 250° F. The rate of cooling is of great importance. If the temperature is reduced too rapidly, oil separation occurs. If the rate of cooling is too slow the inner core of the mass remains softer than the edges, which naturally cool more quickly. This is particularly true when large bulks are involved. In other words, a uniform rate of cooling throughout the mass must be maintained in order to insure a uniform final product.

When thousands of gallons are made at a time the only practical method so far developed has been to draw off the heated mixture into shallow pans about six inches deep, provided with weighted empty cans in the center to obtain more uniform cooling. In this way a steady rate of heat reduction is accomplished yielding a perfect grease without oil separation. Some manufacturers have found it practical to pour the heated mixture directly into shipping containers by stirring the mass periodically, allowing it to cool uniformly throughout its entire contents. This stirring should be continued until the temperature drops to about 230° F.

The above general description brings out four factors that require careful control:

1. Percentage of aluminum stearate.
2. Temperature when mixing.
3. Rate of cooling.
4. Methods of handling.

To Make Corks Acid-proof

To make corks acid-proof proceed as follows: First carefully select the corks, making sure to obtain firm ones of perfect shape. Place them in a solution of glycerin, 2 parts, gelatin, 1 part, and water, 40 parts. Heat to from 112 to 120 degrees F. and keep them there for several hours. It is best to weight the corks down in the solution. After they have been in the solution for the required time remove and wipe off all surplus moisture. They will then be perfectly tight, or closed, retaining at the same time the greater portion of their elasticity. To render them acid-proof they should be treated with a mixture of vaseline, 2 parts, and paraffin, 7 parts, heated to about 105 degrees F. This second operation may be avoided if a little ammonium dichromate is added to the gelatin solution and the corks afterward exposed to the light.

To Soften Old Corks

Old cork stoppers can be cleaned and softened by boiling them, suitably weighted, in a 5 percent solution of sulphuric acid for 15 minutes. After rinsing in water, the corks are boiled in clean water for 15 minutes, and then placed in a 5 percent solution of alum for six hours, and then dried.

Protective Coating for Corks

To prevent the corrosive action of certain preparations, e.g., tincture of iodine, solution of ammonia, hydrochloric acid, etc., on the cork of the bottle in which they are delivered, dip the lower portion of the cork in collodion or celluloid varnish (cement).

Dustproofing Concrete Floors

The United States Bureau of Standards describes the treatment of concrete floors to make them dustproof as follows:

"In ordinary cases it will be found satisfactory to dilute each gallon of water-glass (syrupy) with four gallons of water. The resulting five gallons may be expected to cover 1000 square feet of floor surface, one coat. However, the porosity of floors varies greatly and the above statement is given as an approximate value for estimating purposes.

"The floor surface should be prepared for the treatment by cleaning free from grease, spots, plaster, etc., and then thoroughly scrubbed with clear water. To get the best penetration the floor should be thoroughly dry, especially before the first application, and if practical it is well to let it dry for several days before the first scrubbing. The solution may be applied with a mop or hair broom and should be continuously brushed over the surface for several minutes to obtain an even penetration. An interval of twenty-four hours should be allowed for the treatment to harden. Three applications made in this manner will usually suffice, but if the floor does not appear to be saturated by the third application a fourth should be applied."

Paint Removers

#1—Acetylene tetrachloride (tetrachlor-ethane) works well as a paint or enamel remover. It can be used straight or mixed with alcohol in varying proportions.

#2—Lye .... 2 lb.
      Water .... 1 gal.

Starch or flour, enough to make a paste.

#3—Mix a saturated aqueous solution of the following materials: sodium nitrophthalate, acetone, denatured alcohol, and toluene.

Lubricant for Tapping and Thread Cutting

Sal soda	1½ lb.
Warm water	3 gal.
Lard oil	1 "

Paste for Slipping Belts

#1—Linseed oil	2 parts
Castor oil	2 "
Rosin	1 "
Mutton tallow	5 "

The substances are incorporated by heating.

#2—Another method by which a belt dressing for slipping belts may be simply made is to take a handful or two of rosin and place in a Mason jar, covering it with linseed oil so that the oil layer is as deep as the rosin is thick. The oil and rosin are shaken from time to time during the ensuing several days. The mixture is then applied as desired. It may be thinned out with the addition of more linseed oil if it becomes too thick.

To Sharpen Files

Clean the files with a wire brush and free them from oil and grease by wiping well with alcohol or gasoline. Dry thoroughly, and immerse them in:

Water	1 pt.
Sulphuric acid	7 oz.
Copper sulphate	2 "
Borax	2 "

The above solution slowly etches the files, and dissolves the thin edges which are usually present on a file, but in a curled fashion, preventing the file from biting. The gases evolved in the etching also throw out metal particles. When, by inspection, the files are found eaten sufficiently, remove, wash well in water, and dry, oiling them to prevent rusting.

To Clean Files

Immersion of files in a dilute solution of sulphuric acid, using about one ounce of strong acid to four parts of water, will etch the imbedded iron and steel particles so that they may be readily removed by a stiff wire brush. The files after this treatment should be well washed in water and then oiled slightly with a mixture of machine oil or penetrating oil dissolved in gasoline, wiping off the excess.

Lead and brass filings imbedded in the teeth are best removed with a stiff brush.

Aluminum filings can be removed quite easily by soaking the files in a warm lye solution. The aluminum metal is eaten away, the hydrogen gas which is evolved also helping to throw out the metal particles. Wash well afterwards and oil as before.

To Clean Machinery

Leather belts are satisfactorily degreased with carbon tetrachloride, preparatory to later impregnation with special oils to increase their pliability and durability. Spotted leathers are also readily cleaned with carbon tetrachloride.

Motors of automobiles, airships and airplanes can be cleaned with carbon tetrachloride. This solvent gives thorough, rapid cleaning without introducing a fire hazard. The use of gasoline, benzol, or other inflammable solvents for such cleaning work has often resulted in serious fires or explosions.

Electrical motors can also be cleaned with carbon tetrachloride. The solvent is usually sprayed on to the dirty motor with compressed air, a ventilating fan carrying away the vapors. The use of carbon tetrachloride is absolutely safe, creating no fire hazard, and giving inexpensive yet thorough cleaning.

Printers' type, engraved plates, lithographers' stones, printing machinery, typewriters, and other equipment around a print shop can be easily degreased or ink-cleaned with carbon tetrachloride.

Cementing Blades in Handles

Cements for fastening blades in handles are melted and poured into the hole in the handle. The tang of the blade is then warmed, but not heated enough to take out the temper. It is then inserted into the handle, and allowed to cool, the excess cement being scraped off while tacky, yet firm. The following are good cements for this purpose:

#1—Rosin .... 4 parts
     Iron filings .... 2 "
     Sulphur .... 3 "

The filings should be freed from grease, and should be sifted to remove coarse particles.

#2—Boil together 1 part of caustic soda, 3 parts of rosin, and 5 parts of water till homogeneous and add 4 parts of plaster of Paris. The paste sets in half an hour and is but little affected by water.

#3—Rosin .... 4 parts
     Beeswax .... 1 "
     Plaster of Paris....... 1 "

#4—Thirty parts plaster of Paris, 10 parts iron filings, $\frac{1}{2}$ part sal ammoniac mixed with vinegar to a paste.

Cleaning Composition

The following can be used as a mechanic's hand cleanser, or to degrease machinery, floors, woodwork, or other surfaces that require a detergent and a mildly rough treatment.

#1—Sawdust (finely sifted) 4 lb.
     Potassium carbonate .. 1 "
     Trisodium phosphate .. $\frac{1}{2}$ "
     Soda powder or chips.. 2 "

The above is made into a paste with about a gallon of warm water, and then more water added to make the mass into a creamy paste. The whole can be perfumed with pine oil, oil of sassafras, synthetic oil of wintergreen, or oil of cloves. Owing to the type of sawdust used, the hardness of the water, and the kind of soap chips or powder taken, the amount of water should be varied to suit the needs of the user. A composition of this kind is usually made into a paste.

#2—Shredded soap ...... $2\frac{1}{2}$ lb.
     Fine sand .... 1 "
     Water .... $5\frac{1}{2}$ pt.

This cleaning paste should not be used in the house, as the sand may be carried into the sewage system and accumulate in the sink trap and the local drain connections.

Tempering and Hardening

Small tools such as chisels, knives, plane irons, or molding cutters can be tempered and heat-treated after grinding and fashioning by heating the material to redness in a suitable furnace or forge. Care must be taken not to burn the material as evidenced by scintillations or sparks which are thrown off, even passing through the live coals of the fire. Remove from the fire, and brush off ash, adhering fuel, and scale with a stiff wire brush or a brick or soft stone. Immerse the tool in water until chilled to a temperature which, on again introducing into the water, will not cause the water to boil as vigorously as it did at first. This length of time can only be judged by experience. After this initial cooling, it is slicked up or rubbed bright at the ground end with brick or emery cloth, and the colors observed as they pass down the tool into the ground edge. The colors can be clearly seen if the tool has been cooled to the proper temperature on the first immersion. When the proper color just begins to go into the cutting or chipping edge, the tool is suddenly quenched cold in water. The proper color for the particular tool under treatment is indicated in the following tabulation:

Pale straw, 430° F., for fine cutting edges; dark yellow, 470° F., for razors, etc.; dark straw, 470° F., for penknives, drills; clay yellow, 490° F., for chisels and shears; brown yellow, 500° F., for adzes and plane irons; very pale purple, 520° F., for table-knives; light purple, 530° F., for swords and watch-springs; dark purple, 550° F., for softer swords and watch-springs; dark blue, 570° F., for small fine saws; blue, 590° F. for large saws.

Tempering Liquids

#1—Potassium nitrate .... 1 oz.
    Alum .... 1 "
    Salt .... ¼ lb.
    Water .... ½ gal.

#2—Potassium nitrate ..... 1 oz.
    Sal ammoniac .... ½ "
    Borax .... 1 "
    Salt .... 12 "
    Water .... 1 gal.

Case-Hardening

Some recent investigations on case-hardening materials have shown that such materials may contain (1) a carbon-containing portion, like charcoal, lignite, coal, coke, sawdust, animal charcoal, etc.; (2) a catalyzer such as marble dust, barium carbonate; (3) cyanogen compounds such as potassium cyanide or the ferrocyanide, calcium cyanide, etc.; (4) a binding material such as soap, glue, dextrine, oils, mineral waxes, etc.; and (5) other additions of questionable value, like sand, saltpeter, glass, iron scale, slag, ash, etc. Cyanides, binding materials and other additions are rarely found in hardeners bought and used by the car-load, but are employed in small-scale operations. If the specific gravity of the material is low (0.360) it indicates high percentages of charcoals; if it is high (near 0.850) it indicates the presence of coke in large amounts.

Iron may be case-hardened by heating to a red heat, and then rolling it in a composition composed in equal parts of potassium, ferrocyanide, sal ammoniac and saltpeter, all being pulverized and thoroughly mixed. Plunge, while yet hot, into a bath containing 2 oz. potassium ferrocyanide and 4 oz. sal ammoniac to each gallon of cold water.

Case-Hardening Cast Iron

#1—Salt .... ½ pt.
    Saltpeter .... ¼ lb.
    Prussiate of potash ... ⅛ "
    Cyanide of potash..... ¼ "
    Water .... 5 gal.

Heat the iron to a cherry red, dip in the mixture. If not hard enough repeat the process.

#2—Salt .... 2 lb.
    Saltpeter .... ½ "
    Alum .... ½ "
    Ammonia .... 4 oz.
    Salt of tartar......... 4 "

Pulverize all together and mix thoroughly. Use by powdering over the iron while it is hot, then plunging it in cold water.

To Soften Steel

#1—Sal ammoniac .... 1 gm.
    Salt .... 5 "
    Glycerin .... 80 cc.
    Water .... 100 "

The steel is heated to redness and immersed in the above liquid.

#2—Water .... 2 gal.
    Saltpeter .... ½ oz.
    Pulverized borax ..... ½ "
    Zinc sulphate .... 1 "
    Salt .... 1½ pt.

To soften steel or iron heat it red hot and allow it to cool slowly. This is necessary when the piece is to be drilled afterwards.

Small Iron Parts

To harden small iron parts, such as machine screws, wood screws, punchings, etc., a simple case-hardening process can be used. This is accomplished by dampening charcoal powder with a solution of equal parts of salt and potassium ferrocyanide dissolved in water. The charcoal must be thoroughly wet with the solution. When the solution is first added, the powder will not be wetted with certain charcoals, but one or two drops of alcohol applied to the powder will assist the solution in penetrating the mass. The whole paste is then packed into a sheet iron tray or box, and the iron articles which are to be hardened are placed in the paste so that they are entirely covered. The iron tray is then placed in a muffle furnace, or in an open fire, and slowly brought to redness. When dried out, the powder is poked with an iron rod so that it completely covers the articles which are left exposed when the moisture leaves the mass. An iron cover is placed on the tray or box, and the heating continued, keeping the box red hot for ten or twenty minutes. The box or tray is then removed and plunged in cold water, and the parts washed by shaking.

The articles will then be retained in the box. The water should be immediately driven off by a gentle heat by placing the box in a warm place and the articles, now hardened, protected from rusting by shaking them in a thin spar varnish, lacquer, or a solution of wax in benzol, chloroform, or carbon tetrachloride, and allowing to dry.

HOME CHEMIST'S GUIDE

Paper for Recording Systems

The following solutions, when impregnated on paper sheets or tape, will change color when heated, either by a flame or electrical spark. Its use is suggested in recording systems.

#1—Anilin hydrochloride.. 9.8 gm.
    Potassium nitrate .... 8 "
    Water .... 100 cc.

#2—Nickel nitrate .... 5 gm.
    Sodium thiosulphate.. 3.9 "
    Sodium nitrate ...... 1 "
    Water .... 100 cc.
    Gelatin solution 1%.. 5 "

#3—Gelatin .... 10 gm.
    Salt .... 5 "
    Phenolphthalein ..... 0.5 "
    Water .... 100 cc.

Heat Filter

The following solutions are used in glass cells for preventing the transmission of heat rays, and are frequently employed in projection lanterns, laboratory investigations, etc.

#1—Copper sulphate ..... 0.5 gm.
    Water .... 100 cc.
    Sulphuric acid ...... 1 drop

#2—Ferrous ammonium
    sulphate .... 20 gm.
    Water .... 100 cc.
    Sulphuric acid to clear 5 drops

The above lasts about two weeks. It prevents heat rays from passing, but lets light rays through and is often used in microscopy, a solution being placed between the source of artificial light and the microscope.

To Make Precipitated Chalk

This substance is widely used in making white shoe creams, metal and furniture polishes, talcum powder, tooth cleaning preparations, and putties. It can be made by mixing a solution of limewater, or calcium chloride, with sodium carbonate (soda ash) solution. A voluminous white precipitate is thrown down when the two solutions are mixed. This white calcium carbonate is precipitated chalk, and for use should be washed free from soluble salts.

This is done by allowing the precipitate, or sediment, to settle. The upper clear liquid is syphoned off and discarded. The precipitate is well stirred with at least ten times its own volume of water, allowed to settle, and the clear upper liquid again syphoned off. This process is repeated several times, the last step being to filter the precipitate from the remaining wash water, and drying after being removed from the paper. For an exceptionally pure product, the last washings should be done with distilled water. A Buchner funnel enables the precipitate to be filtered, using suction as an aid to drain off the liquid or wash water.

To Clean Chemical Glassware

The standard bichromate cleaning mixture of the analytical laboratory long since deserved to be displaced. It is dangerous, destructive, and inefficient. Trisodium phosphate as a possible laboratory detergent has been investigated exhaustively and has much to recommend it. A 15 percent solution, heated to about 70° C., has been utilized in many laboratories for cleaning burets and other volumetric glassware with satisfactory results. Trisodium phosphate is sold under the name of TSP and can be used to clean household glassware and automobile windshields, as well as laboratory glassware.—*Industrial and Engineering Chemistry.*

Determining Temperatures

Temperatures higher than that of the room (20° C. or 68° F.) are measured with mercurial thermometers, electrical pyrometers, or optical pyrometers. In estimating the temperatures of various bodies when none of these instruments is available, and where only an approximate determination is to be made, various metals which have known melting points can be used. If, for instance, it is desired to know the temperature of a hot plate upon which fusions or other heating operations are carried out, it is only necessary to place on the plate some pieces of different metals or alloys. For instance, lead which melts at 327° C. or 621° F. will melt if placed upon the plate providing the temperature is at least 621° F. If the lead melts, then the next substance that is quite common and easily procured is zinc. If a globule of zinc is placed on the plate, and it does not melt, then it can be said that the temperature is somewhat lower than 786° F. By this means, close approximations of the temperatures of bjects being annealed, tempered, fused, or enameled can be ascertained. It is best, however, to use the metals in the form of shot, for if they are of a large diameter, then much heat will be radiated by them into the air, thus giving a false temperature. The melting points of some everyday metals are:

Tin	462° F.
Cadmium	608° F.
Lead	621° F.
Zinc	786° F.
Aluminum	1216° F.

Freezing Mixtures

The following are some mixtures which can be used to produce low temperatures for many purposes. In the mixtures below, finely shaved ice can be used for the snow. The original tables call for solid carbon dioxide gas for the dry ice, but there is no doubt that dry ice, being solid carbon dioxide, will, if used, produce the low temperatures mentioned. The initial temperatures given are the temperatures which the substances should

have before mixing to produce the temperature attained by the mixture.

A is the proportion of the substance named in the first column to be added to the proportion of the substance given in Column B. The table gives the temperature of the separate ingredients and the temperature attained by the mixture. Following are from Smithsonian Tables.

Substance	A	B	Initial temperature ° C.	Temp. ° C. attained by mixt.
Sodium acetate	85	H₂O 100	10.7	— 4.7
Sal ammoniac	30	H₂O 100	13.3	— 5.1
Sodium nitrate	75	H₂O 100	13.2	— 5.3
"Hypo"	110	H₂O 100	10.7	— 8.0
Potassium iodide	140	H₂O 100	10.8	— 11.7
Ammonium nitrate	60	H₂O 100	13.6	— 13.6
Calcium chloride	30	Snow¹ 100	— 1	— 10.9
Sal ammoniac	25	Snow 100	— 1	— 15.4
Ammonium nitrate	45	Snow 100	— 1	— 16.75
Sodium nitrate	50	Snow 100	— 1	— 17.75
Salt	33	Snow 100	— 1	— 21.3
66.1% sulphuric acid and 33.9% water	1	Snow 1.097	— 1	— 37.0
	1	Snow 2.52	— 1	— 30.0
	1	Snow 4.32	— 1	— 25.0
	1	Snow 7.92	— 1	— 20.0
	1	Snow 13.08	— 1	— 16.0
Calcium chloride	1	Snow 0.49	0	— 19.7
	1	Snow 0.61	0	— 39.0
	1	Snow 0.70	0	— 54.9
	1	Snow 0.81	0	— 40.3
	1	Snow 1.23	0	— 21.5
	1	Snow 2.46	0	— 9.0
	1	Snow 4.92	0	— 4.0
Alcohol at 4° C.	77	Snow 73.00	0	— 30.0
		Dry Ice		— 72.0
Chloroform	..	Dry Ice	..	— 77.0
Ammonium nitrate	1	H₂O 0.94	20	— 4.0
	1	Snow 0.94	0	— 4.0
	1	H₂O 1.20	10	— 14.0
	1	Snow 1.20	0	— 14.0
	1	H₂O 1.31	10	— 17.5
	1	Snow 1.31	0	— 17.5

¹ Or finely pulverized ice.

Cold Without Ice

#1—The following mixture will create cold without the aid of ice. Take two earthen jars of different sizes so that one will go inside the other. Then take

Sal ammoniac	....	5 oz.
Saltpeter	....	5 "
Sodium sulphate	......	8 "

Mix these together and stir thoroughly into one pint of water previously placed in the larger jar. Then place the preparation to be chilled in the smaller jar, and put the smaller jar in the large one, cover and let remain until contents become as cool as wanted. Other mixtures such as those tabulated can be used.

#2—Sal ammoniac, soda ash, and water is less expensive than the common sodium nitrate, soda ash water mixture usually used.

#3—Equal parts ammonium chloride and saltpeter.

#4—Ammonium nitrate and water.

#5—Ammonium nitrate and soda ash.

Freezing Powders

Four lb. of sulphate of soda, 2½ lb. each of sal ammoniac and nitrate of potash; when about to use add double the weight of all the ingredients of water.

Solid Carbon Dioxide Gas

Dry ice recently has come into extensive use for commercial purposes, especially in ice cream and dairy plants. Its temperature is about 110 degrees below zero or 140 degrees below the temperature of ordinary ice. Although it looks harmless enough it can do considerable damage to the person who handles it with bare hands. Numbness and pain, not only in the fingers but also in the hands and arms are the first symptoms, and in some cases a form of neuritis is produced. It is, no doubt, the easiest substance that can be procured to produce very low temperatures.

Leather Belt Dressing

Melt together 5 oz. of spruce gum with 1 oz. of ozocerite or what is sold also under the name of cerasine (this is a harder paraffin resembling beeswax) and 3 oz. of rosin. When melted, remove from the fire and add 2 oz. of turpentine. Allow the mixture to become cold and add 10 oz. of alcohol. Shake the dressing before applying it with a brush on the inner side of the belt.

How to Remove Moisture

Place calcium chloride in an open dish placed within a larger box containing the substance to be freed from moisture. This substance avidly takes up all available water, but in order to do this the calcium chloride must be in small lumps or granular in form. When the calcium chloride has lost its original shape in the box, it must be replaced by fresh.

Metal-Polishing Bricks

To make metal-polishing bricks, mix 2 parts of pumice stone and 1 of plaster of Paris in water and pour into molds.

Solvent for Many Substances

Benzol is used as a solvent for resins, fats, rubber, sulphur, phosphorus and iodine. If stains of any of these substances are to be removed, moisten the stain with benzol on a rag and rub. If the stain is stubborn, soak the spot in a small dish of benzol until the material has softened and then remove the stain with a clean rag or a piece of blotting paper. This is one of the methods used by dry cleaners for the removal of such blemishes.

Furnace or Forge Clay

Ordinary fire clay can be used in home workshops, but often the setting is never hard because of the lack of heat needed to cause vitrification throughout the whole lining. However, if iron filings and sal ammonia are used with the clay, the whole will, on drying out, become harder than without them and the set cement will not have to be burnt to make it hard. The following can be used:

File clay .... 20 parts
Sal ammoniac .... 1 "
Salt .... 1 "
Iron filings .... 20 "
Sulphur .... 1 "

The sulphur can be omitted if desired.

Prints of Magnetic Lines

Prints of magnetic lines of force can be obtained in a few minutes by the use of velox paper in a darkened room. Lay a sheet of the paper, with the film side up, on the magnet. Sift on iron filings, using cheese cloth bag of filings. Tap the paper slightly. The filings arrange themselves in the lines of force. Hold a gas flame or incandescent lamp a foot above the paper for half a minute to one and a half minutes. Turn out the light, dust off the filings, and immerse the paper in a dish of developing solution. The picture will develop in about a minute, and is then kept from five to ten minutes in a fixing solution of one pound hyposulphite of soda dissolved in water. Wash the print fifteen minutes in running water. The developing and fixing solutions may be kept and used for a large number of prints. These are really negatives, the outlines of the filings appearing as white lines.

If it is desired to print a number of positives, make the negative translucent by applying to the back of it a little Canada balsam dissolved in alcohol or melted paraffin.

To Purify Mercury

#1—The purest mercury is prepared by distillation under diminished pressure, but this procedure is not at all practical for many home laboratory workers.

#2—Covering the mercury with about an eight percent nitric acid solution (say 8 cc. strong acid and 92 cc. water) and bubbling air through the mercury while covered with the acid for a period of twenty-four hours will produce a clean mercury which should be washed free from acid with water and filtered through a dry filter paper having several pin pricks at its apex. This latter operation can also be an initial one if the mercury being purified is very dirty.

#3—If a piece of electric light carbon is placed on the mercury and the whole covered with dilute sulphuric acid, a battery is formed which results in the solution of the baser metals.

Mercury can be purified by shaking with a paste made from concentrated sulphuric acid and mercurous nitrate. It is then separated off by means of a separatory funnel and washed with water, finally with distilled water, and then dried.

How to Make Radio Minerals

Synthetic crystals are composed of lead and sulphur. The lead is first melted, then sulphur is added, the mixture being stirred with a carbon rod until it forms into a black solid mass. After being cooled it is finely powdered, and about 10 percent of its own weight of powdered sulphur is added. The whole preparation is then fused.

Tear Gas Bomb

Any suitable glass container can be used in the preparation of a tear gas liquid. Use a formaldehyde solution. As this solution is unstable, the gas is instantly released and severe smarting of the eyes results.

Artificial Ice for Skating Rinks

#1—This substance is sodium thiosulphate, or photographer's hypo (hyposulphite of soda). The crystals are raked on the floor evenly and then smoothed out with a heavy tailor's iron. The crystals melt in their own water of crystallization, forming an even surface with proper use of the iron.

#2—Equal parts of soda ash and crystallized sodium carbonate and less than half of their amount is taken of sodium sulphate (Glauber's salts). This and water are added. Gum tragacanth has also been added to the mixture.

Cigarette Lighter Fluid

Aviation gasoline is the material used in cigar and cigarette lighters.

High test gasoline, if distilled and the first half of the distillate collected, will be found to yield a good product for lighters. The residual half is discarded. It is good practice to take the first three-sevenths of the distillate in the winter time when cold weather does not volatilize the fluid readily, and in summer use the first half or the first four-sevenths of the distillate. A round-bottomed flask supported upon the usual wire gauze will serve as a distilling flask, or the ordinary side-necked distillation can may be used. Keep the fluid in a stout bottle and stopper with a cork.

Incense

#1—Powdered charcoal ...   5 oz.
  Powdered orris root...   1 "
  Saltpeter, powdered ...   ½ "
  Powdered gum olibanum   ½ "
  Powdered gum sandal-
    wood ....   1 "

#2—Willow charcoal ......   6 oz.
  Benzoin (gum) ....   1 "
  Nitrate of potash .....   ½ "
  Balsam tolu ....   2 dr.
  Sandalwood ....   2 "

Mucilage of tragacanth, enough to form a paste. Mold into cakes.

#3—Benzoin (gum) ....   8 parts
  Balsam tolu ....   2 "
  Storax ....   2 "
  Sandalwood ....   2 "
  Myrrh ....   1 "
  Cascarilla bark ....   2 "
  Denatured alcohol ....   25 "

#4—Benzoin ....   10 oz.
  Charcoal ....   24 "
  Potassium nitrate .....   1 "
  Sassafras, powdered....   2 "

Tragacanth mucilage, enough to mold the cones together.

Stink Bombs

These consist of little glass ampoules or bombs filled with a liquid of a disagreeable odor. The following are suggested to be used as the stench:

Hydrogen sulphide water; carbon disulphide (inflammable at very low temperatures!); ethyl mercaptan; skatole; indole; ethyl selenide; methyl sulphide; pyridine; or phenyl isocyanide.

Permanganate of Potash

This substance consists of shiny dark purple needles and contains a relatively large amount of oxygen which is easily liberated.

Thermos bottles, ice-hot camping or picnic jugs, water bottles, decanters, and the like can readily be freed from obnoxious odors by placing several small crystals of the substance within and adding several tablespoonfuls of water, followed by shaking to expose the inner surface to the action of the chemical. This treatment, followed by several rinsings of clean water, will sweeten the vessel in a way that is remarkable.

Thirty grains of the permanganate dissolved in half a pint of water is a useful cleansing agent for snake bite, the wound being opened and the liquid swabbed about on the raw flesh.

Added to the rain water in a barrel used for washing, permanganate prevents the development of mosquito larvae, a pink solution being obtained in the barrel when sufficient permanganate has been added. The chemical does not kill the larvae but removes the organic matter upon which they feed. The water can be used for other purposes.

In mosquito eradicating campaigns it can be used in marshes in place of oil.

A 5% solution is used to treat seed potatoes to immunize them against fungus. Cuttings or slips of plants, shrubs, etc., which have been immersed along their cut ends in a solution of permanganate, will result in a higher percentage of rootings when placed in cutting sand.

It makes a good wood stain.

How to Make Solidified Alcohol

#1—Make a saturated solution of calcium acetate and filter. Four cc. of this solution are poured into a test tube which can hold about 75 cc. Fifty cc. of denatured alcohol are poured in and the test tube quickly inverted several times to mix the liquids thoroughly. In a moment the mass becomes so firm that the test tube may be inverted without spilling any. This solidified alcohol may be removed from the test tube and burned. It will be noticed that the mass does not melt as is the case with some varieties of solidified alcohol.

In reality the alcohol is still liquid but is held in the interstices of the crystals. If some of the solid is kept undisturbed for several days the crystals will have settled to the bottom of the container and the alcohol will be clear again. Seal in tight cans.

#2—Heat 1,000 parts of denatured alcohol in a large vessel to about 140° F., and then mix with 28 to 30 parts of well-dried soap chips and 2 parts of gum lac. After repeated shaking, complete solution will take place. The solution is put, while still warm, into vessels, and allowed to cool. The admixture of gum lac effects a better preservation and also prevents the evaporation of the alcohol.

#3—Place 1 pt. denatured alcohol in a double boiler and bring to about 60° F., then add 10 oz. powdered soap and $\frac{1}{2}$ oz. gum lac and stir well until dissolved.

#4—Alcohol .... 1000.0 cc.
    Stearic acid .... 60.0 gm.
    Sodium hydroxide .. 13.5 "

Dissolve the stearic acid in 500 cc. of the alcohol. Dissolve the sodium hydroxide in the other 500 cc. of the alcohol. Warm both solutions to 60 degrees C. Then mix them and pour into suitable containers which have previously been warmed to 60 degrees C. and allow the mass to solidify.

Solidified Gasoline

Dissolve 12 oz. finely shaved white soap in 1 pint hot water, working it up to a paste. When slightly cool add 5 oz. household ammonia. Work in $\frac{1}{2}$ gallon gasoline to form a semisolid mass. It may be diluted with either gasoline or water. It will burn when ignited. Usually packed in tubes in a thin state and sold as a spot remover and glove cleaner. Add the gasoline in small quantities, gradually increasing the amount.

Preparation of Gases

The following experiments illustrate the preparation of the various important gases. Oxygen is conveniently prepared by heating potassium chlorate crystals with manganese dioxide. Another method: Drop potassium permanganate crystals in hydrogen peroxide.

Carbon dioxide gas by treating a carbonate, such as baking soda or marble, with an acid.

Hydrogen by an acid on some metals, as zinc and iron.

Sulphur dioxide by heating copper and strong sulphuric acid.

Acetylene by calcium carbide and water. This makes impure gas.

Hydrochloric acid gas by heating salt and strong sulphuric acid.

Ammonia gas by heating any ammonium chemical with lye water or by dropping strong ammonia water on potassium hydroxide.

Nitrogen by heating dry sodium nitrite and ammonium chloride.

Chlorine by heating salt, manganese dioxide, and strong sulphuric acid.

To Determine Polarity

#1—Immersing the wires into a solution of weak sulphuric acid or salt will produce about the negative pole a larger number of bubbles than at the positive pole.

#2—Make a solution of salt and add a few drops of phenolphthalein solution. Cut strips of filter paper to the size desired and immerse in the above solution. Remove and dry. When ready for use, moisten the paper and apply the terminal wires. The negative pole will produce a pink coloration upon the paper.

Soap Bubble Liquids

The common soapy water that has been used for soap bubble blowing can be improved upon in several ways, among them being the inclusion of glycerin, various dyes, and the use of sodium oleate in place of bar soap with its miscellaneous admixture of rosin, and naphtha. The following recipes will produce large bubbles, and at the same time be more resistant to forces that burst them.

#1—White soap, shredded..   5 parts
     Water .... 200 "
Mix and then add:
     Glycerin ....   3 "

#2—Dissolve 10 gm. of sodium oleate powder in 400 cc. of water and allow to stand with occasional shaking until dissolved, which may take several days. Now add 100 cc. of thick (concentrated) glycerin and allow to stand for two or three days, then pour off the clear top solution if sediment is present, and add one drop of strong ammonium hydroxide (ammonia water). The solution appears silky, being colloidal, and will keep for years.

#3—Castile soap ....   1 part
     Water .... 20 "
Dissolve and add:
     Glycerin .... 15 "

Various dyes that can be bought ready mixed will serve as a good tinting substance for colored bubbles, although the colors will be rather pale. However, if a speck of fluorescein is dissolved in the soapy water, the bubbles blown will be of a yellowish green cast, with a slight fluorescence.

Blowing Permanent Bubbles

Bubbles blown with the regular bubble pipe, using the following mixture, will be permanent, in that they are not easily crushed or will not burst, when made by flipping the bubble off the end of the pipe.

Canada balsam is heated at a low temperature and when limpid, rosin is stirred in, together with a small amount of turpentine. About 53 parts of the balsam to 46 of the rosin will produce a liquid for the basis of experiment. It is well to keep the pipe with which the bubbles are blown a trifle warmer than the mixture.

Luminous Paper

To make this oddity coat paper with a glue solution, or ordinary mucilage, and then sift luminous calcium sulphide over the surface before the glue has dried. Any of the luminous paint formulas work well with this glue preparations, but their efficiency is not great, as the water decomposes the alkaline earth sulphide. To prevent this hydrolysis, use a thin varnish upon the paper, such as a spar varnish mixed with turpentine without a drier. The luminous powder is then sifted over the paper and allowed to dry. The luminous powder or paint may be applied to the surface of the paper with a soft hair brush. The gums, such as gum arabic or tragacanth, when made into a mucilage with water can also be used to hold the phosphorescent substance to the paper.

Fire-Extinguishing Powders

These powders act by shutting out the air. They also tend to suppress the flame by virtue of their high thermal conductivity. Any powder that will not burn, such as road dust or talcum powder, will make a good agent for extinguishing fires. However, the following work well. They should be well mixed and the talcum powder or powdered talc used in their compositions should be very fine to

enable the whole mixture to slip between the fingers when thrown on the fire and scatter as a dust.

#1—Fine powdered sal am-
moniac .... 10 lb.
Fine powdered tungstate
soda .... 2 "
Bicarbonate soda ..... 4 "
Talc .... 2 "

This powder is blown or thrown on the fire.

#2—Alum .... 24 parts
Ammonium sulphate... 52 "
Copperas .... 4 "

#3—Salt .... 6 parts
Ammonium chloride... 6 "
Sodium bicarbonate... 8 "

Fire-Extinguishing Liquid

#1—Dissolve sal soda ..... 1 lb.
Tungstate soda .... 1 "
Water .... 3 gal.

In case of fire, throw corked bottles containing the liquid in fire with sufficient force to break bottle.

#2—Carbon tetrachloride. Use as above.

Non-inflammable Fumigant

Moths and beetles that prey upon clothing, carpets, and furniture are to be attacked with a very effective new fumigant devised by the United States Department of Agriculture. A mixture of three parts by volume of ethylene dichloride and one part of carbon tetrachloride is effective against pests of this type. The mixture is cheap, non-inflammable, nonexplosive, non-injurious to stored commodities, and not dangerous to human life. The toxicity of the mixture is approximately five times that of carbon tetrachloride, which is also used as a fumigant.

Waterproof Matches

To 50 cc. of collodion, add 1 part of glycerin or castor oil and coat matches with the well-mixed solution. A solution of candle wax or beeswax in benzol can also be used.

Explosive Matches

The explosive matches sold in novelty stores employ silver fulminate for their action, a small crystal of this substance being placed back of the head of the match and held with varnish. If water-glass is substituted for this process, coating the whole head, the match will sputter and misfire in a decidedly curious way when struck.

Fixed Condensers

The following table gives the size in inches of tin foil that should be used to form condensers of the stated capacities:

Capacity, Microfarads	2 tin foils and 1 mica	4 tin foils and 3 micas
.0001	$1 \times .1$	$.5 \times .1$
.0005	$1 \times .5$	$1 \times .25$
.001	1×1	$1 \times .5$
.002	1×2	1×1
.003	1×3	1×1.5
.004	1×4	1×2
.005	1.5×3.3	1.5×1.6
.006	1.5×4	1.5×2
.008	2×4	2×2
.009	2×4.5	2×2.2
.01	2×5	2×2.5
.02	3×6.6	3×3.3

Fumigating with Formaldehyde

The following formulas are suggested for formaldehyde fumigation: Place in mixing pan, chlorinated lime .... 12 oz.
Water (add and stir to paste) 4 "
Formaldehyde, U. S. P. solution .... 1 lb.
Pour over the moistened lime.

The above is sufficient to fumigate 1,000 cubic feet room space.

Sodium dichromate .... 10 oz.
Formaldehyde, U. S. P..... 1 lb.
Sulphuric acid, commercial. 1½ oz.

The acid can be added to the formaldehyde and the mixture kept on hand for use. This solution is added to the dichromate, which has been spread out in a layer over the bottom of the vessel. One of the drawbacks of this method is that the residue is somewhat corrosive, and if a metal container is used it should be removed and washed out with water as soon as possible.

Caustic soda (commercial), ground or contused, lumps or sticks .... 6 oz.
Formaldehyde, U. S. P. solution .... 1 lb.
Aluminum sulphate, saturated solution .... 2 oz.
Formaldehyde, U. S. P..... 8 "
Pour this mixture on unslaked lime .... 1 lb.

Use only fresh unslaked lime or failure will result. It is necessary for proper fumigation to have the premises heated to 70° F. or over. A good rule to use for proper size of vessel is to have it ten times the capacity of the volume of the ingredients used.

Phosphorescent Substance

Heat the following for one half hour, using a porcelain crucible. A Mekker, Fisher or other high temperature burner should be used to produce sufficient heat.

#1—Calcium carbonate (precipitated) .... 100 gm.
Sodium carbonate (chemically pure) .... 2 "
Salt .... 0.2 "
Sulphur .... 30 "
Bismuth nitrate ...... 0.2 "

#2—The following gives a pale green light when viewed in the dark after exposing to a bright light:

Zinc sulphide (precipitated) 15 gm.
Magnesium chloride ...... 2 "
Calcium chloride .... 1 "
Strontium chloride .... 1 "
Barium chloride .... 1 "
Ammonium tungstate .....0.002 "

The mixture should be heated for half an hour at a high temperature.

Fluorescent Screen for X-Rays

The following preparation is suitable as a fluorescent screen for small X-ray tubes.

#1—Sodium tungstate ..... 29 gm.
    Calcium chloride ..... 11 "
    Sodium chloride ...... 58 "

The whole is intimately mixed, and heated in a crucible. The result of the reaction produced by the heat is that calcium tungstate is formed, which crystallizes out from the molten sodium chloride as the mass cools. After cooling, the mass is removed from the crucible and washed with water to dissolve the excess sodium chloride. The powder is then dried and sprinkled on a gummy sheet of stiff paper, and when dry makes a good fluorescent screen for experimental purposes.

#2—Powdered scheelite (naturally occurring calcium tungstate) when powdered and sprinkled upon a stiff sheet of paper or card coated with gum arabic solution makes a suitable X-ray fluorescent screen. The scheelite can be sifted upon the tacky card or paper by shaking it from a small cloth bag.

#3—Precipitated calcium tungstate, mixed with lime and heated in a current of hydrochloric acid gas, will be converted into crystalline calcium tungstate, which can also be used as a fluorescent screen.

The following are fluorescent under various ultra-violet rays and X-rays. They offer a wide field for experimentation by amateurs. Aesculine, anthracene ammonium and barium platino-cyanide, barium sulphide, boracic acid, the fluoride, sulphate, sulphide, platino-cyanide and tungstate of calcium, chlorophyll, corundum, curcumine, daturine, fluoresceine, eosine, erythrosine, fluorspar, obsidian, potassium acetate, quinine salts in acid solution, rhodamine B, strontium sulphide and platino-cyanide, succinic acid, uranium salts, uranium glass, willemite, zinc sulphide.

Under intense ultra-violet radiations, the following are fluorescent: white of boiled egg, pearl buttons, teeth, finger nails, freckles, white paper, Ivory soap.

LACQUERS

Old Tooth Brush Handles

An excellent label lacquer and general utility cement may be prepared from the pyroxylin handles of discarded tooth brushes. The bristled end is broken off and the handle dissolved in enough of a solvent such as butyl acetate, acetone or ether-alcohol to give a glycerin-like consistency. About 300 cc. of solution generally results. The color of the original handle is unimportant since even the dark ones give an almost colorless film.

The lacquer so prepared is not only useful for protecting labels but has been used successfully for sealing leaks in apparatus, notably vacuum distillations and sealing bottles against moisture. It is a good library paste since it does not wrinkle paper. It may be used to cement pieces of glass together. It has also been dyed with organic dyes or mixed with handy pigments for decorative effects.—A. H. Taylor, in *The Chemist-Analyst*.

Pale-Colored Lacquer

Shellac (bleached)	4 oz.
Gum sandarac	4 "
Gum elemi	1 "
Denatured alcohol	1 gal.

Allow to dissolve in a warm place for several days. Strain off, and add to the yet undissolved material ½ gallon of alcohol. This will cause further dissolution, which is to be strained and added to the first solution of lacquer.

The above pale-colored lacquer can be tinted green by using a mixture of 6 ounces of turmeric and 1 ounce of green gamboge, grinding portions of the two colors with some of the lacquer, and diluting with more lacquer to obtain the shade desired.

Lacquer for Brass

Shellac	4 oz.
Annatto	4 "
Dragon's blood	4 "
Gamboge	4 "
Saffron	1 "
Alcohol	5 qt.

A General Lacquer

Gum mastic	8 parts
Camphor	4 "
Gum sandarac	12 "
Gum elemi	4 "
Alcohol	300 "

Transparent Lacquer

Powdered gum sandarac	4 parts
Turpentine	7 "
Spirit of turpentine	28 "

Dissolve the turpentine and the powdered gum sandarac over a low fire in the spirit of turpentine.

The following lacquer is suitable for flowers:

Gum mastic	8 parts
Camphor	6 "
Sandarac	15 "
Shellac	15 "
Alcohol	40 "

Universal Lacquer

Gum sandarac	12 parts
Shellac	6 "
Gum mastic	6 "
Gum elemi	3 "
Denatured alcohol	150 "
Venice turpentine	6 "

Heat to dissolve, using precautions from fire.

Bronze-Colored Lacquer

Dissolve ¾ lb. of shellac and ½ lb. of sandarac in 3 qt. of alcohol, and add enough extract of dragon's blood and turmeric to produce the desired color.

Bookbinders' Lacquer

The following recipes are recommended: Pulverize and dissolve 3 oz. of shellac, 1½ oz. each of sandarac, mastic, and benzoin in 1¼ pt. of denatured alcohol, then add 1½ oz. of Venetian turpentine. Allow to settle.

Strong Lacquers

The following are very adherent lacquers:

#1—Shellac, flake	75 parts	
Boric acid	2 "	
Oil of lavender	¼ "	
Denatured alcohol	160 "	

The borax improves the adhesive quality of the shellac but the quantity should not be exceeded, for fluffing off of the shellac will occur.

#2—Gum sandarac	46 parts
Alcohol	64 "

Dissolve the above and to this add:

Alcohol	200 parts
Turpentine	50 "
Oil of lavender	2 "

#3—Gum sandarac .... 3 dr.
    Canada balsam .... 3 "
    Gum mastic .... 3 "
    Turmeric .... 6 "
    Saffron .... 3 scr.
    Alcohol .... 12 oz.

Dissolve and add turpentine, 120 minims.

Lacquer for Maps

A lacquer for paper, drawings, and maps is made of gum dammar, 35 parts, dissolved in 180 parts of acetone. Mix 40 parts of this solution with about 30 parts of collodion.

A mixture of gum dammar dissolved in acetone, added to a solution of celluloid in acetone, will produce a clear varnish-like lacquer.

Dammar Lacquer

Dammar lacquer is prepared by treating dammar resin with turpentine or with light mineral oil, with or without the application of heat. It is generally believed that the lacquer made by the cold process is the better. The usual proportions are 5 to 6 pounds of resin to 1 gallon of solvent. The resin is only partially dissolved so that commercial dammar lacquers always show more or less turbidity.

Four Good Lacquers

#1—Gum lac .... 10 parts
    Strong ammonia water 30 "

Dissolve by shaking, but not by heating because of the decomposition of the ammonium hydroxide. After applying this lacquer, the metal should be dried and heated.

#2—Gum sandarac .... 10 parts
    Rosin .... 3 "
    Glycerin .... ½ "
    Alcohol, a sufficient quantity to dissolve.

Dissolve the two rosins in sufficient alcohol and add the glycerin.

#3—Gold-Colored Lacquer for Brass Not Dipped:

Alcohol .... 4 gal.
Turmeric .... 3 lb.
Gamboge .... 3 oz.
Gum sandarac .... 7 lb.
Shellac .... 1½ "
Varnish .... 1 pt.

#4—Place 25 parts of mastic and 250 parts of sandarac in a fine sieve, and suspend the latter in a vessel containing 600 parts of denatured alcohol in such a manner that the resins are just covered with the alcohol. This will dissolve by virtue of the difference in densities of the solution and solvent.

METALS

Black on Brass

The blackening of brass is perhaps the most important or most widely used coloring operation in the workshop. Also, it is the easiest to carry out, a cupra ammonium chloride or sulphate being the agent used to produce the effect.

As this liquid cannot be purchased in the open market, it must be made, but its preparation is easy. Copper sulphate or copper nitrate is used as the base solution, and to it there should be added a solution of soda ash or sal soda. This will precipitate basic copper carbonate. In adding the solution of the soda, the amount must be controlled so that all of the copper carbonate is precipitated, yet not dissolved again, as will be the case if a large amount or an excess amount of the carbonate or soda solution is used.

In adding the soda solution, allow the precipitate to settle, then add more, allow to settle, then add still more of the soda solution. In this manner, the point at which no further precipitate forms on the addition of the soda solution is easily ascertained, and after this no more should be added. The precipitate is allowed to settle and the clear water poured off. Fresh water is then added, the whole shaken, and allowed to settle, pouring off and adding fresh water again. The paste of carbonate of copper is then collected and laid away for use. To make up the blackening solution some of the paste is dissolved in household ammonia until a deep blue solution is formed. The brass is then immersed in this deep blue solution. The solution can be stoppered and used for other blackenings at a later date if desired.

Brass can be blackened by immersion in a slightly warm solution of powdered malachite mineral dissolved in ammonium hydroxide, or the solution can be applied to the brass by means of a brush and the brass or copper heated.

Solutions for Blacking Brass

#1—Prepare the following two solutions:

A.

Nitrate of copper......... ¼ oz.
Water .... 1 "

B.

Nitrate of silver.......... ¼ oz.
Water .... 1 "

Mix A and B, clean the brass thoroughly, and dip in the solution for a moment only. After removing from the solution, the brass is heated to the annealing point to produce the desired black color which may be rubbed glossy with linseed oil, or lacquered.

#2—Dissolve 10 gm. of copper nitrate in 60 cc. of water and apply to the brass, which should be cleaned so that the copper solution will not gather in drops. The brass is then heated to decompose the copper nitrate, the resulting product finally being copper oxide, which is permanent.

Instead of heating to decompose the copper nitrate, apply:

Sodium sulphide .... 10 gm.
Muriatic acid .... 5 cc.
Water .... 100 "

When the brass, covered with the film of copper nitrate, comes into contact with this sulphide solution, copper sulphide is formed, which deposits upon the brass. In this manner the heating process is eliminated.

#3—The following produces a good black on brass instrument parts. Free the brass from grease by sponging with gasoline or carbon tetrachloride. Wipe dry and immerse in strong nitric acid. This will cause copious brown fumes to be generated, which should not be breathed. Wash in water after a few seconds' immersion in the acid and then place the object in the following solution until the desired depth of color is produced:

Muriatic acid .... 12 parts by weight
Arsenic trioxide .. 1 " " "
Iron sulphate .... 1 " " "

Remove and wash well, and dry. Both of the above solutions can be used again, the nitric acid spending itself first.

#4—Ammonia water ...... 16 cc.
Ammonium hydroxide,
    strong .... 16 "
    Water .... 16 "
    Sodium carbonate .... 1 gm.

Add to the above, copper carbonate powder until no more of the powder will dissolve. Immerse the brass article in the heated solution.

To Get a Dull Black

Dissolve copper scraps in strong nitric acid which has been diluted with an equal amount of water. After the copper has been dissolved, add more copper to reduce the acidity, and then immerse the well cleaned brass article in the solution until the desired depth has been produced. Remove and wash well with water. The brass can now be polished with linseed oil to give a bright shiny appearance. This method is useful in coloring brass instrument parts.

Brown on Brass

A solution of bismuth nitrate in water to which several drops of hydrochloric acid have been added slightly to clear the solution of the oxychloride which is formed, can be used, keeping the temperature of the bath about 100° F.

Green Bronze on Brass

Ferric nitrate .... 2 oz.
Sodium hyposulphite .... 2 "
Water .... 1 pt.

The articles are allowed to remain in the liquid until the desired tint is acquired. Rinse, dry, and polish with cloth.

Steel Gray on Brass

Antimony sulphide .... 1 part
Iron filings .... 1 "
Hydrochloric acid .... 3 "
Water .... 3 "

Allow to react and when gas is no longer evolved, heat gently and immerse the metal in the solution.

Silver on Copper

Cream of tartar........... 6 oz.
Tin metal .... 8 "
Water .... 1 qt.

Heat, and immerse the copper in the solution.

Violet on Brass

(a) Lead acetate .... 4 oz.
    Water .... 5 pt.
(b) Sodium hyposulphite .. 9 oz.
    Water .... 5 pt.

Make the two solutions, a and b. When it is desired to color the brass,

mix equal portions of each, and heat the resulting solution to 170° to 180° F., put the cleaned brass articles in the solution until the desired shade has been obtained.

Solutions for Coloring Iron or Steel

Black:

#1—Bismuth chloride ..... 2 parts
    Mercuric chloride .... 4 "
    Copper chloride ...... 2 "
    Hydrochloric acid .... 12 "
    Alcohol .... 10 "
    Water .... 100 "

#2—Copper-nitrate solution
    (10 per cent)....... 70 parts
    Alcohol .... 30 "

#3—Mercuric chloride .... 5 parts
    Ammonium chloride .. 5 "
    Water .... 100 "

Brown:

#1—Alcohol .... 45 parts
    Iron-chloride solution.. 45 "
    Mercuric chloride .... 45 "
    Sweet spirits of niter
    (ethyl nitrite + alcohol) .... 45 "
    Copper sulphate ...... 30 "
    Nitric acid .... 22 "
    Water ....1000 "

#2—Nitric acid .... 7 parts
    Alcohol .... 14 "
    Copper sulphate ..... 28 "
    Iron filings .... 1 "
    Water .... 100 "

Blue:

Iron chloride .... 4 parts
Antimony chloride .... 4 "
Gallic acid .... 2 "
Water .... 10 "

Bronze:

Manganese nitrate solution
    (10 per cent)........... 7 parts
Alcohol .... 3 "

Brown on Steel or Iron

#1—Alcohol .... 1½ oz.
  Tincture of iron ...... 1½ "
  Corrosive sublimate ... 1½ "
  Sweet spirits of niter.. 1½ "
  Blue vitriol .... 1 "
  Nitric acid .... ¾ "

Mix and dissolve in 1 qt. of warm water and apply the mixture to every part with a sponge or rag, and expose to the air for 24 hours, when the loose rust should be rubbed off with a steel scratch brush. Use the mixture and the scratch brush twice, and more if necessary, and finally wash in boiling water, dry quickly, and wipe with linseed oil or varnish with shellac.

#2—Sulphate of copper..... 1 oz.
  Sweet spirits of niter.. 1 "
  Water .... 1 pt.

For a deep color, apply, dry, and then apply again.

Black on Iron and Steel

A beautiful black polish is obtained by boiling 1 part of sulphur with 10 of turpentine. A coat as thin as possible is laid on the article to be polished, which is then held over a flame until the black polish makes its appearance.

Black on Copper

Potassium or sodium sulphide 6 gm.
Strong ammonia water..... 5 cc.
Water, enough to make...1000 cc.

Do not heat this solution, as it will decompose and spend itself without producing a good color.

Antique Green on Copper

Sal ammoniac .... 3 gm.
Acetic acid .... 10 cc.
Salt .... 1 gm.
Cream of tartar........... 1 "
Copper acetate .... 1 "

This should be made into a paste with a little water and smeared over the copper and allowed to remain on overnight.

Olive Green on Brass

Sodium hyposulphite ..... 45 gm.
Iron nitrate .... 8 "
Water, enough to make....1000 cc.

The objects must be immersed for several minutes in the heated solution.

Bright Blue on Copper

Lead acetate .... 15 gm.
Hypo .... 25 "
Water, enough to make...1000 cc.

The articles are immersed in the above for about a quarter of a minute. Sugar of lead is another name for the lead acetate.

Gray on Copper

White oxide of arsenic.... 3 gm.
Hydrochloric acid (strong). 5 cc.
Water .... 25 "

The oxide is first dissolved in the acid by warming, and the solution diluted with the water. The quantities used are open to wide variations. The solution works more rapidly when strong and warm. In this solution brass and copper receive a steel-gray deposit of arsenic, quite adherent.

Blue on Iron

Antimony trichloride ..... 25 parts
Strong nitric acid .... 25 "
Hydrochloric acid .... 50 "

Tie a rag to a stick and apply the mixture freely. After rubbing the article with a flannel it may be polished on a polishing head until an even, clear blue is obtained.

Bluing Steel

To blue gun-barrels, etc., dissolve 2 parts of crystallized chloride of iron; 2 parts chloride of antimony crystals; 1 part gallic acid in 4 or 5 parts of water; apply with a small sponge, and let dry. Repeat this two or three times, then wash with water, and dry. Rub with linseed oil to deepen the color.

Yellow on Nickel

#1—Ammonium sulphide .. ¼ oz.
    Water .... 1 gal.

The nickel object is passed through this solution, rinsed off in water, and then wiped. The work should be lacquered afterward if possible.

#2—Barium sulphide ...... ¾ oz.
    Water .... 1 gal.

The solution is used at a temperature between 100° and 150° F. It will be found that various shades are produced with varying temperatures.

Iridescence on Zinc or Nickel

#1—Make a solution of:

Copper tartrate .... 150 gm.
Sodium hydroxide .... 200 "
Water, enough to make....1000 cc.

This solution is used as a bath for the metal, heating the solution to about 110° F. If the solution is used cold, then the varying colors which are produced are easy to control, the object being removed and washed and dried when the desired shade has been reached.

#2—Copper sulphate ...... 50 gm.
    Cream of tartar....... 50 "
    Sodium carbonate .... 150 "
    Water ....1000 cc.

Dissolve the copper sulphate in half of the water, the other two chemicals in the other half and then mix the two solutions. The solution is used as the first, and produces varying oxides of copper on the nickel or zinc.

Antique Green on Brass

Sodium hyposulphite ...... 6 gm.
Nickel ammonium sulphate. 6 "

Dissolve the above in 100 cc. of water, heat the solution to near boiling and immerse the cleaned articles. Photographer's hypo may be used in this formula. The nickel compound is also known as double nickel salts.

Light Green on Brass

Copper sulphate .... 8 gm.
Ammonium chloride .... 2 "
Water, enough to make....1000 cc.

Use as in the previous coloring solutions.

Black Anti-Rust for Steel or Iron

Bismuth chloride .... 1 part
Mercury bichloride .... 2 "
Copper chloride .... 1 "
Hydrochloric acid .... 6 "
Alcohol .... 5 "
Water, sufficient to make... 64 "

Universal Solution for Metals

Prepare a solution of 15 gm. of sodium thiosulphate in 60 cc. of water and add to it a solution of 4 gm. of lead acetate in the same quantity of water. Metals to be colored are placed in the solution which is then gradually heated to the boiling point. The hot solution gives iron the effect of blue steel, zinc becomes bronze, and copper or brass changes successively yellowish-red, scarlet, deep blue, and white with a rose tint.

Bronze on Metals

Surfaces may be bronzed by applying gold bronze, which is a brass or copper alloy hammered into thin flakes, with a suitable varnish to cause it to adhere to the object.

Banana oil is used as the vehicle for the bronze powder, but any spar varnish thinned out with turpentine will serve as well. It is well to add a small amount of drier, such as Japan driers, to the mixture. Amyl acetate, in which a small amount of celluloid is dissolved, can also be used as a vehicle. About 25 parts of the amyl acetate and 1 of celluloid is satisfactory.

In silver bronzing aluminum flake, or aluminum bronze, is used instead of the bronze powder, the operation being the same as when the brass flakes are used. Of course, the product results in a silvery surface upon the object. The aluminum powder catalyzes the hardening of the spar varnish, if the varnish and not the banana oil is used, the result being that the aluminum bronze dries quicker than the vehicle—spar varnish —alone.

Green Bronze

Sodium nitrate .... 1 oz.
Ferric nitrate .... 6 "
Water .... 8 "

Immerse the articles in the above solution until the desired shade has been produced, remove and wash in clear water. The process is completed by then dipping into the following solution:

Ferric chloride .... 8 oz.
Water .... 1 pt.

Remove and allow to dry without rinsing in water. The work can then be lacquered.

Copper Dip for Iron and Steel

Dissolve 1½ oz. of copper sulphate in 1 gal. of water. Then add 1 oz. of sulphuric acid and mix well. The articles must be well cleaned, then dipped in the solution for a few seconds only. The shortest possible time in which the articles will be covered with copper should be employed for good adherence. Remove the work, rinse in cold water, then in hot water, and dry. The solution can be used repeatedly until it refuses to plate copper on the iron or steel in about 15 seconds.

Oxidized Finish for Copper, Bronze and Silver

Dissolve ½ oz. of potassium sulphide in 1 gallon of water and use at a temperature of about 130° F. Before being oxidized, the article must be cleaned. It is then dipped in the above solution. The high lights are brought out by polishing lightly with a piece of felt carrying rouge. The finish can be protected with a thin coat of lacquer.

Antique Bronze on Copper

#1—Copper acetate .... 1 part
      Potassium bitartrate ... 1 "
      Salt .... 1 "
      Ammonium acetate .... 3 "
      Glacial acetic acid...... 3 "

Mix the above and spread upon the well cleaned copper. Allow to remain overnight. Due to the uneven decomposition which is set up on the metal, the result is that the copper is streaked blue and dark green. The film may then be rubbed with a soft cloth dampened with oil or wax.

#2—Copper sulphate ...... 8 gm.
      Sal ammoniac .... 1 "
      Cream of tartar....... 3 "
      Salt .... 3 "
      Water .... 12 cc.

Bronzing Brass

Ferrous sulphate .... 50 gm.
Potassium permanganate .. 10 "
Hydrochloric acid .... 5 "
Water enough to make....1000 cc.

The brass, having been freed from grease and immersed in nitric acid diluted with an equal amount of water, is washed and immersed in the above solution. It is removed when the desired shade is produced, and can then be dried and the color may be further enhanced by heating over an iron plate or in an oven.

Bronzing Zinc

Ammonium chloride ...... 1 gm.
Potassium oxalate .... 1 "
Vinegar .... 10 cc.

Acetic acid can no doubt be used in this well known formula, about half a cubic centimeter of the glacial or strongest acetic acid being used to 10 cc. of water. No matter in what form the acetic acid is used, whether in vinegar or the glacial acid, the work should be rubbed up with the mixture, using a cloth to produce the tint desired.

Bronze on Iron or Steel

#1—Iron (ferric) chloride. 10 gm.
    Copper sulphate ...... 10 "
    Water .... 250 cc.
    Nitric acid .... 5 "

Immerse the iron or steel, which has been cleaned with emery cloth, in the above mixture and dry at room temperature. Suspend it over the vapors from heated alcohol to make the coating permanent.

#2—Sweet spirits of niter.. 3 oz.
    Gum benzoin .... ½ "
    Tincture of chloride of
      iron .... ½ "
    Sulphate of copper.... 2 dr.
    Alcohol .... ½ oz.

Mix and add 1 quart of water.

#3—Copper sulphate ...... 2½ oz.
    Nitric acid .... 2 "
    Tincture of iron chlo-
      ride .... 3 "
    Strong solution of anti-
      mony chloride ...... 6 "
    Water .... 5 "

Mix and dissolve. Sponge on the iron or immerse.

#4—Iron chloride .... 2 oz.
    Gallic acid .... 1 "
    Strong solution of anti-
      mony chloride ..... 1½ "
    Water .... 4 "

Mix and dissolve.

Bronzing Solution

Dissolve sufficient cellulose acetate in acetone to obtain a thin, flowing mixture. Place the bronze metal powder in this and stir thoroughly. If desired, celluloid chips may be used in place of the cellulose acetate.

Brushed Brass on Brass

This finish is often used on brass beds and is produced by a mechanical surfacing. A cloth is rubbed over the cleaned brass, free from lacquer, using finely ground pumice stone (graded and sold as #1 Pumice), and alcohol. The pumice scratches the surface, producing the brushed effect. Any adhering pumice powder left by the evaporation of the alcohol is removed with a cloth. Alcohol is used to remove any particles of lacquer which may have been upon the brass from a previous lacquering operation. The brass is then lacquered to prevent tarnishing.

Dipping Fluids for Brass, Copper, Zinc

Brown to black shades: For brass —Dissolve 5 oz. iron nitrate or chloride in 1 gal. water. For copper— Dissolve 5 oz. iron nitrate and 2 oz. potassium sulphocyanide in 1 gal. of water. For zinc—Same as for brass.

Brown to red shades: For brass— Dissolve 1 lb. each of iron nitrate and sodium hyposulphite in 1 gal. of water. For copper—Heat 8 oz. potassium carbonate and 1 oz. sulphur in 1 gal. of water.

Steel gray: For brass—Dissolve 8 oz. arsenic chloride in 1 gal. water. For copper—Use the same solution as for brass, only heat to 100° F. For zinc—Dissolve 4 oz. copper sulphate and 4 oz. of ferrous chromate in 1 gal. of water.

Olive green: For brass—Iron chloride, 8 oz. in 1 gal. water. For zinc —Dissolve 4 oz. ferrous chromate in 1 gal. of water.

Temper Colors on Iron or Steel

The steel is heated, the following colors being produced at the temperatures indicated:

Color produced	Deg. F.
Pale yellow	418
Straw	446
Brown	491
Purple	536
Pale blue	572
Dark blue	599

To Blacken Aluminum

White arsenic	1 oz.
Sulphate of iron	1 "
Hydrochloric acid	12 "

Dissolve and then add 12 oz. of water. Clean the aluminum with emery or steel wool, and then immerse in the solution, removing when the required depth of color is produced. The aluminum will be attacked if it is cleaned of grease with lye water as is the usual procedure for metals preparatory to coloring them.

To Copper Aluminum

Cream of tartar	30 gm.
Copper sulphate	30 "
Sodium carbonate	25 "
Water	1000 cc.

Dissolve the copper sulphate in half the water, the cream of tartar and the soda in the remaining part of the water, and mix the two solutions. Clean the aluminum well with steel wool and immerse in the mixture.

Copper Amalgam

Although mercury will amalgamate with copper sheet to produce a bright silvery surface, this method cannot be used to produce an amalgam of copper because the copper is only alloyed on the surface. However, finely divided copper metal, such as that obtained by precipitation, can be alloyed readily with mercury to produce a pliable copper amalgam. To produce the copper in finely divided form, suspend several strips of zinc or iron in a solution of copper sulphate or copper nitrate. The iron or zinc will dissolve, precipitating the copper out upon its surface in the form of a fine powder. Collect this powder, and if the solution is still blue, further powder may be precipitated out by allowing more iron or zinc to act on the solution. Wash the precipitated copper well with running water and pour onto it a solution of mercuric nitrate which can be made by dissolving a globule of mercury in nitric acid. Allow the mercury chloride solution to act for about ten minutes, until the color has changed somewhat. Pour onto the precipitated copper contained in a mortar several times its weight of mercury metal and knead the mass under hot water by means of a pestle. The mercury will then amalgamate with the copper.

The product can be used to take impressions, fill holes in copper work, or serve as an electrical conductive cement to join pigtails to carbon brushes, and also to join certain metals together. For this latter operation, the metals, which must have been cleaned, are heated to about 180° F., the copper amalgam rubbed on at the contact surface and pressed firmly together, reheating slightly, applying clamps, and allowing them to remain on until the metal joint has become cold.

Gold Amalgam

One method by which copper, silver or brass articles can be plated with gold is by amalgamation. It should only be attempted on a small scale in the home, because of the danger of poisoning from mercury fumes, the metal actually volatilizing at room temperature. The mercury is warmed in a crucible, under a hood which will carry off the objectionable vapors. The gold, preferably in small shavings, should then be added, and by stirring dissolved in the mercury, forming the amalgam. The gold slivers can be heated directly with the mercury to hasten formation of the gold amalgam. After the amalgam has been prepared, it is rubbed on the well cleaned article, which receives the amalgam, and after heating the object to volatilize the mercury, leaving the free gold on the surface, the work is burnished and polished.

Sodium Amalgam

Sodium metal combines with mercury forming sodium amalgam. This substance placed in a cold ammonium chloride solution generates gases and causes a volcanic-like fluffy mass to form and run from the vessel.

Metal That Expands on Cooling

Lead .... 9 parts
Antimony .... 2 "
Bismuth .... 1 part

Melt the lead and then incorporate the bismuth and antimony. Use just enough heat to melt the lead. This melt is good for taking impressions from dies, castings, and filling holes in metals.

To Protect Metals from Rust

Mechanical equipment, tools, etc., which are to be taken out of service and stored can be effectively protected from rust by applying the following paint, which is warmed to make it liquid so that it can be applied with a brush:

Pure tallow .... 4 lb.
Pure white-lead .... 2 "
Pure linseed oil .... 1 qt.

In order to mix the tallow and white-lead (which may be either heavy paste or soft paste), it will be necessary to heat the tallow slightly. The white-lead should be added and thoroughly incorporated while the tallow is still in liquid or semi-liquid condition. The linseed oil may be added at the same time. If heavy paste white-lead is used the entire amount of linseed oil called for in the formula will be needed, but if soft paste is used, a slightly smaller amount of linseed oil will be enough. Either raw or boiled oil may be used, as desired.

This tallow and lead compound may be applied to the metal with an ordinary four-inch wall brush, after having made sure the parts to be coated are clean and dry. Although the preservative is not expensive, it is not necessary to pile it on to any greater thickness than ordinary plastic paint.

On removal from storage the machines may be made ready for service by simply wiping off the coating, then lubricating the working parts in the usual manner.

The following fluid will prevent iron from rusting: $1\frac{3}{4}$ pints each of linseed oil and varnish, 1 quart of turpentine, and $1\frac{1}{2}$ ounces of camphor. Heat the mixture over a low fire, stirring constantly, then immerse the articles for a few moments, or apply the varnish with a brush and allow to dry.

The following will be found suitable for use in protecting metals from rusting, whether the object is to be used or laid away while idle. The solution is painted on.

Gum mastic .... 10 parts
Camphor .... 5 "
Gum sandarac .... 5 "
Gum elemi .... 5 "

Denatured alcohol, enough to dissolve. Then add an equal amount of alcohol to the solution.

The following solution produces a coating of phosphatic iron upon iron or steel and guards against rust:

Phosphoric acid, concentrated .... 25 cc.
Manganese dioxide (pyrolusite) .... 1.5 gm.
Water .... 1000 cc.

The articles to be treated are boiled for about four hours in the above solution, an iron tank or tinned baking pan being used as a vessel. Hydrogen gas is released along with other objectionable gases, so the heating should be done outdoors. Remove and heat the articles on a hot plate to a temperature such that a drop of water, if allowed to fall upon the objects, is instantly evaporated. At this temperature the work should be plunged into linseed oil and heated to dryness.

To Keep Nails from Rusting

In the home workshop, especially if the shop is in a damp cellar, nails and tacks are frequently rendered worthless by rust. If they are covered with a solution of one ounce of shellac in a pint of water, thrown upon the floor to remove surplus solution, and then allowed to dry, the adherent shellac coating will protect them from further rusting. A solution of rosin in alcohol, made very dilute, can be used for the same purpose.

To Remove Rust from Metals

♯1—A solution of ammonium citrate is perhaps the best substance for removing rust from metals such as instruments, tools and machine parts. A tablespoonful of ammonium citrate dissolved in a quart of hot water makes a solution that removes rust quickly and effectively. If cold water is used, the same amount of substance can be taken, but the length of time

the articles are to be left in the solution should be increased. Rinse the cleaned objects in clear water and dry thoroughly, preferably with the aid of heat.

♯2—Immerse the articles in a strong solution of tin chloride (stannic chloride) in water, until the rust can be removed with a brush.

♯3—Ten grams of tin chloride are dissolved in 100 cc. of water. This solution is added to one containing 2 grams of tartaric acid dissolved in 100 cc. of water. After allowing the solution to act upon the stain, rinse and wipe object with alcohol to dry.

♯4—Immerse the article in equal parts of muriatic acid and water.

♯5—Amyl acetate .... 2 oz.
       Acetone .... 1 "
       Cylinder oil .... 1 "

Mix the ingredients and put in a wide mouth bottle. Keep corked when not using.

Cleaning Small Metal Parts

In the manufacture of cutlery, wire novelties, small metal objects turned in lathes, and other similar products they frequently become covered with oil or grease. Before the products are packed for shipment they must be cleaned, and this is usually done by dipping them in some solvent and then drying them in sawdust. The parts are usually revolved, together with the sawdust, in a large drum which absorbs the solvent solution and polishes the pieces at the same time.

Removing Varnish from Metal

An old varnish finish on metal can be removed by dipping the metal in a solution made by pouring ammonia (strong ammonia water) into the same quantity of denatured alcohol. If the article is too large to be dipped, apply the solution with a soft brush. Keep the solution away from flames and work out of doors, if possible, or at least near an open window. See that the articles remain moist until the varnish has softened; then wipe the metal clean with a rag.

Thermite Welding

Thoroughly mix ferric oxide and aluminum powder, using about equal quantities of each; a slight excess of aluminum powder is an advantage. Place this mixture in a conical container, such as an old tin funnel or crucible with the bottom hole covered with a piece of heavy paper.

At the top of the powder spread about a half teaspoon of powdered magnesium. This is topped with a level teaspoon of potassium permanganate heaped in the center. Make a depression in this heap.

Fill a box with sand and on the sand place the iron to be welded. Make a form of the sand to surround the joint on all sides except the top. Just above the mold, place the thermite mixture, held by means of a wire tripod.

Place from 4 to 6 drops of glycerin quickly in the depression of the potassium permanganate and stand away. A stream of white-hot molten iron soon will run into the mold and form a weld. Large pieces should be preheated to redness.

Low Melting Alloys

Alloys melt at a temperature lower than that of any constituent that is contained in them. The following well known alloys have found wide use in instances where a low melting alloy is required, such as fuses, and the mounting of radio crystals. In the latter case a low temperature is needed to prevent the decomposition of the crystal and a corresponding loss in sensitiveness which would oc-

cur if a high melting point alloy were used as an imbedding material. Their low melting point makes them well adapted for home mechanics in making casts of various objects, because a forge or melting furnace, which usually requires an air blast, is not necessary.

Impressions can be taken from many objects, using a low melting point alloy, without fear of injuring the objects. Examples are impressions from wood, for it can be seen that if an alloy, which melts in boiling water or below the temperature of boiling water, is brought into contact while liquid with wood, the wood will not char. This of course is not true with an alloy having a high melting point. Some of the more important alloys which melt at a low temperature are as follows, the amounts of the constituents being by weight:

Alloy	Tin	Lead	Bismuth	F.
Newton's	3	2	5	212°
Rose's	3	8	8	200°
Erman's	1	1	2	199°
Mellott's	5	3	8	200°
D'Arcet's	3	5	8	176°

As Erman's solder consists of tin and lead in the ratio of 1:1, and plumber's half and half solder also has this composition, this alloy can be made by melting half and half solder and adding an equal amount, by weight of course, of bismuth.

When cadmium is added to low melting alloys, the melting point is still further lowered.

	Tin	Lead	Bismuth	Cadmium	F.
Wood's metal.	2	4	7	1	158°
Harper's "	4	4	7	1	180°
Lipowitz's "	4	8	15	3	150°

Any of the above, and Lipowitz's in particular, can be alloyed with mercury to further reduce the melting point.

This is accomplished by melting the alloy and after removing from the source of heat, introducing the mercury and stirring with an iron rod. Do not breathe the fumes from heated mercury, as they are poisonous.

Some Other Low Melting Compositions

#1—Lead	1	2	3
Tin	1	2	3
Bismuth	1	1	1
Melting Point.	258° F.	283°	311°

#2—Bismuth, 7 parts; lead, 6 parts; cadmium, 1 part. Melts at 180° F.

#3—Bismuth, 7 to 8 parts; lead, 4; tin, 2; cadmium, 1 to 2. Melts at about 155° F.

A low melting alloy, such as described above, can be used by heating until it is the consistency of wax, and then the warmed and cleaned metal surfaces to be cemented together are smeared with it. Pressing the parts together and allowing to cool will cause adhesion.

The alloy is made by allowing zinc scraps to remain in copper sulphate until a quantity of metallic copper is formed upon the zinc. This is removed, washed, mixed with strong sulphuric acid in a mortar and mixed with mercury in the proportion of about one of copper powder to two of mercury. Rubbing the whole will cause the mercury to amalgamate with the copper, and at this stage the amalgam or low melting alloy should be removed, washed thoroughly until free from acid as tested with litmus paper, and dried. When it is to be used, it should be heated, when it becomes soft as wax by pounding with a pestle in a mortar. In this softened state it can be spread upon any surface, to which, as it cools and hardens, it adheres tenaciously.

Some cadmium, tin, bismuth alloys which melt in boiling water consist of the following:

	Parts		
Cadmium	1	1	1
Tin	2	3	1
Bismuth	3	5	2

The following alloys also have low melting points and can be utilized in the filling of holes in pewter and other soft metals.

Homberg's Alloy—Bismuth, lead and tin, equal parts.

Krafft's Alloy—Bismuth, 50 parts; lead, 20 parts; tin, 10 parts.

Newton's Metal consists of bismuth, 8 parts; lead, 5 parts; tin, 3 parts. Melts at 202° F.

Melt the lead first, then add the tin, and finally the bismuth.

How to Make Pewter

Pewters can be used in the manufacture of toy soldiers or other figures in the molding sets now sold for such purposes. In fact any lead alloy can be used, even type metal, which unfortunately breaks easily in toys. If pewter is used for the home manufacture of such articles, it is best to select one in which there is no copper, as this will require a high melting temperature.

#1—Common Pewter—Pure tin, 82 parts; lead, 18 parts.

#2—Plate Pewter—Tin, 90 parts; antimony, 7 parts; bismuth, 2 parts; copper, 2 parts.

#3—Best Pewter—5 lb. tin to 1 lb. of lead.

#4—Tin, 83 parts; antimony, 17 parts. Some lead is added in most cases.

#5—Tin, 4 parts; lead, 1 part. Used for mugs, steins, etc.

#6—Tin, 100 parts; antimony, 8 parts; copper, 4 parts; bismuth, 1 part. Very fine.

#7—Triple Pewter—Tin, 79 per cent; antimony, 15 per cent; lead, 6 per cent; as the last. Used for small articles, syringes, toys, whistles.

#8—Britannia is an excellent pewter and is made by melting together equal parts of brass, bismuth, antimony and tin and then adding melted tin, until it acquires the proper degree of color and hardness. The addition of the latter amount of tin can be omitted if desired.

Yellow Metal Alloys

The following are yellow metal alloys:

Brass usually is composed of two-thirds copper and one-third zinc, but lead or tin is sometimes added.

Red copper, 66 parts; zinc, 34 parts; lead, 1 part.

Copper, 66 parts; zinc, 32 parts; tin, 1 part; lead, 1 part.

Copper, 64.5 parts; zinc, 33.5 parts; lead, 1.5 parts; tin, 0.5 part.

Yellow Brass for Turning—Copper, 20 lb.; zinc, 10 lb.; lead, 1 to 5 oz. Add the lead last.

Red Brass for Turning—Copper, 24 lb.; zinc, 5 lb.; lead, 8 oz. Add the lead last.

Red Brass, Free, for Turning—Copper, 160 lb.; zinc, 50 lb.; lead, 10 lb.; antimony, 44 oz. Melt in order given.

Another Brass for Turning—Copper, 32 lb.; zinc, 10 lb.; lead, 1 lb.

Medals—Copper, 50 parts; zinc, 4 parts. Copper, 89 parts; tin, 8 parts; zinc, 3 parts, or copper, 95 parts; tin, 5 parts.

Bronze Metal—Copper, 7 lb.; zinc, 3 lb.; tin, 2 lb., or copper, 1 lb.; zinc, 12 lb.; tin, 8 lb.

Statuary Metal—91.4 parts copper, 5.53 zinc, 1.7 tin, 1.37 lead; or copper 80, tin 20.

Best Red Brass for Fine Castings—Copper, 24 lb.; zinc, 5 lb.; bismuth, 1 oz. Put in the bismuth last before pouring off.

Bronze Metal—Copper, 7 lb.; zinc, 3 lb.; tin, 2 lb., or copper, 1 lb.; zinc, 12 lb.; tin, 8 lb.

Cock metal for valves on pewter urns—Consists of copper, 20 lb.; lead, 8 lb.; litharge, 1 oz.; antimony, 3 oz.

Pinchbeck's Alloy for Jewelry—Copper, 88.8 parts; zinc, 11.2 parts; or copper, 2.1 parts; brass, 1.0 part.

Rolled Brass—Copper, 32 parts; zinc, 10 parts; tin, 1 to 5 parts.

Soft Brass—Copper, 4 parts; zinc, 1 part.

Tobin Bronze—This alloy is nearly similar in composition and properties to the alloy Delta Metal. Copper, 61.2; zinc, 27.4; tin, 0.9; iron, 0.1; lead, 0.3.

Macht's Yellow Metal—This alloy consists of 33 parts of copper and 25 parts of zinc. It has a dark golden yellow color.

Light colored "brasses" consist of:

			Parts			
Lead 70	..	...	..	..	84	42.5
Zinc	82	...	..	..	..	42.5
Tin	..	66.7	90	85	..	...
Antimony . 20	11	11.1	7	10	16	15.0
Copper 10	7	22.2	3	5	..	...

In making these alloys melt the copper first, add all the rest but the antimony, and add this just before pouring.

White Metal Alloy

Ordinary brass, 32 oz.; lead, 2 oz.; tin, 2 oz.; zinc, 1 oz.

German Silver

This alloy has been varied so widely in constituents and proportions that a typical composition would not cover the wide ranges used in its manufacture. Perhaps the following will give the best idea of its composition:

Copper .... 50 to 65 parts
Nickel .... 13 to 18 "
Zinc .... 19 to 31 "

It can readily be seen that German silver does not contain silver.

Frick's German Silver—55.39 parts copper, 17.4 nickel, 13 zinc.

Bullet Metal

Ninety-eight parts lead to 2 arsenic. For round shot the fused metal is dropped from a high elevation in a shot tower into water.

Bronze for Statuary

Copper	65	90	84	72	85	8 parts
Lead	2	..	2	2	2 ..	"
Tin ...	5	2	5	3	3	2 "
Zinc ..	30	6	11	23	10	.. "

Bell Metal

Fine—71 copper, 26 tin, 2 zinc, 1 iron.

For Large Bells—Copper, 100 lb.; tin, from 20 to 25 lb.

For Small Bells—Copper, 3 lb.; tin, 1 lb.

Rivet Metals

#1—Copper, 32 oz.; tin, 2 oz.; zinc, 1 oz., for riveting copper or brass.

#2—Tin, 6 lb.; copper, 64 lbs.

Metal for Impressions

Lead, 3 lb.; tin, 2 lb.; bismuth, 5 lb.

Making Type Metal

The following are type metal compositions: (#1 is the most commonly used.)

	Lead.	Antimony.	Copper.	Tin.
#1	9	1	..	..
#2	5	1	..	..
#3	10	1	..	..
#4	70	18	2	10
#5	60	20	..	20
#6	55	25	..	20
#7	55	30	..	15

Tombac—Copper, 16 lb.; tin, 1 lb.; zinc, 1 lb.

Red Tombac—Copper, 10 lb.; zinc, 1 lb.

Cymbals and Gongs

One hundred parts of copper with about 25 of tin. To give this alloy a sonorous property to the highest degree, the piece should be heated after casting and then plunged into cold water.

Metal for Organs

Pipe metal for organs consists of equal parts of tin and lead. This alloy is cast instead of rolled in the desired form of sheets, in order to obtain a crystallized metal, which produce a finer tone. The metal can be planed with a carpenter's plane.

Speculum Metal for Mirrors

Equal parts of tin and copper form a white metal as hard as steel. Less tin and a small quantity of arsenic added to the alloy forms a white hard metal of high luster. Two lb. copper, 1 lb. tin, 1 oz. arsenic, form a good speculum metal. An alloy of 32 copper, 16.5 tin, 4 brass, 1.25 arsenic is hard, white, and of brilliant luster.

Dentists' Molds and Dies

#1—Very hard. Tin, 16 parts; antimony, 1 part; zinc, 1 part.

#2—Softer than the former. Tin, 8 parts; zinc, 1 part; antimony, 1 part.

Dental Alloys

#1—Tin, 91.63 parts; silver, 3.82 parts; copper, 4.4 parts.

#2—Tin, 36.78 parts; silver, 48.32 parts; gold, 14.72 parts.

Babbitt Metal

Tin .... 49 parts
Antimony .... 5 "
Copper .... 1 "

Duralumin

Copper 4.0%
Manganese 0.5%
Magnesium 0.5%
Aluminum .... Remainder

Welding Iron or Steel

The borax usually used in making welds between iron or steel can be improved by adding to it about one-tenth of its bulk of sal ammoniac. The steel or iron is heated in the forge until it begins to burn, as evidenced by the bright scintillations that are thrown out through the coals. The metal is then removed, the borax-sal-ammoniac mixture sprinkled upon the butt which has been previously made, the work inserted with due care not to pick up clinkers, ashes, or coals, and then, when it has been brought to the same heat as before, removed and the weld made.

Plating Without Electric Current

Many articles can be made to receive a good coating of different metals without using a battery or dynamo for producing the electric current. This simple process is entirely practical, the work taking on a good plate which afterwards can be buffed or burnished to a bright luster.

The principle depends upon the fact that different metals placed in metallic solution set up electric currents when they are in contact with each other. The metal in solution is plated out upon the metal which acts negative in the battery formed by the two metals.

The following is a powder which, when moistened with water, forms a paste that can be rubbed over copper or brass, to cause a plate of nickel to be formed:

Nickel ammonium sulphate   60 parts
Magnesium powder ....   3 "
Chalk .... 30 "
Talc ....   7 "

The copper or brass should be free from grease, and the above mixture wet with water and rubbed on the surface of the metal. Zinc dust can be substituted for the magnesium powder if some tartaric acid is also added to the mixture. Ordinary talcum powder of the toilet variety can be used in the formula, and for experimental purposes, the chalk can be omitted as it acts as an agent to prevent too rapid action. A simplified formula would be to use equal parts of all constituents, except the chalk, by volume.

Silver Plating

Certain compounds containing silver readily give up their metal to other metals when brought into intimate contact with them in the presence of water. Silver is actually precipitated or plated out upon the metal, and with the aid of polishing agents such as chalk, whiting, or rouge, in the mixture, becomes highly polished. Such coatings of silver deposited in this manner are not very durable, as their layers are so thin that they are easily removed by wear. However, for many objects, such a silver coating is of value, and the following formula will be found to produce admirable coatings. In almost all cases, the powders should be moistened just before using, for if they are wetted, silver chloride is formed which changes chemically into various sub-chlorides by exposure to the light. Iodized salt is not recommended, as its presence would undoubtedly tarnish the silver film, due to the formation of silver iodide.

Caution should be observed in the mixtures containing potassium cyanide, as this substance is very poisonous.

#1—Silver nitrate .... 1 part
    Salt (not iodized) .... 1 "
    Cream of tartar ...... 14 "

The mixture, which should be in the form of a powder, is touched with a damp cloth to which it adheres, and rubbed on the clean and bright metal to be silver plated. The silver plates out from the mass, and is polished by the cloth.

#2—Silver nitrate .... 1 part
    Potassium cyanide .... 3 "

This mixture is moistened with water to form a paste and rubbed on the article to be plated. Take care in using this powder not to inhale the dust.

#3—Whiting .... 10 parts
    Salt .... 12 "
    Cream of tartar ...... 7 "
    Silver nitrate .... 4 "

The whiting, salt, and cream of tartar are powdered in a mortar, and then the silver nitrate powdered and sifted into the first batch. The whole should then be sifted and placed in well corked bottles. The salt should be iodine-free (not iodized), as this is liable to cause tarnishing through the formation of silver iodide. Some of the powder is taken, mixed to a paste with water and rubbed on the cleaned metal surface. The whiting acts as a polishing agent.

#4—Silver nitrate .... 15 gm.
    Potassium hydroxide .. 15 "
    Water .... 50 cc.

Dissolve the silver nitrate in half of the water, the potassium hydrate in the other half and when ready to use the fluid, mix the two solutions together. The metal to be plated should be clean and to plate, it is immersed in the solution, using slight motion to remove air bubbles. The work is removed after several minutes, washed and dried, after which it is buffed lightly. The silver nitrate solution can be kept in blue glass bottles, the cork (do not use a rubber stopper) being waxed.

#5—Silver nitrate .... 15 gm.
    Potassium cyanide .. 7 "
    Cream of tartar ...... 15 "
    Whiting .... 125 "

The above mixture is made into a paste with water and rubbed upon the article to be plated. As poisonous potassium cyanide is used it is well to burn the rubbing cloth after using to prevent accidental poisoning from this source.

Silver Nitrate from Old Spoons

The silver scraps should be dissolved in a mixture of strong nitric acid and water, equal parts of each. Using a little heat to cause dissolution, the reaction will proceed of its own accord. This forms a silver nitrate solution, but as there is a chance that nitric acid remains in the solution, more silver metal is added and the whole heated to boiling until the acid refuses to attack the freshly added silver. The solution should then be filtered if necessary, the paper washed with water, the filtrates combined and evaporated almost to the crystallizing point, then allowed to cool and evaporate slowly. Silver nitrate will crystallize out. The crystals can then be used in any of the formulas in which silver nitrate is used.

Preparing Silver Chloride

To prepare silver chloride for use in following formulas, take a solution of silver nitrate and add a solution of common salt, or potassium chloride. This will precipitate silver chloride in the form of a white cloud. Continue to add the chloride solution until no further precipitation takes place, which shows that all of the silver is now in the form of the chloride. Filter off the silver chloride and wash it well with water by pouring water through the filter upon which it rests. Scrape from the filter paper, dry away from the light, and preserve in blue or amber colored glass bottles with a waxed cork. This can be used in the following formulas:

#1—Silver chloride .... 1 part
    Cream of tartar ...... 2 "
    Salt .... 3 "

Apply, using water to make a paste.

#2—Silver chloride .... 1 part
    Cream of tartar ...... 14 "

Water is used in the plating operation.

For Copper or Brass

Clean the metal thoroughly, using dilute nitric acid followed by rinsing in water. Use the following:

#1—Silver nitrate .... 1 oz.
    Sal ammoniac .... 1 "
    Salt .... ¼ "
    Sodium hyposulphite .. 2 "
    Precipitated chalk .... ½ "
    Water .... 1 qt.

The above must be shaken from time to time, and kept in brown glass bottles well protected from the light. For best results it should be made up fresh as needed.

A solution for plating objects either gold or silver without the aid of a battery can be made as follows:

#2—Take one ounce of silver nitrate and dissolve in one quart of distilled water (clear rain water will answer). When thoroughly dissolved throw in a few crystals of hyposulphite of sodium which will form a brown precipitate but which will redissolve if sufficient hypo is used. A slight excess of this salt must be used. The solution thus formed may be used for coating small articles of steel, brass or German silver, by simply dipping a sponge in the solution and rubbing it over the surface of the article to be plated. A solution of gold in the same way may be made and applied in the above manner by using gold chloride instead of the silver nitrate.

Silvering Powder for Coating Copper

#1—Nitrate of silver ..... 30 gr.
    Common salt .... 30 "
    Cream of tartar ...... 3½ dr.

Mix, moisten with water, and apply.

#2—Dissolve 10 parts nitrate of silver in 50 parts of distilled water; also 25 parts of potassium cyanide in sufficient water to dissolve it. Pour the two together, stir well, and filter. Add 100 parts precipitated whiting or chalk and 400 parts of cream of tartar. This paste is spread by a brush or a pad of old linen, all over the surface of the reflector, and allowed almost to dry, when it is briskly rubbed over by another clean dry rag.

#3—Nitrate of silver ...... 1 part
    Cyanide of potassium... 2 "
    Chalk .... 5 "

Mix to a paste with water and apply to the cleaned copper or brass surface.

#4 A—2 parts lime, 5 of grape sugar, 2 of tartaric acid, 650 of water. The solution is filtered and well corked.

B. Dissolve 20 parts of nitrate of silver in 20 of aqua-ammonia, and then add 650 of water.

Just before using mix solutions A and B together, shake well and filter. Metals and dry vegetable substances, such as wood buttons, ivory, etc., can be silvered with this fluid, it is claimed.

Tin on Iron

The pieces of iron, previously cleansed and rinsed in cold water, are placed in the following solution as soon as it boils. They are immediately covered with a film of tin of a white luster. The bath is maintained at the proper strength by small additions of chloride of tin. This bath is convenient for a preliminary tinning of zinc; when the ammonia alum may be replaced by any other kind of alum, or by sulphate of alumina; but for wrought and cast iron and steel this substitution cannot be made.

#1—Ammonium alum ..... 25 gm.
    Stannic (tin) chloride . 2 "

Water, enough to make 1 liter.

#2—Saturated solution cream
    of tartar .... 1 liter
    Tin chloride .... 20 gm.

Boil articles in above, allowing them to touch pieces of tin.

Brass on Iron or Steel

By immersion, a color resembling brass is given to small articles of iron or steel by stirring in a tub, containing water, 1 quart; sulphate of copper and chloride of tin, about ⅕ of an ounce each. The shades are modified by varying the proportions of the two salts.

Copper on Aluminum

Copper sulphate .... 6 gm.
Sodium carbonate .... 5 "
Cream of tartar .... 6 "
Water .... 200 cc.

Boil the aluminum articles in the above solution.

White Metal on Iron

The white metal plate which is formed on the iron or steel by this process is a mixture of antimony and arsenic metals. The color is almost that of silver, and depends largely upon the amount of care taken in cleaning and polishing the iron or steel previous to the actual plating, which is performed without the use of an electric current:

Powdered hematite mineral 8 parts
White arsenic .... 1 "
Antimony trichloride ..... 4 "
Alcohol .... 100 cc.

The above is heated in a vessel which is placed in boiling water, for about half an hour. The cleaned and polished iron object is then swabbed with the mixture, until plated. In swabbing, the cotton used as the swabbing and polishing device is stirred about in the solution, taking up some of the white powder in the bottom of the vessel as well as the liquid. The arsenious acid (white arsenic) and hematite do not dissolve in the alcohol to any great extent, so this means must be adopted to get the maximum amount of material into contact with the iron. The solution can be used over again, adding alcohol to that lost by evaporation during the warming process.

Zinc Plating

To determine if an article has been thoroughly zinc plated or galvanized the American standard test is as follows: prepare a neutral solution of sulphate of copper of specific gravity of 1.185, dip for one minute, wash and wipe dry; the wire must stand 4 dips without a permanent coating of copper showing on any part of the object.

Nickel on Brass or Copper

Boil in a copper vessel a saturated solution of zinc chloride. By this is meant a solution of the chemical in water until the water will dissolve no more. When boiling, add an equal quantity of water to the solution.

Bring again to a boil and add hydrochloric (muriatic) acid drop by drop, until the precipitate which is first formed is dissolved. Remove from the fire and add powdered zinc until the bottom of the vessel is nearly covered with a precipitate of zinc. Now add nickel nitrate until the liquid assumes a strong green color. The articles to be plated are then hung in the solution by means of a zinc wire which is wound about a rod of zinc.

A few pieces of zinc are also placed in the solution. Bring the solution again to the boiling point and boil for several minutes or until the articles are covered with a coating of nickel. Rinse the articles thoroughly in water and polish. Before being plated, the articles must be thoroughly cleansed and washed in a solution of 1 lb. of lye in 2 qt. of water. Use this solution hot, dip in the articles so that all grease and dirt is removed, using a brush if necessary, and wash well in clean water. If a heavier plate is desired, brush well the first coating of nickel with a wire brush, then dip again in the solution and boil.

Gold on Brass or Copper

Gold chloride, 1 oz.; sodium cyanide, 16 oz. Dissolve in 2 gal. of water. Mix then with a solution containing sodium sulphate, 5 oz.; sodium hydrate, 3 oz.; water, 2 gal.; mix well and boil. While hot, dip in the articles to be plated. If the action is slow, add a little cyanide, dissolved in water.

Silver on Copper and Brass

Silver nitrate .... 2 oz.
Water .... 3 qt.

Dissolve and add:

Sodium cyanide .... 7 oz.
Dissolve in water .... 3 qt.

Heat the mixture to about 200° F. Dip the copper or brass articles in until a uniform coating of silver has been deposited upon them. Remove and wash in water. Polish with a paste of rouge and water.

Metal Gilding

Dissolve scrap gold, such as earrings, scarf pin shanks or cuff buttons, using about 15 gr. of the scrap or old gold, in a mixture of one part of nitric acid and three parts of hydrochloric acid (aqua regia). Concentrate the solution to make sure that the excess of the acid is broken down, leaving a solution of gold chloride. Add to the resulting solution, one pint of warm water in which 60 gr. of potassium cyanide have been dissolved, stirring well. Filter the solution and preserve. To gild metals, heat the solution until it is quite warm but not boiling hot, then suspend the metal to be gold plated in the solution. The metal must be free from grease.

Stiffening Copper and Brass

A simple method of making copper or brass springy, much like that of phosphor bronze, is by hammering the metal upon a hard surface with a steel faced hammer. Frequent turning of the metal will prevent any possible curling. The metal does not necessarily have to be beaten to such an extent that it is reduced perceptibly in thickness during the operation.

Galvanizing

Iron or steel articles can be galvanized without electroplating. The articles should be cleaned first in an acid pickle consisting of dilute sulphuric acid. After loose scale and dirt is removed, they are washed and quickly dried in a flame, for if they are air dried they are liable to rust before the galvanizing can be accomplished. Heat the article, holding with tongs or pair of pliers, and immerse, while hot, in a solution of zinc chloride. While still hot immerse in molten zinc metal. The zinc will attach itself to the iron in a smooth even layer. If portions remain that have not received the zinc coating, immerse the iron again, while hot, in zinc chloride solution and dip again into the molten zinc. Do not heat the zinc too hot as it will burn. Wash the articles well, to remove the zinc chloride. Some workers sprinkle sal ammoniac or zinc chloride powder on the heated metal while it is immersed in the zinc.

For galvanizing on metals, the following also can be used:

Zinc dust .... 45 parts
Sal ammoniac .... 15 "
Magnesium powder .... 3 "
Chalk .... 30 gm.
Talc powder .... 7 parts

It is used in the same manner as the previous mixture.

Copper Plating

The articles, thoroughly cleansed and free from all traces of grease and oil, are placed in a bath composed as follows, first attaching them to a sheet of zinc—zinc with wire or zinc strips —Copper Sulphate, 1 oz.; Water, 3 qt. Dissolve the sulphate in the water, adding a few drops of sulphuric acid, until the liquid is clear. When plated, remove, wash and then polish with rouge and water.

Behavior of Metals

The following is the "electromotive series" of some important elements. This tabulated arrangement of metals in a series enables one to determine some interesting and useful properties of a metal in question. All the elements or metals above a given one in the series, or as it is sometimes expressed, all those having a higher *electrode potential,* will displace it from its solution. The displaced metal will also displace any other metal below it in the series. Thus metallic iron placed in a solution of copper sulphate will displace the copper from the solution, the iron itself passing into solution. The copper, in turn, will precipitate out a metal lower in the series; thus copper, if placed in a solution of silver nitrate, will displace the silver, the silver being precipitated in the form of a sludge or loose film upon the copper. Similarly, a strip or sheet or rod of zinc placed in lead acetate will produce, upon the zinc, metallic lead. This experiment, when carried out, results in the formation of a beautiful mass of lead plates that bear a striking resemblance to a tree, hence the mass of lead has been called a lead tree.

Hydrogen has an interesting location in the series. Any metal before hydrogen will, under ordinary conditions, produce hydrogen gas when it is immersed in acids of certain strengths. Thus, as is well known, zinc or iron will produce hydrogen gas when immersed in dilute sulphuric acid.

Electromotive Series of the Elements

Potassium	Chromium	Copper
Sodium	Cadmium	Arsenic
Barium	Iron	Bismuth
Strontium	Cobalt	Antimony
Calcium	Nickel	Mercury
Magnesium	Tin	Silver
Aluminium	Lead	Palladium
Manganese	**Hydrogen**	Platinum
Zinc		Gold

Metal Polishes

Metal polishes are fundamentally alike, whether they are in the form of a liquid, paste, or powder. There is incorporated in the various types soaps, abrasives, and a liquid to keep the abrasive in suspension, some of the liquids used at the same time acting as solvents or scale looseners.

The abrasive used in the preparation determines the work the polish is to be used upon. Those containing whiting, precipitated chalk, tripoli, jeweler's rouge, etc., are used for fine polishing, while those consisting of siliceous materials are used for coarse or dull surfaces. Scents are usually added, and often the preparation is colored.

Pine oil has been used in many metal polishes. It softens the oxidizable material or unoxidizable material without affecting the metal, and at the same time imparts a body to the polish and helps hold the abrasive more firmly in suspension. A typical formula is as follows:

Red oil soap .... 8 lb.
Tripoli (natural earth) .... 8 "
Pine oil .... 8 "

This pine oil formula cleans as it polishes and possesses a fragrant, pleasant pine odor. It is noninflammable, and does not possess any ingredients that injure metal surfaces.

A metal polishing paste that contains no alkali acid, or cyanide, is not dangerous to handle, does not scratch metals, and is noninflammable at room temperatures is one of the following compositions:

#1—Precipitated chalk .... 5 parts
Ortho dichlorobenzene .. 1 "

This metal paste apparently cleans by actually dissolving the oxides of nickel, silver, copper and aluminum, these being the tarnishes which are usually produced on the discolored metals. At the same time, its action upon the metals themselves is negligible. Little rubbing is required. It should be remembered that ortho dichlorobenzene is not the same as para dichlorobenzene, which is a widely used moth repellent.

#2—Sal ammoniac, 10 parts, is dissolved in 75 parts of water and 5 parts of chalk.

To Polish Silver

Boil the silverware in an aluminum pot or pan containing a solution of two tablespoons of baking soda in a quart of water.

Proceed as above, using alum, salt and cream of tartar and an enameled pan.

#1—Sodium hyposulphite .. 4 oz.
    Water .... 12 "

Rub dry and polish with whiting.

#2—Prepared chalk .... 2 oz.
    Ammonia water ...... 2 "
    Water, to make ...... 8 "

#3—Powdered alum .... 3 dr.
    Common salt .... 8 oz.
    Soft soap .... 4 "
    Water .... 40 "

#4—Kieselguhr .... 8 parts
    Kaolin .... 30 "
    Tartaric acid .... 3 "

#5—Kieselguhr .... 28 parts
    Kaolin .... 10 "
    Sodium hyposulphite .. 3 "

#6—Crude oleic acid ..... 16 lb.
    Mineral oil .... 4 "
    Kieselguhr .... 5 "
    Lemon oil ....1 to 2 oz.

Mix the liquids and gradually mix part of the liquid to a paste with the kieselguhr, avoiding lumps, then thin out.

#7—Fuller's earth .... 2 oz.
    Whiting .... 1 "

#8—Precipitated chalk .... 1 oz.
    Whiting .... 1 "
    Hyposulphite soda .... ¼ "

#9—Precipitated chalk .... 1 oz.
    Whiting .... 1 "
    Bicarbonate soda .... ¼ "

#10—Kieselguhr .... 8 oz.
    Paraffin .... 2 "
    Paraffin oil .... 6 "
    Oleic acid .... 1 "

Melt the paraffin with the paraffin oil, and mix with the kieselguhr; then add the oleic acid and then perfume with oil of cedar or oil of pine. Whiting can be used instead of kieselguhr.

#11—Sal ammoniac .... 1 part
    Lime .... 2 "
    Lubricating oil .... 1 "

Add water to the lime and sal ammoniac and then add the lubricating oil. Use a cloth. It is best to prepare this as needed.

#12—Dried sodium carbonate 1 part
    Soap .... 4 parts
    Flour of emery ...... 25 "

Water, enough to make a paste.

#13—Rottenstone .... 4 oz.
    Oxalic acid .... 1 "
    Sweet oil .... ½ "

Oil of turpentine, enough to make a paste.

#14—Precipitated chalk .... 1 lb.
    Oleic acid .... 1 "
    Alcohol .... 8 oz.

#15—Prepared chalk .... 2 oz.
    Aqua ammonia ...... 2 "
    Water .... 8 "

Auto Metal Polish

#1—Put in a 2-gallon jar 4¾ lb. of Tripoli and 8 oz. of oxalic acid, add 1 gal. of water. It is then ready for use.

#2—Tripoli .... 1 lb.
    Whiting .... 1 "
    Powdered pumice ...... 8 oz.
    Kerosene .... 3 "
    Crude oleic acid ...... 3 "

Vaseline, enough to make a paste.

#3—Place 2 oz. of sulphuric acid in an earthen vessel and add 1 qt. of cold water; after cooling, add 2 oz. each of tripoli and jeweler's rouge.

#4—Oleic acid .... 1 lb.
    Kerosene .... 1 pt.
    Tripoli powder .... 8 oz.

#5—Prepared chalk .... 8 oz.
    Red tripoli .... 1½ "
    White tripoli .... 3 "
    Rouge, dry .... 3 "

Water, enough to make a paste.

For Brass and Copper

#1—Take 3 parts of rottenstone to 1 part of powdered soap. Mix and moisten with water before using.

#2—Powdered pipe clay .. 112 lb.
    Soap chips .... 16 "
    Tartaric acid .... 1¼ "

#3—Mix 3 oz. pumice flour, 3 oz. whiting, 1 qt. oleic acid. Thin with gasoline and add color and odor to suit.

#4—Place 3 lb. powdered pumice stone, 1 lb. whiting and ½ lb. oxalic acid crystals in 1 gal. of water. Let set 24 hours, stirring occasionally.

#5—Rottenstone .... 16 oz.
    Paraffin .... 8 "
    Kerosene .... 16 "

Oil of mirbane to perfume.
Melt the paraffin, incorporate the rottenstone, add the kerosene, and the oil of mirbane when cold.

#6—Precipitated chalk .... 10 oz.
    White bole .... 4 "
    Carbonate lead ...... 5 "
    Carbonate magnesia ... 1 "
    Oxide iron .... 1 "

#7—Whiting .... 8 oz.
    Turpentine .... 2 "
    Alcohol .... 1 "
    Spirit of camphor ..... ½ "
    Aqua ammonia .... 2 dr.

Apply and allow to dry before polishing.

#8—Oxalic acid .... 1 part
    Peroxide iron .... 15 parts
    Rottenstone .... 20 "
    Palm oil .... 60 "
    Petrolatum .... 5 "

#9—Infusorial earth .... 1 part
    Soda ash .... 1 "

Sift both together.

#10—Kieselguhr .... 20 parts
    Kaolin .... 10 "
    Photo hypo .... 3 "
    Rottenstone .... 2 "

Mix.

#11—Rottenstone and flour emery together make a good material for polishing iron and steel. The materials may be formed into a cake or slab by mixing with boiling suet and then pouring into square or oblong molds. Crocus and rottenstone mixed in the same way with a little rouge form the best combination for brass or copper and kindred materials.

#12—Refined tallow ...... 80 lb.
    Rottenstone .... 16 "
    Oxalic acid .... 1 "

Powder the acid, mix with the powdered rottenstone, and mold with the tallow into bars, like soap.

#13—Powdered tripoli .... 3 oz.
    Tartaric acid .... 1 dr.
    Powdered pumice .... ½ oz.
    Gasoline .... 14 "

Shake well, and apply with a cloth until the dirt is removed; then polish with chamois.

#14—Rottenstone .... 8 oz.
    Oxalic acid .... 2 "
    Cottonseed oil .... 3 "

Add gasoline to form a creamy fluid.

#15—Kieselguhr .... 100 gm.
    Calcium chloride .... 6 "
    Jeweler's rouge ...... 1 "
    Ammonia water .... 1 cc.
    Water .... 150 "
    Oil of cedar or citro-
      nella .... 1 "

Silver Cream Polish

#1—Water .... 2 gal.
    Photographic hypo .. 1 oz.
    Cream of tartar ...... 1 "
    White neutral soap .. 2½ lb.
    Infusorial earth ...... 10 "
    Whiting .... 6 "
    Spirits camphor ...... 2 oz.
    Denatured alcohol .... 1 pt.
    Gum camphor .... 2 oz.
    Ammonia .... 1½ "

Add 2 gal. more water.
Start with 2 gal. water, add the soap powder and heat until dissolved; then add hypo and cream of tartar. Then add infusorial earth, also called fossil flour, and whiting, and stir into a smooth paste. Cool off and add spirits camphor and ammonia. Then add remainder 2 gal. water and stir the whole into a creamy mass.

#2—Infusorial earth .... 2 parts
    Turpentine .... 4 "
    Ammonia water ...... 4 "
    Water .... 5 "

#3—Whiting .... 15 parts
    Baking soda .... 2 "
    Citric acid .... 1 "

Moisten when ready to use.

Fluids and Pastes

#1—Carbon tetrachloride .. 2½ gal.
    Gasoline (straight) ... 1½ "
    Chloroform .... 1 oz.

Mix.

#2—Turpentine .... 1 part
    Fine emery .... 1 "
    Jeweler's rouge .... 2 "
    Vaseline .... 2 "

#3—Water-glass .... 5 lb.
    Oleic acid .... 5 "

Heat the oleic acid almost to boiling point. Heat the water-glass in another vessel and pour it into the oleic acid with constant stirring. Take enough kieselguhr to make a cream when mixed with one pint of kerosene and when the first mixture has cooled somewhat mix the two solutions together.

#4—Oxalic acid .... 1 oz.
    Kerosene .... 1 qt.
    Rottenstone .... 11 oz.
    Machine oil .... 1 "

The rottenstone is a mineral and should be in the form of a fine powder. It should be mixed with the powdered oxalic acid, and then kerosene mixed with the oil, the two resulting mixtures then being incorporated with a wooden paddle or spatula. The oxalic acid acts as a solvent for the rust, and this preparation is particularly good for cleaning brass or copper. The oil that is left on the surface can be washed off in straight gasoline if the work is to be painted. If it is to be lacquered, it is best to wash in benzene or toluene or carbon tetrachloride, as the gums left by the gasoline sometimes interfere with the adhesion of the lacquer.

To Clean Nickel Plate

Nickel plate that has become blackened and which cannot be cleaned by the polishes given above should be rubbed with a wad of steel wool or rag tied to a stick, the rag or steel wool being wet with a lye water solution. Although this treatment seems rather severe, the nickel will not be damaged, for it is insoluble in the caustic. Rubber gloves will offer protection to the hands when using this effective treatment. The nickel plate is then copiously bathed with water, to the last rinse of which may be added vinegar, which will assist in removing remaining caustic by neutralization. The usual polishes will then brighten the metal surface.

Electric Cleaner

The removal of grease, dirt, rust or scale from metals can be accomplished by using the object as anode or cathode in hot alkaline solutions, and passing a direct current through the solution via the work to be cleaned and another metal plate. The work to be cleaned can be attached to either the positive or negative terminal of a direct current supply, using a metal plate as the other electrode. The work to be freed from dirt and scale is immersed in the sodium hydroxide or lye solution, which is heated.

The current produces, on electrolysis of the caustic, a strong flow of gas bubbles tearing off the scale as they form. As much as from 40 to 80 amperes per square foot of work-area is used.

Electroplating

In using the different plating solutions, the proper anode must be used. This is a sheet or lump of the metal, usually the same as that to be plated, and is connected by means of a wire to the anode, or positive terminal of the battery or source of direct current. In copper plating, a sheet of copper is placed in the copper plating solution, connected to the positive binding post of the battery, and the work upon which the copper is to be plated is connected to the negative terminal, or wire, of the battery. An ammeter and rheostat are placed in series with the circuit at any advantageous point. A voltmeter is also used to read the difference in potential across the battery, or the work and the anode.

Good contact should be made between the work and the battery with which it is connected. Any source of direct current may be used. Wet batteries or dry cells will not be suitable in most instances. For plating at home or for use with small tanks a storage battery or dynamo is excellent.

The work to be plated must be absolutely clean. Cleaning the article to be plated is often the most difficult part of plating.

The current should be regulated to secure best results. Using a plating solution requiring say, one amp. per sq. ft., then for every square foot of surface to be plated, one ampere should be used. An article that is nine inches by eight inches (72 square inches) would therefore require half an ampere of current as shown by the series ammeter, when plating. This is equivalent to a small stream of bubbles coming off the work when it is being plated.

Pure chemicals should be used, and distilled water, if it is possible to secure same, is ideal. It is better to use pure chemicals and tap water than distilled water and impure chemicals. As a rule, plating solutions are not expensive, as they can be used over and over again in small plating. This is due to the fact that the plate is very thin and the solution has not decreased, in plating out, any appreciable extent its metallic constituent, although other factors cause a change of the solution which entails making up from time to time with other chemicals.

Cleaning the Work

Rust, scales and other metal oxides can generally be loosened, and often removed entirely, by immersing the corroded article in a pickle made of a diluted acid or a mixture of acids, and then washing in clean water. Green verdigris and similar forms of corrosion may be removed by dipping in a mixture of equal parts sulphuric acid and water, to which has been added a half part of nitric acid and a small amount of hydrochloric acid. The articles should be strung on a wire, and immersed in the dipping mixture for a few minutes, until the corrosion has been loosened, and then rinsed with clean water. After this, they may be brushed with a wire-brush, and again washed in water. If the verdigris is not all off, they must be again washed in the acid pickle until clean.

A mixture of 1 part of sulphuric acid in 20 parts of water will loosen the oxides on copper and zinc or their alloys. If the surface of a copper or brass article is deeply corroded and green, use a pickle of:

Sulphuric acid .... 4 parts
Nitric acid .... 2 "
Water .... 5 "

Pickling in sulphuric acid has the advantages of being rapid and inexpensive, of reaching all parts of irregular specimens, and of being readily handled by inexperienced operators. In general the samples are immersed for from 5 to 30 minutes in sulphuric acid of concentration 2 to 15 per cent by weight, and at temperatures from 25 to 60° C. Other reagents for pickling include hydrochloric acid, hydrofluoric acid (which is especially useful for cleaning sand castings), and solutions of sodium-acid sulphate. Make a pickle of:

Sulphuric acid .... 6 parts
Muriatic acid .... 1 "
Water .... 150 "

This is useful for removing rust on iron and steel articles which are to be plated.

Oxides on pewter, lead, Britannia metal, or soft solder are removed by a hot lye solution.

Lacquers should be removed by dissolving off in alcohol. Many objects, metal parts, and castings are satisfactorily degreased previous to electroplating by using carbon tetrachloride, which rapidly removes adhering grease, and leaves the objects in a dry, greaseless state. Cleaning is ordinarily accomplished by dipping the articles in the solvent.

Black Nickel Plating

Nickel ammonium sulphate. 8 oz.
Zinc sulphate .... 1 "
Sodium sulphocyanate ..... 2 "

Ammonium or potassium sulphocyanate can be used instead of the sodium salt.

In this, as well as in the alkaline black-nickel solutions, even slight changes in voltage produce marked differences in the proportion of the metals precipitated and hence in the color and physical properties of the deposits. Thus in the above sulphocyanate solution a good black deposit is produced with 0.5 to 0.7 volt (between anode and cathode); while if the voltage be increased to 1.5 to 2 volts, a light-colored, bright nickel deposit is secured. In the operation of such solutions, therefore, control of the voltage is more important than is the control of the current density. The latter probably will not, under good conditions, exceed 1 ampere per square foot.

If the zinc content of the solution is increased very much above that indicated by the above formula, grayish deposits, with high zinc content, are produced. If, on the other hand, the zinc content of the solution is

greatly reduced or actually eliminated, the deposit is nearly pure nickel, with a light or bright nickel color.

A bath prepared from the ingredients here listed, kept neutral with an excess of suspended zinc carbonate, and operated with nickel anodes, will give satisfactory black deposits upon brass, copper, and zinc; upon brass plated with copper; and upon steel plated with copper, nickel, or zinc. The deposit is probably a mixture of nickel, nickel sulphide, zinc, and organic matter of undetermined composition.—From Bureau of Standards Paper "Black Nickel" Plating Solutions.

Gray-Black Nickel Plate

	Ounces per or gallon	Grams per 1000 cc.
Nickel ammonium sulphate	6	45
Zinc sulphate	½	3.8
Ammonium carbonate	5	37.5
Arsenic trioxide	0.7	5
Sodium hydroxide	0.7	5
Sodium cyanide	6	45

Use nickel anode as in black nickel plating process.

The work should be carefully cleaned and degreased before being nickel plated. If there is an old deposit of nickel upon it, this must be removed either by filing and then polishing to remove file marks, or immersed in a mixture of:

Nitric acid .... 1 part
Oil of vitriol............. 2 "
Water .... 1 "

The oil of vitriol is first carefully added to the water with gentle stirring. After cooling, the nitric acid may be added. The work for stripping should be dry, and should be carefully watched in order to avoid excessive corrosion of the base metal. The work should be left in the solution only long enough to remove the nickel deposit. The solution can be used again on other objects to remove the nickel from them.

After removing from this stripping solution, the work must be washed with water, and then plated. It should not be touched with the hands between stripping and plating as grease will be distributed on the surface. The plating wire should be soldered to the work before it is stripped of nickel.

A nickel anode must be used with the nickel plating solutions. This can be a sheet of nickel, or a rolled lump. This nickel must of course be connected to the positive wire of the battery, the work as usual being connected to the negative terminal of the direct current source.

Good nickel plating baths for copper or brass are:

#1—Nickel sulphate .... 50 gm.
    Ammonium chloride . 25 "
    Water to make .... 1000 cc.

The size of the work determines the amount of current needed, although a good rate of current can be judged when the object being plated is covered with only a very thin film of bubbles, these bubbles rising very slowly from the work. The voltage should be about 2.3. In this formula, cast nickel anodes one-half of the area of the cathode surface are satisfactory.

#2—Nickel ammonium sul-
    phate .... 80 gm.
    Water .... 1000 cc.

Nickel ammonium sulphate is sold under the name of double nickel salts. The solution previously described in which ammonium sulphate and nickel sulphate are used duplicates this double salt, due to hydrolysis. The above solution should not be used for nickel plating iron or steel.

#3—Nickel sulphate ...... 6 gm.
    Nickel phosphate ..... 3 "
    Nickel citrate .... 3 "
    Benzoic acid .... 1.5 "
    Water .... 200 cc.

The amounts above can be taken in any multiple.

#4—Nickel ammonium sul-
    phate .... 100 gm.
    Ammonium sulphate . 40 "
    Citric acid .... 10 "
    Water .... 2000 cc.

Heat to dissolve the chemicals, and then add small quantities of ammonium carbonate to neutralize the acid. Test with blue litmus paper for acidity, the litmus turning red when the acid has been completely neutralized. The solution is best used neutral. This is known as Powell's Nickel Solution.

#5—Nickel sulphate ..... 340 gm.
    Nickel ammonium .. 68 "
    Magnesium sulphate . 23 "
    Boric acid .... 23 "
    Water .... 1890 cc.

Use a current strength (density) of 12 to 15 amperes for every square foot of surface to be plated, if the cathode is not moved, and if agitated, use 20-24 amperes per sq. ft. Cadmium chloride may be added in small amounts from time to time.

#6—Nickel sulphate .... 6 oz.
    Nickel ammonium sul-
    phate .... 2 "
    Salt (not iodized) .... 4 "
    Epsom salts (pure) .... 2 "
    Sodium sulphate ...... 2 "
    Boric acid .... 1 "
    Water .... 1 gal.

Use at 26°. A pH value of 6.8 is desirable.

If zinc objects are to be plated with chromium, clean first in 20% hydrofluoric acid, plate with the above nickel solution, and then chromium plate.

Nickel Plating on Lead

Nickel sulphate .... 32 oz.
Magnesium .... 26 "
Ammonium chloride ...... 2.1 "

Water, enough to dissolve above, and then enough in addition to dilute to one gallon. A small quantity of cadmium chloride acts as a brightener in this solution.

Nickel Plating Bath

Nickel sulphate .... 4 oz.
Nickel ammonium sulphate. 6 "
Boric acid .... 2 "
Glycerin .... 1 "
Water .... 1 gal.

Nickeling on Zinc

Nickel sulphate .... 40 gm.
Sodium citrate .... 35 "
Water enough to make .. 1000 cc.

Use about 3 volts. The anode area should be about 2½ times as great as the cathode, or work to be plated.

A nickel bath for thick deposits of nickel consists of:

Nickel sulphate .... 50 gm.
Ammonium tartrate neutral 30 "
Tannic acid .... ¼ "
Water enough to make....1000 cc.

Do not use a large current strength (amperage) in plating with this solution.

A nickel plating solution for iron or steel is the simplest of all the plating solutions and consists of about 75 grams of nickel ammonium sulphate (double nickel salts dissolved in water) the resulting solution being then diluted to make a volume of 1000 cc.

Gun Metal Plate

Potassium cyanide .... 60 gm.
Arsenic trioxide .... 30 "
Nickel ammonium sulphate 60 "

Water, enough to dissolve above salts and then a further addition of water to make the solution have a volume of one liter. Brass anodes are used with the bath warm, and the same current as for nickel plating. The metallic articles to be plated are of course cleaned and hung on the negative wire from the source of the direct current.

Plating Brass on Metals

#1—Copper cyanide ..... 45 gm.
 Zinc cyanide .... 15 "
 Sodium cyanide .... 67.5 "
 Sodium carbonate .... 15 "
 Ammonium chloride . 15 "

Water, enough to dissolve the chemicals. The resulting solution is then diluted to 1000 cc. with water. Use brass anode.

#2—Copper cyanide .... 3 oz.
 Zinc cyanide .... 1 "
 Sodium cyanide ...... 4½ "
 Sodium carbonate .... 2 "
 Water .... 1 gal.

To every 100 gallons of the above solution add 1 quart of ammonium hydroxide (about one half diluted). The above is a good "flashing" solution for brass plating zinc, previous to chromium plating.

In the Morris & Johnson's formula for brass plating a solution is made by dissolving, in 1 gal. of water, cyanide of potassium, 1 lb.; carbonate of ammonia, 1 lb.; cyanide of copper, 2 oz.; cyanide of zinc, 1 oz. The solution is to be used at a temperature of 150° F., with a large brass anode and a strong current strength.

The following is Reseleur's brass plating solution:

Sodium carbonate (dry)   10 gm.
Copper(ic) acetate ....   14 "
Sodium bisulphite .....   14 "
Zinc chloride, fused....   14 "
Potassium cyanide (100
    percent) ....   40 "
Ammonium chloride ..   2 "
Water to make one liter (1000 cc.).

Use about 2.7 volts and a current density about the same as in normal nickel plating. The sodium salts should be dissolved in about 400 cc. of warm water. The copper and zinc salts dissolved in about 200 cc. of water and the two solutions mixed, stirring the second slowly into the first. Dissolve the cyanide in the remainder of the water and stir into the mixture, which is just produced from the first and second solutions. The cyanide will dissolve the precipitate. Now add the ammonium chloride and boil the solution for about an hour, replacing the water which evaporates, and the solution is ready for use.

A brass plating solution that is less troublesome to make and which does not have to be boiled is made from:

Sodium carbonate ....   8 oz.
Sodium bisulphite ....   8 "
Copper carbonate ....   4 "
Zinc carbonate ....   4 "
Potassium cyanide ....   4 "
Arsenic trioxide ....   1/10 "
Water ....   2 gal.

Dissolve the copper carbonate and the zinc carbonate in water and then add the soda carbonate and soda bisulphite. Dissolve in warm water the cyanide of potassium and the white arsenic, and pour this liquid into the other, which becomes rapidly decolorized; add distilled water to make 2 gal. or slightly more.

Brassing Without Battery

To brass small articles of iron or steel put them in a quart of water and ½ oz. each of sulphate of copper and chloride of tin. Agitate the articles in this solution until desired color is obtained.

Bright Plating Lead

For plating lead with copper use:

Sodium cyanide ....   3 oz.
Rochelle salts ....   1/4 "
Water ....   1/4 gal.

Add copper cyanide to the warm solution until no more dissolves. To every gallon of this solution add 1 pint of a solution of:

Lead acetate ....   2 oz.
Sodium hydroxide ....   2 "
Water, enough to make a pint.

This sodium plumbate solution acts as a brightener. Use the bath at 160° F. (70° C.).

Cadmium Plating

Cadmium hydroxide ......   48 gm.
Sodium sulphate ....   60 "
Sodium cyanide ....   120 "
Glycerin or turkey red oil..   12 "
Nickel sulphate ....   1.5 "
Water .... 1000 cc.

Copper Plating

Copper can be plated directly upon iron or steel by simply immersing the iron or steel in a solution of copper sulphate. The copper so precipitated on the steel is not adherent, and is so thin that it will not stand wear. Using the electric current, copper can be plated on iron or steel using certain solutions. These solutions used for copper plating iron or steel are alkaline and therefore do not contain free acid, because the acid will attack the steel with or without the passage of the current. A typical copper plating solution for iron or steel is:

Sodium sulphite .... 20 gm.
Sodium carbonate .... 20 "
Sodium bisulphite .... 20 "
Cupric acetate .... 20 "
Potassium cyanide .... 20 "
Water ....1000 cc.

This is made up by dissolving the sodium salts in part of the water, and the copper acetate in about the same quantity of water, the two solutions then being mixed. The potassium cyanide is then dissolved in the remaining amount of water and added to the mixture, which dissolves the precipitate.

Another copper plating solution for iron or steel, zinc or tin:

Copper cyanide .... 3 oz.
Sodium cyanide .... 4 "
Sodium carbonate .... 2 "
    Water to make 1 gal.

Some platers add about one-eighth of an ounce of sodium thiosulphate (photographer's hypo) to each gallon of solution to produce a very bright deposit of copper. The solution is used warm, and from about 3 to 6 amperes of current are used for every square foot of area to be plated. Faster deposits can be plated out if the quantities of copper and other chemicals are increased, and also the current as indicated by the ammeter in series with the circuit. If the copper deposit becomes dark, then more cyanide is added. The concentration of sodium carbonate gradually increases during the course of operations. If the concentrations of copper cyanide and sodium cyanide are correctly adjusted, however, the presence of excessive amounts of sodium carbonate will not seem to be especially disadvantageous, and in usual practice no efforts are made to remove the excess of sodium carbonate. It may be removed, however, by cooling the solution and crystallizing out some of the excess sodium carbonate. It should not be neutralized with an acid.

Another copper plating solution for iron, steel, tin or zinc:

Rochelle salts .... 5 oz.
Copper sulphate .... 1 "
Water .... 1 qt.

Dissolve each chemical in a pint of water and then mix the two solutions. Dissolve the precipitate, which is formed by adding a solution of sodium hydroxide (caustic soda). The solution will become deep blue. Clean the work and plate, for small articles using about one or one and a half amperes. This current is ascertained without an ammeter by observing the bubbles which form on the object being plated. A very small stream of bubbles is desired. About 15 minutes of plating will produce good deposits. Remove the work immediately after turning off the current. Nickel can be plated directly upon this copper plate.

An alkaline copper solution for iron, steel, tin or zinc is prepared as in the previous plating solution, the cream of tartar and the soda being dissolved together, the copper sulphate in another portion of water, the two mixed and cleared with sodium hydroxide solution:

Cream of tartar .... 6.7 oz.
Sodium carbonate .... 15 "
Copper sulphate .... 6.7 "
Water .... 10 qt.

Another copper plating solution for iron or steel is made as follows: Prepare a solution of 1½ lb. potassium cyanide in 1 gal. of water. Set aside one-quarter of this solution. The remainder is now warmed, and copper carbonate is added. At first it dissolves quite easily, but as the solution acquires more copper, the reaction takes place more slowly. When no more carbonate is dissolved, allow to settle. Pour off the clear liquid as completely as possible, and filter the remainder, adding the filtered solution to the clear liquid which has been poured off. Now add the cyanide solution originally set aside, and the solution is then ready for use.

Chromium Plating

The article to be plated is cleaned of rust and grease by the energetic application of emery and a bath in soapy water. After this preliminary cleaning, a wire scratch brush spun by a motor will usually prepare the surface satisfactorily for plating. Of course, the article must be very smooth and perfect if a bright, glossy plated surface is desired. Under exactly the right conditions, 'a chromium deposit can be obtained that requires little or no rouging and buffing to bring it to a mirror-like brilliancy. Indeed, the beginner will have no difficulty in obtaining good coatings, even if not as bright as he would like, because the current can be loaded into the bath without any danger of depositing "mud" or burning the work.

A good plating solution is composed of 33 oz. of chromic acid (trioxide of chromium or chromic acid anhydride) dissolved in 1 gal. of water with about $\frac{1}{3}$ oz. of sulphuric acid added to it. The solution is used at about 130° F. and it should never be allowed to fall below 100° F. or bright deposits will not be produced. One may add chromic acid crystals to the solution from time to time as it becomes weaker. Considerable latitude is possible here since some plating baths contain as much as 55 oz. of the chromic acid crystals to a gallon of water.

In chromium plating high amperage is required.

Iron, steel, brass, and copper can be chromium plated directly, provided they are clean. Fasten the article to be plated to a heavy copper wire and connect it to the negative side of the storage battery. A sheet of lead is used as the positive element and is connected to the positive terminal of the battery. A heavy-duty rheostat should be included in the circuit, and it is well to provide a single-pole switch to short-circuit this rheostat in case overheating of the resistance wire makes it necessary to remove the rheostat from the circuit. All the connecting wires should be heavy enough to carry the current without becoming warm.

It is somewhat difficult to chromium plate interior portions or indentations of objects because of the poor "throwing power" of chromic acid solutions. When this problem arises, place the lead plate nearer the indented portion of the object so that it may be completely plated.

When removed from the plating bath, the articles should be rinsed in a bath of water and then thoroughly washed in running water. Springs, such as those upon calipers, should not be plated while under tension, for they are likely to break.

Pinholes in chromium plated iron objects can be detected by immersing the plated work in a solution of 2 oz. each of strong sulphuric acid and copper sulphate dissolved in a quart of water. The appearance of red specks will indicate the presence of pinholes in the chromium layer.

Chromium plating should be performed in a well-ventilated room, as the chromium acid spray evolved is most unpleasant. The amateur plater can lay a wet newspaper on top of the plating bath vessel to overcome this objectionable feature. Before attempting to plate chromium, it is necessary that the article be free from oil and grease, or the chromium will not adhere to the work, and dark spots will show. Bright deposits of chromium can only be secured within a narrow range of temperature and current density. The most effective temperature range is between 104° and 122° F.

The most effective current density is between 50 and 200 amperes per sq. ft. Within these ranges good deposits are secured at high temperatures and low current densities, or high current densities and low temperatures. The amount of the deposit increases with current density, but decreases with rise in temperature. For general work the best current density is 100 amperes per sq. ft., with a temperature of 113° F.

Good chromium plating solutions:

	Gm. per Liter.	Oz. per Gal.
#1—Chromic acid	250	33
Chromium sulphate	3	0.4
Chromium carbonate	7	1.0
#2—Chromic acid anhydride	48 oz.	
Iron chromate	1 "	
Sodium sulphate	½ "	
Water	1 gal.	

Use this bath at about 32° and have the current strength 75 amperes per square foot of surface to be chromium plated. A 3-5 minute plate is sufficient to ensure lasting service. The chromic acid anhydride can be purchased under the name chromium trioxide or chromic acid crystals.

Silver Plating

#1—Silver cyanide	25 gm.
Potassium cyanide	27 "
Water ....1000 cc.

A sheet of silver is used as the anode.

#2—Silver chloride	10 gm.
Potassium cyanide	20 "
Water enough to make.1000 cc.

In these two solutions, the cyanide is made into a solution with water and added to the silver compounds in water.

Silver plating solutions can be modified by adding a brightener, which may consist of about 35 cc. dissolved or shaken up with 1000 cc. of either of the above two silver plating solutions.

This brightener solution thus formed is shaken in a bottle and allowed to stand for a day or two before using. Of this brightener solution, 0.7 cc. is taken and added to every 1000 cc. of the fresh carbon disulphide-free silver plating solution.

Tin Plating

Tin (stannic) chloride.....	30 gm.
Salt (not iodized).........	15 "
Sodium hyposulphite	15 "
Sodium hydroxide	90 "

Water enough to make a liter of solution.

Tin anodes must be used with the above.

Tin plating without using electric current is possible with this solution:

Ammonium alum	25 gm.
Stannic (tin) chloride.....	2 "

Dissolved in 1000 cc. of water. If iron or steel articles are immersed in the above boiling solution, they will be plated with a bright coating of tin. Ammonium alum is sold also under the name of ammonium aluminum sulphate.

Zinc Plating

Ammonium citrate	40 gm.
Zinc sulphate	100 "
Ammonium chloride	25 "
Water ....1000 cc.

Zinc anodes should be used.

Lead Plating

#1—Lead silico-fluoride 50 to 80 gm.
  Hydrofluorsilicic
    acid ....100 to 150 "
  Gelatin ....   ½ "

Water to make 1000 cc.

#2—Lead acetate .... 1 lb.
  Water .... 1 gal.

Add potassium cyanide dissolved in part of the gallon of water to the solution of lead acetate (sugar of lead) which is dissolved in the remaining part of the water. This addition of potassium cyanide will precipitate lead cyanide which will, on further addition of the cyanide, dissolve. It is this clear solution that is formed which is used as the plating bath. Lead sheet anodes are to be used for these two lead plating solutions.

Cobalt Plating

Cobalt platings upon metal renders the metal resistant to rusting and oxidation. A typical cobalt plating bath is made as follows:

#1—Cobalt ammonium sul-
    phate .... 200 gm.
  Water ....1000 cc.

This can be plated about four times as fast as ordinary nickel plating solutions.

#2—Cobalt sulphate ...... 312 gm.
  Sodium chloride ...... 19.6 "
  Boric acid ......Nearly saturated
  Water ....1000 cc.
(Specific gravity is 1.25 at 15° Cent.)

Cobalt plating from the above two solutions on brass, iron, steel, copper, tin, lead and other metals is firm, adherent, uniform and much harder than nickel plate. These surfaces may be buffed to an excellent finish of high luster and brilliant white. The electric conductivity of these solutions is higher than that of standard nickel solutions so that cobalt may be de-posited at a lower voltage for a given speed. This solution can be deposited 15 times faster than nickel plating solutions.

Cobalt deposits remarkably well in indentations of the objects plated. The high speed of deposit does not require agitation of the solutions. Since the cobalt plate is so much harder than nickel, one-fourth the weight gives the same protection as nickel. Ornamental work not subject to great wear requires only one-minute deposit, and fifteen-minute deposits withstand great friction or atmospheric attack.

Cobalt plated skates showed far greater resistance to corrosion, wear and scratching than similar nickel plated skates. Similar results are obtained with automobile parts.

Iron Plating

Ferrous sulphate .... 150 gm.
Ferrous chloride .... 75 "
Ammonium sulphate ...... 100 "
Use this solution at about 200° F.

For iron plating dissolve in 200 cubic centimeters of water, 10 grams of potassium ferrocyanide and 20 grams of Rochelle salts. Then add a solution consisting of 3 grams of persulphate of iron and 50 cubic centimeters of water. For use, a solution of caustic soda is added slowly, keeping the whole well stirred, until a clear yellow liquid is obtained. Another solution is prepared by evaporating and crystallizing equal parts of sulphate of iron and sulphate of ammonia. A solution of the double salt is thus made which yields a good white deposit of iron.

Gold Plating

Gold chloride .... 160 gr.
Potassium cyanide .... .2 oz.
Sodium phosphate .... 9.5 "
Sodium bisulphite .... 1.6 "
Water .... 1 gal.

Dissolve the cyanide and bisulphite in water. Dissolve the sodium phosphate in another portion of the water. To this add the gold chloride dissolved in the remaining water. Then add the cyanide-bisulphite solution to the solution containing the gold. Use gold anode.

Metallochromes

This is the name given to varicolored deposits upon brass or copper plates by means of an electric current. The electrolyte or liquid used is usually composed of sodium plumbate, made by dissolving litharge in, or treating lead nitrate or acetate with, a potassium hydroxide (caustic potash) solution.

The copper or brass article should first be nickel plated, using one of the nickel plating solutions described for copper or brass, and then suspended as an anode (connect with the positive wire of a battery) in the following solution:

Lead nitrate .... 5 gm.
Water .... 250 cc.
    Dissolve and mix with a solution of:
Sodium hydroxide .... 50 gm.
Water .... 50 cc.

Allow to settle and use top clear liquid.

The negative wire of the battery, or cathode, should be placed about half an inch from the surface of the plate which is immersed in the solution. Soon beautifully colored rings appear on the plate, which spread out as the electrolysis proceeds.

The pointed wire can be replaced by a bare wire bent into various shapes such as crosses, stars, scrolls, circles, or letters and these bent wires placed parallel with the copper or brass plate which is to be colored.

The plate is removed when the desired color has been produced. It is well washed in water, and, after it has dried, is then coated with a colorless lacquer.

Other solutions that can be used as the electrolyte are:

Litharge .... 60 gm.
Potassium hydroxide ...... 100 "
Water .... 900 cc.

The potassium hydroxide is first dissolved in the water and the litharge then added, the whole being boiled for half an hour, replacing any water that is removed by evaporation. The solution should then be allowed to settle and the clear top liquid poured off and used as the electrolyzing bath.

Figures or designs cut from paper, and glued to the metal sheet, will produce the design in plain metal while the outside ground area will be colored, if plated, using one of the foregoing solutions. The paper figure or design must be made impervious to the solution, however, by coating with wax, or a varnish. The paper is, of course, removed afterward.

Manganese sulphate solution can also be used as the electrolyzing liquid.

Welding Platinum to Copper

Platinum is used in many laboratory operations, principally in electrolytic operations as electrodes. Although thin sheets of platinum or the small diameters of platinum wire are not expensive, this metal can be readily welded to copper wire to reduce the amount of platinum wire which would be needed.

To unite platinum wire with copper wire, one end of each wire should be held in a Bunsen flame. When red hot, the wires are pressed together, the fusion or weld then being complete. If the wires are small and the applied pressure causes collapsing of the wire, they can then be welded by squeezing together while still red rot, using a pair of forceps, the forceps of course being held in the flame and heated red hot also.

Casting Metals

A mixture that will eliminate the effect of sand burning into, or adhering onto, castings which are poured in sand molds is equal parts of ethylene glycol and 200 mesh silica flour. The ethylene glycol is familiar as a liquid coolant for automobile radiators, and silica flour is nothing more than the fine dust from silica. The mixture is applied to the molds by brushing. When the metal is poured, the glycol evaporates from the heat of the metal, forming a gas blanket, and at the same time decomposing, forming a layer of soot. This sooty layer effectively prevents the sand of the mold from burning into the casting, thus eliminating much labor in cleaning the cold castings.

Silicate Enamel

A rather inexpensive enamel is made by mixing various pigments with water-glass, applying to any metal surfaces, and baking on. For white, zinc white (zinc oxide) can be used; green, use chromic oxide; red, use one of the oxides of iron, which also gives brown tones: lampblack can be used with the silicate for a black; various other chemical or earthy pigments can be used. The mixture of water-glass and pigment is applied to the metal work, and baked on by placing the work in an oven which is heated to about 200 degrees, the heat being raised slowly, to avoid spattering of the water-glass.

Enameling Metals

The metal is fired with a frit, paste, ground coat, or flux as it is called,

which is usually white but can be any color. This frit contains, for colored enameling, oxides of different metals which impart their characteristic colors to the frit, thus showing up on the metal which it is desired to enamel. Jeweler's enamels of different colors are used as made. These are excellent for enameling by amateurs. A common frit is:

Borax	3	parts
White glass	12	"
Sand (white)	3	"
Red lead	16	"

This is fused in a crucible, cooled, and powdered. For colored enamels the following holds true, using this base, or frit.

Black enamels are made with dioxide of manganese, or oxide of iron, to which more depth of color is given with a little cobalt. *Violet* enamel of a fine hue is made from peroxide of manganese, in small quantity, and soda ash. *Red* enamel is made from oxide of copper. *Green* enamel is produced by a mixture of yellow and blue, but is generally obtained from oxide of copper, or with the oxide of chromium.

For *yellow* enamel take one part of white oxide of antimony, with from one to three parts of white lead, one of alum, and one of sal ammoniac. Each of these substances is to be pulverized, then all are to be exactly mixed, and exposed to a heat adequate to decompose the sal ammoniac. This operation is complete when a yellow color develops.

A beautiful *blue* enamel color is obtained from the oxide of cobalt, and it produces it with such intensity that only a very little can be used lest the shade should pass into black. A *white* enamel may be prepared with a *calcine* formed of 2 parts of tin oxide and 2 parts cryolite.

PAINTS AND HOW
TO MIX THEM

General Painting Facts

There are many jobs of painting for which only a comparatively small amount of paint is needed. For jobs of this kind, mix your paint according to the following simplified directions.

Paint which gives a gloss finish is used for practically all exterior painting.

To make a gloss paint, mix soft paste white-lead with an equal measure of linseed oil. Then add a gill each of turpentine and drier for every gallon of paint.

Follow identically the same procedure in using heavy paste white-lead except increase the amount of linseed oil slightly and stir it in a little at a time.

These directions give a fairly heavy paint such as is generally used for a gloss finishing coat. If for any reason a thinner paint is wanted, add more linseed oil and turpentine. Thus, for priming new, unpainted wood increase the quantity of paint by half with a mixture of linseed oil and turpentine, using two parts oil and one part "turps."

Where a dull or so-called flat finish is desired, as for interior decoration on either woodwork or plaster walls, a flatting liquid instead of linseed oil should be mixed with the white-lead. The best material for this purpose is flatting oil, but turpentine may be used if flatting oil cannot be obtained. It produces a flat finish which is remarkable for its beauty, washability and durability.

To make flat paint, mix together equal parts of heavy paste white-lead and flatting oil (or turpentine). Pour the flatting liquid into the white-lead a little at a time, stirring thoroughly before adding each additional quantity. If turpentine is used, add one tablespoon of drier for each pint of paint. If flatting oil is used, add no drier.

Flat paint, mixed as directed, may be used for undercoats as well as the finishing coat on woodwork and for all coats on plaster except the priming coat. For the priming coat on unpainted plaster, it is better to use a special primer, which will seal all fine cracks and porous places in the surface.

One of the special advantages of making paint from white-lead is that it can be colored to the exact tint you want simply by adding tinting colors ground-in-oil.

The more commonly used colors-in-oil may be purchased in one and five-pound cans or in small tubes at most paint and hardware stores. Where there is only an ounce or so of tinting material needed, it may be found convenient to buy the tubes of color, but whenever considerable quantities are needed it is advisable to purchase the color in cans for these are, compared to the tube colors, much lower in price.

If difficulty is experienced in obtaining the Chinese blue called for in the formulas, Prussian blue may be substituted.

In buying colors-in-oil, specify exactly the color desired. It is not sufficient to say "chrome yellow." Medium chrome yellow, the most commonly used, is a deep yellow. Lemon chrome yellow is a lighter, more greenish yellow.

Chrome green might mean any one of the three chrome greens—light, medium or dark. Of these, medium chrome is most satisfactory for general use since it can, by the addition of a little Chinese blue and lampblack, be substituted for dark chrome green, or by the addition of a little lemon chrome yellow will answer the purpose for light chrome green. If medium chrome green is not easily obtainable it can be made up by mixing lemon chrome yellow and Chinese or Prussian blue. It is advisable, however, to use the straight green when possible.

Various grays can be produced by adding lampblack to white-lead. If no black tinting material is at hand, a gray can be produced by using a little Chinese blue and Venetian red. A gray produced by using lampblack and white-lead may be made warmer by the addition of small amounts of French ochre, Venetian red or medium chrome yellow, and may be made cooler by employing a little Chinese blue in the mix.

Formulas for securing a number of popular colors are listed below. These formulas give the amount of color-in-oil required to tint one gallon either of gloss paint or flat paint made with white-lead. A lesser or greater quantity of paint may be tinted to the desired color simply by decreasing or increasing proportionately the amount of color-in-oil called for by the formula.

color is desired, add a little Chinese blue to the pink, greens, drabs and grays and a little chrome green with a touch of blue to the cream, yellow and buff. To soften or gray a color, add a little lampblack. To lighten a color, simply use less color-in-oil or more white-lead; to darken it, add more color-in-oil.

As colors-in-oil of different manufacturers vary in strength, the foregoing formulas are at best only approximate. Therefore, add the color-in-oil gradually (stir in a drop or two at a time) and stop when the desired tint is reached, even if the formula calls for more. So also, if the tint is too light, add more color-in-oil until the tint is exactly right. Before adding the tinting colors thin them to about the same consistency as the white paint with linseed oil, flatting oil or turpentine, depending upon whether gloss or flat paint is being used.—Courtesy National Lead Co.

Raw and Boiled Linseed Oil

Raw linseed oil with a drier is somewhat better than boiled linseed oil for paint to be used on wood, but boiled linseed oil without drier may be used

Tint	Colors-in-Oil	Gloss Paint	Flat Paint
Pink	Venetian Red	1⅛ oz.	1½ oz.
Light Blue	Chinese Blue	½ oz.	¾ oz.
Light Green	Med. Chrome Green	9¾ oz.	13 oz.
Green	Med. Chrome Green	2 lbs.	2¾ lb.
Cream	Lemon Chrome Yellow	⅛ oz.	⅙ oz.
Yellow	Lemon Chrome Yellow	4¼ oz.	5¾ oz.
Buff	Med. Chrome Yellow	2¾ oz.	3¾ oz.
Light Drab	Burnt Umber	1½ oz.	2 oz.
Dark Drab	Burnt Umber	5 oz.	6¾ oz.
Light Gray	Lampblack	½ oz.	¾ oz.
Dark Gray	Lampblack	1¼ oz.	1¾ oz.

A little Venetian red added to any of the above colors except the greens will give a warmer tint. In the case of the greens, the warmer effects are secured by adding yellow. If a colder

if desired. The results will be quite satisfactory. Boiled linseed oil is particularly desirable for paint to be used on metal, plaster, concrete, and stucco. A variety of oil sometimes sold as boiled oil is raw oil to which drier has been added. The danger that this so-called "bung-hole boiled" oil may have been made with poor drier, or too much drier, makes it preferable to buy raw oil and add your own drier.

Paint for Outside Wood

Ingredients	Priming Coat	Second Coat	Third Coat
Heavy paste white-lead.....	100 pounds	100 pounds	100 pounds
Pure raw linseed oil	4 gallons	1½ gallons	3½-4 gallons
Pure turpentine	2 "	1½ "	1 pint
Pure drier	1 pint	1 pint	1 "
How much paint it makes...	9 gallons	6 gallons	6½-7 gallons
Square feet it should cover..	5,175 sq. ft.	3,600 sq. ft.	3,900-4,200 sq. ft.

For repainting outside wood use the ingredients as given above for second and third coats.

Mixing the Paint

The steps to be taken in mixing white-lead paint are:

1st. Take the proper amount of white-lead required by the directions which follow. "Break up" or soften it in a large pail with just enough oil to bring it to a workable paste. Use a wooden paddle to stir.

2nd. Add tinting colors, if the paint is to be tinted, mixing them thoroughly into the white-lead.

3rd. Put in drier. Stir thoroughly.

4th. Add the remainder of the oil required by the formula. Stir thoroughly.

5th. Put in the turpentine.

Stir until the whole mass is thoroughly mixed. Strain through wire or cloth screen. The paint is now ready to apply.

For the first or priming coat on new, unpainted outside wood the paint should be thin. Use the following:

The painter may exercise his own discretion in using a larger or smaller quantity of oil according to whether the wood is oil-absorbing, such as white pine, poplar and bass-wood, or less permeable, such as yellow pine, cypress, spruce and hemlock. The painter may find it advisable, in rare cases, to increase the quantity of turpentine for extremely sappy or resinous woods. Where this is done a corresponding decrease should be made in the specified amount of linseed oil.

Raw linseed oil with drier is somewhat better than boiled linseed oil for making paint to be used on outside wood, but boiled linseed oil without drier may be used if desired. The results will be quite satisfactory.

The same precautions must be taken in preparing to paint a floor as in the preparation of any other surface. If the old paint is rough and scaly or thick and gummy, the floor should be cleaned down to the wood by planing, burning and scraping or by the use of a liquid paint remover. If the last method is used the surface must be brushed afterward with a coat of strong vinegar to destroy any trace of the alkali in the remover. Make sure that every part of the floor is firm and solid. There should be no spring to it when stepped on. After sandpapering and cleaning, the floor is ready for painting.

To Prevent Settling of Pigment

As the vehicle in a flat paint is largely turpentine, naphtha or turpentine substitute, instead of the linseed oil in a gloss paint, the pigment quickly settles to the bottom of the can when painting, necessitating constant stirring while painting. A paste containing aluminum stearate added to the paint will prevent the pigment from settling out. The paste is made as follows:

Dissolve about 25 lb. of aluminum stearate in 100 lb. of turpentine, naphtha or turpentine substitute. This is easily done by sifting the aluminum stearate slowly into the solvent, heating gradually, and stirring constantly until complete solution is effected. A better way to insure a perfect solution and prevent any particles from settling to the bottom is to make a paste with the aluminum stearate with as little naphtha or turpentine as possible and then add the total quantity of solvent to be used. Apply heat after the full amount of both ingredients has been mixed together. The resulting product will be a jelly-like substance which should be used as a stock flatting agent.

To the regular formula for flat paint, add 5% by volume of this aluminum stearate jelly. In other words, if your formula calls for a total of 100 gallons, five gallons of aluminum stearate jelly should be used.

Besides giving a flatting effect, aluminum stearate also imparts to paint a water resisting property, which is of considerable value.

White Paint Formulas

Priming coat:

Heavy paste white-lead... 100 lb.
Pure raw linseed oil....... 3 gal.
Pure turpentine .... 3 "
Pure drier ....1½ to 2 pt.

The preceding formula makes 10 gallons of paint, which should cover about 5,750 square feet, one coat.

Priming coat for plaster walls:

Heavy paste white-lead... 100 lb.
Pure boiled linseed oil..... 7 gal.
Pure turpentine .... 1 "

This makes 11 gallons of paint, which should cover 5,500 square feet, one coat.

First Coat:

Heavy paste white-lead.... 100 lb.
Pure raw linseed oil....... ½ gal.
Pure turpentine .... 2 "
Pure drier .... 1 pt.

This makes 5 to 6 gallons of paint, which should cover about 3,500 to 4,200 square feet, one coat.

Second coat for plaster walls or new inside wood:

Heavy paste white-lead.... 100 lb.
Pure raw linseed oil ...... ½ gal.
Pure turpentine .... 2 "
Pure drier .... 1 pt.

Makes 5½ gallons of paint, which should cover about 3,300 square feet, one coat.

Third coat for plaster walls or new inside wood:

Heavy paste white-lead.... 100 lb.
Pure turpentine .... 2 gal.
Pale varnish (suitable for
enamel) .... 1 pt.
Pure drier .... ½ "

This makes 5 to 6 gallons of paint, which should cover about 3,500 to 4,200 square feet.

Third coat, oil gloss finish for plaster walls:

Note: The following formula should be used only as a base for dark colors, as light-colored paint containing considerable raw linseed oil will yellow badly when used on interiors.

Heavy paste white-lead.... 100 lb.
Pure raw linseed oil ....3 to 3½ gal.
Pure turpentine .... 1 pt.
Pure drier .... 1 "

This makes about 6 to 6½ gal. of paint and should cover 3,600 to 3,900 sq. ft.

Third coat, enamel finish for plaster walls:

Heavy paste white-lead...   3 lb.
Floor varnish ....   1 gal.

This makes about 1 gal. paint and will cover about 600 sq. ft.

Third coat, eggshell gloss finish for plaster walls:

Heavy paste white-lead....   100 lb.
Pure turpentine ....1½ to 2 gal.
Floor varnish ....   ¾ "
Pure drier ....   ½ pt.

This makes 5¼ to 5¾ gal. and will cover 3,150 to 3,450 sq. ft.

To Color White Paint

Where colored paint is wanted, it can be secured simply by adding tinting colors according to the shade or tint desired. These tinting colors are known as "colors-in-oil" and can be bought from any dealer who handles paint materials.

There is scarcely any limit to the number of shades and tints obtainable by coloring white-lead paint but only shades and tints of certain colors are desirable for exterior painting. Any of the colors listed can be varied indefinitely simply by increasing or decreasing the amount of tinting materials specified.

Most of the color formulas given call for the use of two or more tinting materials, but it should be remembered that simpler colors may be obtained by the use of one coloring pigment. Mixed with white-lead, varying quantities of lampblack will produce a pleasing range of grays, chrome yellow will produce yellows, chrome green will produce greens, Chinese blue will produce blues, Venetian red will produce pinks, and so on.

Formulas for colored paint are at best always only approximate, as some allowance must be made for slight variations in the strength and tone of different manufacturers' colors. Chrome yellows and ochres, for example, vary quite noticeably both in strength and tone.

The tinting colors should be added to the white-lead before the paint is thinned to painting consistency. Never put in all at once the entire quantity of colors called for. Weigh out the color and put it in gradually, noting the effect. Stop when the desired shade or tint is arrived at, even if the formula calls for more. So also, if the color is too light, add a little more tinting matter until the color is exactly right.

Where tinting colors are used in sufficient quantity to alter the consistency of the paint, add ½ pint of linseed oil and turpentine (combined) to each pound of coloring material. The proportion of the turpentine to linseed oil should follow the particular white-lead formula being used.

The following formulas with the exception of those marked "No white-lead" are based on the use of 100 pounds of heavy paste white-lead.

Dark Venetian Red
　　Venetian red .... 100 lb.
　　Indian red .... 40 "
　　No white-lead.

Pale Greenish Yellow
　　Heavy paste white-lead 100 lb.
　　Medium chrome yellow   5 oz.
　　Medium chrome green. 1¼ "

Buff
　　Heavy paste white-lead 100 lb.
　　French ochre ....   2 "
　　Medium chrome yellow ½ "

Light Yellowish Green
　　Heavy paste white-lead 100 lb.
　　Medium chrome green. 1½ "
　　Medium chrome yellow ½ "

Reddish Yellow
　　Heavy paste white-lead 100 lb.
　　French ochre .... 14 "

Grayed Blue Green
  Heavy paste white-lead 100 lb.
  Chinese blue .... ¼ "
  Medium chrome yellow ½ "
  Lampblack .... 3 oz.

Yellowish Brown
  Heavy paste white-lead 100 lb.
  French ochre .... 86 "
  Venetian red .... 3 "
  Lampblack .... 1 "

Pale Buff
  White lead .... 100 lb.
  French ochre .... 1 "
  Chrome yellow .... 3 oz.

Olive Green
  White lead .... 100 lb.
  Chrome yellow .... 1 "
  Medium chrome yellow 7 oz.
  Lampblack .... 1 "

Medium Gray
  White lead .... 100 lb.
  Lampblack .... ¼ oz.

Olive Green
  White lead .... 100 lb.
  Medium chrome yellow 19 "
  Medium chrome green. 1 "
  Lampblack .... 2½ "
  —Courtesy National Lead Co.

Paint for Stucco or Brick

Stucco, concrete work and the mortar in brick or stone work should be allowed to stand and dry at least a year before paint is applied. If painted within a year, it may be aged artificially by washing with a solution made by dissolving two pounds of zinc sulphate in one gallon of water or with ordinary carbonic acid water.

Boiled linseed oil should be used as specified wherever possible, especially on stucco and concrete. If boiled oil is not available, raw oil and a drier may be used.

For painting stucco or brick, apply three coats of paint mixed according to the following formulas:

Priming coat for stucco and brick:
Heavy paste white-lead.... 100 lb.
Pure boiled linseed oil..... 7 gal.
Pure turpentine .... 1 "
This makes 11 gal. of paint and should cover 5,500 sq. ft.

Priming coat for concrete and stone:
Heavy paste white-lead.... 100 lb.
Pure boiled linseed oil..... 5 gal.
Pure turpentine .... 1 "
This makes 8¾ gallons of paint and should cover about 4,375 sq. ft., one coat.

Second coat for concrete and stone:
Heavy paste white-lead.... 100 lb.
Pure linseed oil (⅓ boiled,
  ⅔ raw) .... 3 gal.
Pure turpentine .... ½ "
This makes 6½ gallons of paint and should cover about 3,900 sq. ft., one coat.

Second coat for stucco and brick:
Heavy paste white-lead.... 100 lb.
Pure linseed oil (⅓ boiled,
  ⅔ raw) .... 4 gal.
Pure turpentine .... 1 "
This makes 7⅞ gallons of paint and should cover 4,725 sq. ft.

Third coat, gloss finish for stucco, brick, concrete, stone:
Heavy paste white-lead.... 100 lb.
Pure linseed oil (⅓ boiled,
  ⅔ raw) .... 3½ gal.
Pure turpentine .... 1 pt.
This makes 6½ gallons and should cover 3,900 sq. ft.

If pure boiled linseed oil is not available, use pure raw linseed oil and add pure drier not to exceed 1½ pints in any of the above formulas.

Painting Concrete Floors

The foregoing priming coat for concrete and stone may be used in priming concrete floors, but the second and third coats must be made to produce a harder finish than is necessary in the case of concrete and stone walls, as floors are subjected to much more severe usage than walls. The following formulas will produce the hard finish needed:

Second coat for concrete floors:

Heavy paste white-lead....	100 lb.
Pure raw linseed oil.......	1 gal.
Pure turpentine	2 "
Pure drier	1 pt.

This makes 6 gallons of paint and should cover 3,600 sq. ft.

Third coat for concrete floors:

Heavy paste white-lead....	100 lb.
Pure raw linseed oil.......	½ gal.
Pure turpentine	¾ "
Floor varnish	1 "
Pure drier	½ pt.

This makes 5⅛ gallons of paint and should cover 3,075 sq. ft.

When the third coat is dry the floor should be finished by applying a coat of wax or a high-grade floor varnish. The third coat should be tinted with a little lampblack to match the natural color of concrete.

Outside Paint for Metals

Good paints for metal surfaces may be prepared by mixing red-lead or sublimed blue-lead ground in oil with linseed oil and drier according to directions on the kegs in which the pigments are sold. Paint from dry red-lead should be mixed in the following proportions just before it is used:

Red-lead, dry	50 lb.
Raw linseed oil...........	1¾ gal.
Oil drier	1 pt.

This will make 2½ gallons of red-lead paint.

The finishing coats for oil tanks and other structures which need protection from the sun's heat should be white or light colored. Aluminum paint may be prepared by mixing aluminum bronzing powder, preferably polished, with good outside spar varnish in the proportion of 2 pounds to the gallon. Add the varnish to the dry pigment, a little at a time, stirring well after each addition.— U. S. Dept. Agr. Farmers Bulletin 1452.

Paint made of pure red-lead successfully combats causes of corrosion. It is insoluble in water, unaffected by ordinary atmospheric gases, adheres closely to metal, and is a true rust preventive. Pure red-lead has excelled every other material in all kinds of tests, ancient and recent, both in the laboratory and in the field. Nearly all the railroads of the country use it for the protection of bridges and building skeletons. It is used on every vessel in the United States Navy, on gas holders and oil tanks, farming implements and machinery, tin roofs, pipes, water tanks and troughs; in fact, pure red-lead paint is used wherever metal needs protection against corrosion.

Dark green for exterior and interior metal:

Heavy paste red-lead......	100 lb.
Pure linseed oil	10½ gal.
Paste medium chrome yellow	15 lb.
Paste Chinese blue........	52 "

This makes 18 gallons of paint, which should cover about 10,800 sq. ft., one coat.

Light brown for exterior and interior metal:

#1—Heavy paste red-lead..	100 lb.
Pure linseed oil.......	2⅝ gal.
Paste lampblack	12 oz.

Or:

#2—Pure dry red-lead..... 100 lb.
      Pure linseed oil....... 4¾ gal.
      Paste lampblack ..... 13 oz.

The first formula makes 4¾ gallons of paint and the latter 5¼ gallons of paint, which should cover respectively about 2,850 and 3,150 sq. ft., one coat.

Black for exterior and interior metal:

Heavy paste red-lead ..... 100 lb.
Pure linseed oil........... 15 gal.
Pure turpentine .... 1 "
Paste lampblack .... 52 lb.
Paste Chinese blue........ 16 "

This formula makes 25 gallons of paint and should cover 15,000 sq. ft., one coat.—Manufacturers of Dutch Boy White-Lead.

Aluminum in Outside Paint

As is well known, aluminum paint consists of aluminum powder with a mixing varnish. The aluminum powder is manufactured by a stamping process, and each particle is a minute disk or plate. In the paint film these disks float to the surface overlapping, and thus form a metallic film which protects the vehicle from the various disintegrating effects to which subjected.

Use is made in the Navy also of a so-called red-lead paint for priming coat of steel, which is a compound paint containing as pigment, a mixture of red-lead, zinc oxide, iron oxide, and magnesium silicate. Aluminum stearate is used in the vehicle to assist in holding the pigment in suspension to prevent settling. This paint has the advantage of being considerably lighter in weight and cheaper than straight red-lead paint, and can be made up and issued ready-mixed; also having comparatively smaller amounts of red-lead, the danger of lead poisoning is correspondingly reduced.— Bureau of Standards Specifications for red-lead paint composition.

Paint for Porch Floors

Porch floors require protection against moisture from the damp space beneath the porch. This space is frequently left without sufficient ventilation. If the soil is damp the porch floor will absorb a great deal of moisture, which is almost certain to cause blistering and peeling. To prevent trouble of this sort give the underside of the floor, also the tongued and grooved edges of the boards, whether soft or hard wood, a coat of paint mixed as follows:

#1—Red-lead .... 66 lb.
     White-lead .... 34 "
     Pure raw linseed oil... 5 gal.
     Pure turpentine ...... 1 "
     Pure drier .... ¼ pt.

This makes 8¾ gal. of paint and should cover about 5,250 sq. ft., one coat.

#2—Heavy paste white-lead 100 lb.
     Pure raw linseed oil... 4 gal.
     Pure turpentine ...... 2 "
     Pure drier .... 1 pt.

This makes 9 gal. of paint and should cover 5,175 sq. ft.

Whitewash for Outdoors

When a good, durable, exterior whitewash for improving the appearance of farm buildings, fences, or trees is desired, any of the following formulas will produce as fine an appearance as could be desired.

#1—Dissolve 15 lb. of common salt in 7½ gal. of water. To this solution add 50 lb. (1 sack) of hydrated lime or the putty made by carefully slaking 38 lb. (½ bushel) of fresh quicklime. Mix thoroughly until a thick paste is formed and strain through a fine screen before using. Thin to desired consistency with fresh water.

♯2—The substitution of 5 lb. of dry calcium chloride for the salt in the foregoing formula produces a mixture that does not chalk and is quite desirable.

The following formula produces a whitewash that has a yellow tinge when first applied. However, this color disappears within a few days and a very white and durable coating results.

♯3—Dissolve 12 lb. of salt and 6 oz. of powdered alum in about 4 gal. of hot water. Add 1 qt. of molasses. Make a thick cream by thoroughly mixing 50 lb. (1 sack) of hydrated lime with about 7 gal. of hot water. Add the clear solution to the lime, stirring vigorously. Thin to desired consistency.

In the foregoing formula, 38 lb. (½ bushel) of fresh quicklime may be substituted for the hydrated lime. The quicklime must be carefully slaked and screened before use.

Formula ♯4, which follows, has also been found to be very satisfactory. It is white, does not rub or chalk, and is quite weather-resistant. Taking everything into consideration, this formula may be considered as the best and most practical for any use.

♯4—Soak 5 lb. of casein in about 2 gal. of water (preferably hot) until thoroughly softened (about 2 hours). Dissolve 3 lb. of trisodium phosphate in about 1 gal. of water and add this solution to the casein. Allow this mixture to dissolve. Prepare a thick cream by mixing 50 lb. (1 sack) of hydrated lime in about 7 gal. of water, stirring vigorously. Dissolve 3 pt. of formaldehyde in about 3 gal. of water. *When the lime paste and the casein solution are both thoroughly cool, slowly add the casein solution to the lime, stirring constantly.* Just before using, slowly add the formaldehyde to the batch, stirring constantly and vigorously. Care must be taken not to add the formaldehyde too rapidly, as this may cause the casein to jell, thus spoiling the batch. The cold lime paste produced by carefully slaking and screening 38 lb. (½ bushel) of quicklime may be substituted for the hydrated lime if desired. This formula is useful as a size for walls prior to painting or papering.

Caution. Do not make up more of this formula than can be used in one day.

♯5—Soak 10 lb. of casein in about 4 gal. of water (preferably hot) until thoroughly softened (about 2 hours). Dissolve 6 lb. of trisodium phosphate in about 2 gal. of water and add this solution to the casein. Allow this mixture to dissolve. Make a thick, smooth cream of 25 lb. of whiting and 50 lb. (1 sack) of hydrated lime, with about 7 gal. of water, stirring vigorously. When the two mixtures are cold, slowly add the casein-phosphate solution to the lime paste, stirring constantly. To this mixture, just before use, slowly add 5 pt. of formaldehyde dissolved in about 3 gal. of cold water, stirring constantly and vigorously. The cold lime paste resulting from the careful slaking and screening of 38 lb. (½ bushel) of quicklime may be used instead of the hydrated lime if desired.

Caution. Do not make up more of this formula than can be used in one day.

Note. In either formula ♯4 or ♯5 borax may be substituted for the trisodium phosphate if the latter is not available. The borax mixes are not quite as durable and weather-resistant as those containing the trisodium phosphate, but will give satisfaction in most cases.

#6—Slake a half-bushel of lime in boiling water, keeping it covered while slaking. Strain, add a peck of salt dissolved in warm water; three pounds of ground rice boiled to a thin paste, one-half pound of powdered Spanish whiting, and one pound of glue dissolved in warm water. Stir all and let the mixture stand for several days before using. Apply hot if possible.

Colors for Whitewash

There are three factors to be considered in connection with colors used to tint whitewash and cold water paints—first, that they shall not react chemically with the lime; second, they shall be insoluble in water; and third, the mixing shall be as nearly perfect as possible.

The following pigments may be purchased as dry powders and added to any of the whitewash formulas given above. The amount of pigment necessary will depend upon the shade of color desired. It is always advisable to prepare a small sample and allow it to dry before mixing any considerable quantity so as to be sure that the desired shade will be obtained.

Greens—Chromium oxide, opaque or chromium oxide, hydrated. These are known as chromium or chrome oxide greens and should not be confused with mixtures of chrome yellow and Prussian blue, known as chrome greens, which are not lime-proof.

Yellows—Those made by using precipitated hydrated iron oxides are most satisfactory. Ochre, raw sienna, lemon cadmium, orange cadmium and golden cadmium are less suitable as they may change in shade, lack strength or be affected by light. Chrome yellow is not lime-proof.

Reds—Indian red made from pure ferric oxide is highly recommended. Madder lake and toluidine vermilion

are alkali fast but have little strength and are fugitive to light.

Blues—Ultramarine and cobalt blue are the only good ones.

Blacks—Magnetic black oxide of iron is safe. Ivory black and carbon black are non-reactive with lime but they are lacking in strength.

Whites—Lime itself is satisfactory. Lithopone and ground marble are also used as white pigments.

Browns—Pure precipitated brown oxide of iron, or mixtures of the magnetic black oxide of iron with turkey or Indian red are highly recommended. Sienna and turkey umber are lacking in strength, but may give good results.

Violets—Cobalt violet and mixtures of the reds, whites and blues suggested above are satisfactory.

Fire-Resistant Lime Paint

White whitewash cannot be said to make a structure fireproof, but the following formula has been found to be quite effective as a fire retardant. Its use will prevent splinters and rough surfaces from igniting quickly and, when properly applied, a considerable degree of fire-resistance is secured. Best results will be obtained if this mix is applied with a high-pressure spray pump or paint gun so that all crevices and cracks are thoroughly filled.

Formula: Soak 5 lb. of casein in about 4 gal. of water (preferably hot) until thoroughly softened (about 2 hours). Dissolve 3 lb. of borax in about 2 gal. of water and add this solution to the casein. Allow this mixture to thoroughly dissolve. Prepare a thick cream by thoroughly mixing 50 lb. (1 sack) of hydrated lime with about 7 gal. of water or by carefully slaking 38 lb. (½ bushel) of quicklime and straining the paste through a fine screen. When both the lime and casein mixtures are cold, slowly add the borax-casein solution to the lime, stirring constantly and vigorously. Thin to desired consistency.

Caution. Do not prepare more of this mixture than can be used the same day.

Rust Prevention

The corrosion or rusting of metal can be prevented by applying a good coat of whitewash. A coat of whitewash will save trouble on the farm or in a contractor's yard if applied to all metal surfaces exposed to the weather—such as plowshares, mold boards, scrapers, picks, shovels, structural shapes, reinforcing rods, etc. If the implements or tools are allowed to stand out in the open, formulas #1 or #4, pages 182 and 183, should be used, but if stored under cover and not disturbed, the simple lime and water mix will do.

Whitewash on Asphalt

Whitewash will frequently be found of great assistance in connection with mop coats of asphaltic preparations such as are used for waterproofing walls, reservoirs, slabs, etc. Where the black surface is exposed to direct sunlight, and particularly in hot climates, trouble is sometimes experienced because of the asphalt softening. This causes the coat to sag and wrinkle, or even to melt and run. This difficulty may be entirely stopped, or at least greatly reduced, by applying a good coat of whitewash to the black surface. The formula to be used will depend upon the durability desired. If the exposure is short, the plain lime and water mix will be good, while for longer exposure formulas #1 and #4 are recommended. All whitewash formulas are given by courtesy of National Lime Association.

Removing Old Paint

Four formulas for paint removers are:

#1—Equal parts of acetone and carbon bisulphide, with 2 oz. of paraffin added for each quart of mixture. The paraffin prevents too rapid evaporation after the remover has been applied. The mixture should not, therefore, be brushed more than is necessary, as brushing disturbs the film of paraffin.

#2—Three parts of amyl alcohol and one of grain alcohol.

#3—Four parts of grain alcohol, six of gasoline and one of amyl acetate.

#4—Five parts of alcohol, five of benzol and one-half part of amyl acetate.

On old paints that have become very hard two or more applications of the remover may be necessary.

Putting Drier in Paint

By boiling raw linseed oil (10 parts) with manganic peroxid (1 part) that has been thoroughly dried and placed in a bag in the oil, a good drier is obtained. It can be taken as a rule never to add too much drier to a paint. A teaspoonful or so is sufficient to a pint.

Painting Blackboards

#1—The blackboard, if needing paint badly, should first be given a coat of black oil paint. This is followed by a flat coat, or the can of paint used in the first coating can be allowed to settle, the cover carefully removed, the oil poured off, and turpentine substituted. The flat paint so produced is used as the second coat.

#2—A solution of logwood chips in warm water can be applied to the blackboard, and allowed to dry. A solution of copperas (iron sulphate), made by dissolving about a quarter of a pound of the chemical in a quart of water, is then applied, thus forming iron tannate in the fibers of the board. Several coats of the logwood decoction and the iron sulphate solution may have to be applied if the board is very absorptive.

Luminous Paints

The most satisfactory luminous paints are those composed of luminous zinc sulphide and radio-active substances. The radio-responsive zinc sulphide is in the form of crystals, and not the usual type of zinc sulphide which is prepared by a dry or wet process. Various radio-active materials, such as radium bromide or meso-thorium, are used. Other luminous paints are made from specially prepared impure sulphides of calcium, strontium, or barium. These paints, however, are luminous only under certain conditions and only for short periods immediately after exposure to sunlight. Luminous paints cannot be made from phosphorus, and any attempt to do so is extremely dangerous.

Practically all luminous paints have for their base a luminous sulphide which is produced either by precipitation or formed during calcination. The production of these usually starts with a white salt of almost any of the metals of the second group of the periodic system; namely, calcium, strontium, barium, and zinc. Next there is the substance known as the exciter. It is usually in the form of a salt of one of the heavy metals, such as manganese, copper, bismuth, uranium, thorium, etc., in the proportion of one part to one thousand parts of the base, or even one hundred thousand parts of the base. One of the most important steps in the manufacture of these paints is the embedding or dispersing of the exciter throughout the base. Merely grinding the small amount mentioned above into the base is not sufficient to secure good dispersion. This is indicated when attempts are made to produce a luminous product in this manner, phosphorescence being produced only in a few spots. Probably one of the best ways in which to disperse an exciter thoroughly is to secure it in the form of a very dilute solution and then evaporate in contact with the base.

Apparently there is no satisfactory explanation of the action which causes the light rays. Some investigators attribute the action to the formation of a double sulphide which by its molecular structure produces the phenomenon. It has also been likened to the action of the older grades of lithopone which upon exposure in damp weather to sunlight turned black, and which, during certain periods of dry weather, would revert to the normal white color.

One of the difficulties with the ordinary types of luminescent substances is that they do not continue to emit light rays for any considerable period of time, and some radio-active salt is necessary to prolong their efficiency. There is a field of investigation open for the production of some substance that will take the place of these radio-active salts.

A large number of formulas are made up with lithopone as a base, since that material contains zinc sulphide which might be satisfactorily activated, and at the same time possesses very distinctly valuable pigmentary properties. In experiments the exciter was dissolved in about 10 cc. of 95 per cent alcohol and thoroughly mixed into a paste with 100 grams of the lithopone base. These mixtures were dried in an oven, and afterward calcined with a flux by the aid of a blast lamp. The resulting hard, sintered masses were then taken from the crucible and powdered in a mortar. The powders were exposed to the sunlight and then examined for light effects in a dark room. There are given below the results of a few of the experiments conducted.

#1—Strontium carbonate. 100 gm.
    Sulphur .... 30 "
    Sodium carbonate ... 2 "
    Sodium chloride .... 0.5 "
    Manganese sulphate.. 0.2 "

Emits a yellow phosphorescence.

#2—Calcium sulphate ... 100 gm.
    Carbon .... 30 "
    Sodium carbonate ... 2 "
    Sodium chloride .... 0.5 "
    Manganese chloride .. 0.2 "

Emits a bright red phosphorescence.

#3—Calcium sulphate ... 100 gm.
    Carbon .... 30 "
    Sodium carbonate .. 2 "
    Sodium chloride .... 0.5 "
    Uranium sulphate ... 0.2 "

Emits a greenish-yellow phosphorescence.

#4—Strontium carbonate... 60 gm.
    5% solution of bismuth
      nitrate in alcohol.... 12 cc.
    5% solution of uranium
      nitrate in alcohol.... 6 "

Mixed, dried and calcined.
Emits a green phosphorescence.

In more recent experiments, the best dispersion and brightest phosphorescence was produced in the following manner. One hundred grams of zinc sulphate was dissolved in a small amount of distilled water, and one-tenth of a gram of manganese sulphate and one-tenth of a gram of uranium sulphate dissolved in 20 cc. of water were then added. This mixture was then evaporated to dryness. Thirty grams of sulphur were then added to the dry mixture with 2 grams of sodium carbonate and 0.5

grams sodium chloride. The mixture was ground and calcined at a high temperature, at which point the sulphur probably converted part of the zinc into sulphide, throughout which was dispersed the exciting reagents. The sodium carbonate and sodium chloride were used as a flux. The result of the calcination was a hard, sintered mass which, when ground up and exposed to the action of sunlight or ultraviolet rays from a mercury quartz tube, gave forth temporary luminescence.—Courtesy, Scientific Section of Paint and Varnish Manufacturers' Association.

Other formulas for luminous paint are:

#1—Pure lime .... 300 parts
    Sulphur (flowers) .... 120 "
    Starch .... 40 "
    Solution bismuth nitrate
      (0.5% in alcohol)... 20 "
    Potassium chloride ... 3 "
    Salt .... 3 "

The dried mixture should be heated to a very high temperature.

#2—Heat with a blast flame, or a Mekker burner:

Strontium carbonate .... 100 gm.
Sulphur (flowers of)..... 80 "
Sodium chloride .... 0.5 "
Potassium chloride ...... 0.5 "
Manganese chloride or sul-
    phate .... 0.3 "

The crucible in which the substances are heated should be covered so as to cause complete conversion of the carbonate into the sulphide of strontium. The sodium and potassium compounds act as fluxes.

Luminous paints should be admixed with a clear dammar varnish. Many of the luminous paints decompose when water is mixed with them, and for this reason, water solutions of gum arabic, gum tragacanth, or other water soluble gums or resins cannot be used with success, so alcoholic solutions of the gums are used.

#3—

Calcium oxide	15 gm.
Strontium hydroxide ..	5 "
Sulphur	8 "
Magnesium oxide	1 "
Sodium carbonate	3 "
Lithium sulphate	1 "
Bismuth nitrate solution	6 cc.

The bismuth solution is made by dissolving 0.3 grams of bismuth nitrate in 100 cc. of water. The above mixture is heated in a red hot crucible for half an hour.

Paint Removers

#1—

Acetic ether	2 oz.
Amyl acetate	2 "
Strong ammonia water.	1 "
Acetone	1 "
Alcohol	1 "

Mix and put into airtight container. Apply to spot and let stand a few moments, then rinse with alcohol and allow to dry.

#2—

Benzene	4 parts
Yellow wax	½ "
Fusel oil	3 "
Alcohol (denatured)...	1 "

The wax can be omitted if desired. It also makes a good softener for paint brushes.

#3—

Water-glass (solution)..	5 parts
40% lye solution.......	1 "
Ammonia water (strong)	1 "

The following paint and varnish removers are inflammable; in applying them care should be taken to see that, when left upon the painted surface, their evaporization does not constitute a fire hazard.

#1—

Benzene (benzol).	2 parts by volume
Anilin	1 " " "
Amyl acetate (pear oil)	1 " " "

#2—

Benzol	2 parts by volume
Anilin	2 " " "

Oil of mirbane (nitrobenzene), enough to produce odor.

#3—

Denatured alcohol.	1 part by volume
Benzene (benzol).	1 " " "

A good formula for the removal of paint or varnish from surfaces consists of benzol (benzene), alcohol and lye. Dissolve as much of the lye in alcohol as will dissolve. When cool add benzene so that the resultant solution is twice as great as the alcohol solution. This mixture should be shaken before use. A handful of flour added to about a pint of the mixture, it is said, keeps the liquid from evaporating, holding it to the paint to be removed, thus causing a more complete removal.

A strong solution of oxalic acid can be used on some paints and varnishes to effect their removal.

Furfural, benzene, monochloride and paraffin wax, when mixed, have also been used to remove paint and varnish.

Another good mixture consists of 5 parts of water-glass with one part of lye and an equal amount of water.

Automobile Paint Remover

Benzol	75 parts
Fusel oil	20 "
Yellow wax	5 "

Dissolve the wax on the benzol and add the fusel oil. Apply to the paint. When softened, use scraper, throwing the scrapings on new paint. These scrapings will soften the new paint, and the two can then be scraped off together.

Cleaning Old Paint Brushes

#1—Suspend the brush in a can containing a solution of 1 part of sodium carbonate in 3 of water, in such a manner that it hangs several inches from the bottom of the container. Let it stand from 12 to 24 hours in a warm place. The dried paint will be softened so that it may be washed out with soap and water. Brushes which have become as hard as stone can be restored by this process.

One of the most useful liquids for cleaning paint brushes is amyl acetate, also called banana oil, or pear oil. This inflammable substance has a pleasant odor and is used in lacquers. In removing paint from brushes, the amyl acetate is used straight, undiluted with other liquids. It should be used so that the entire bristle length of the brush is covered with the liquid, and allowed to soak into the dried oxidized film of hard paint. The brush should hang upright in the vessel used, and the top kept closed if possible. When the paint has become loosened, the liquid can be poured off, allowed to settle, thus removing the pigment, and used again for other brushes. It must be borne in mind, however, that this re-use of the liquid makes it imperative to wash the second brush cleaned in the fluid with fresh amyl acetate.

#2—Ordinary soapy water, especially if used hot, will loosen much paint from recently used paint brushes. Many of the soap powders now on the market are good paint removers, if used hot.

The following will be found serviceable to loosen paint from brushes:

Trisodium phosphate ...... 1 lb.
Hot water .... ½ gal.

Soak the brushes in this liquid, working the bristles from time to time if possible. When the paint has been removed, wash the brush in running water until absolutely clean.

The following has also been used:

#3—Sal soda crystals....... 1 lb.
Water .... 3 pt.

Benzol (benzene) and turpentine are good removers of paint from brushes. A method generally used by many painters is to wash the brushes immediately after using in turpentine, gasoline, kerosene; or suspend the brushes upright, hanging by their handles, and not resting upon their bristle ends, in a can of linseed oil. This will keep the brushes soft and the pigment will be loosened by dilution and fall to the bottom of the can. The oil acquires a hard film on its surface, which is no detriment to the brush that is being soaked.

Slow-Drying Putty

Raw linseed oil, which dries much more slowly than boiled oil, may be mixed with precipitated chalk and kneaded to a dough to form a putty that remains soft for quite a time.

Tool-Marking Paint

In laying off work for subsequent cutting with shears, or for drilling, bending, etc., a liquid chalk will be found to be of value, especially where the work has a surface with many contours. To make this liquid chalk, fill a pint can about half full of powdered chalk or whiting and cover with its own volume of water, adding about a tablespoon of glue to the mixture and stir well.

Stain for Table Tops

C. R. Hoover, in *Industrial and Engineering Chemistry,* June, 1923, suggests the following modification of the usual procedure for the production of a stain of superior fire-resisting and preserving qualities:

To warm, clean, dry wood apply, working in well with a stiff brush kept hot, a hot solution of 100 g. of potassium chlorate, 100 g. of zinc sulphate (heptahydrate), and 20 g. of copper sulphate (pentahydrate) in 1000 cc. of water. When the first coat is dry apply a coat of a warm solution of 110 cc. of anilin and 175 cc. of concentrated hydrochloric acid with water to make 1000 cc. Allow the wood to dry 15 to 24 hrs. and repeat the application of the two solutions as described above. While the wood is still wet with the second coat of anilin hydrochloride solution, warm the wood very carefully with a gas flame, but do not heat any portion of the surface which appears dry. Allow the wood to dry and the stain to develop for 48 hours, then wash thoroughly with boiling water and dry for 15 to 24 hrs. Apply a coat of melted paraffin and impregnate by carefully heating the surface of the wood with a gas flame. After the wood has cooled, warm gently with a flame and wipe off excess paraffin. An electric or gas iron is an excellent substitute for a gas flame in the impregnation of wood. With ordinary usage, the paraffin treatment should be repeated about twice each year.

To Paint on Galvanized Surfaces

Oil paints do not adhere readily to galvanized surfaces unless the surfaces have been weathered long enough to give them a coating of zinc oxide or sulphide. This weathering can be done artificially by painting the galvanized surface with a weak solution of copper sulphate or vinegar. In the case of copper sulphate, metallic copper is plated on the zinc coating. The vinegar should be washed off with water, using a garden hose with a fine spray. When absolutely dry the surface can be painted with any oil paint.

Hot Water Paint

Mix 20 lb. slaked lime and 1 lb. powdered glue, and sufficient water

and soluble anilin color to give desired tint. Dissolve in hot water with constant stirring.

PAPER

Fireproofing Paper

Practically the same chemicals are used in rendering paper fireproof as are used for wood. Pass the paper through a solution of:

Ammonium sulphate	70 parts
Borax	50 "
Zinc chloride	2 "
Glue soaked in water	2 "
Water, about	800 "

The borax is dissolved in part of the water and the ammonium sulphate and zinc chloride added. The glue is dissolved in the rest of the water and the two solutions mixed.

Another formula:

Ammonium sulphate	8 parts
Boracic acid	3 "
Borax	2 "
Water	100 "

Non-combustible paper may be made by mixing with the pulp a fluid obtained by adding to an aqueous solution containing $1\frac{3}{4}$ oz. of pure tallow soap, just enough alum completely to decompose the soap. The paper made with this requires no size.

Waterproof Wrapping Paper

A waterproof wrapping paper may be made by dipping paper into the following solution and then hanging it over a string to dry: Dissolve 12 oz. of alum and 2 oz. soap in 2 qt. of water. Boil, add $7\frac{1}{2}$ oz. of beeswax, and stir thoroughly.

To Write on Paper with Water

This type of paper may be of especial interest to some readers as suitable for some practical purpose, but as a party stunt, or trick, it will have a wide appeal. The prepared paper is written upon with water, ginger ale, etc., and actually writes in ink. A clean new pen point must be used.

Tannic acid .... 3 parts
Iron sulphate .... 1 "

The iron sulphate should be heated in an evaporating dish until the green crystals turn to a white powder. This calcined green vitriol is mixed with the tannic acid and thoroughly rubbed into the unglazed paper by the use of a smooth board. The excess of the chemicals is shaken off and the paper kept in a dry place until wanted. Heated copper sulphate and tannic acid will produce a brown color when water is used on the paper treated as described.

Current-Detecting Paper

Paper which indicates polarity of electric current may be made as follows:

Salt .... 10 gm.
Phenolphthalein .... 1 "
Water .... 150 cc.

Dissolve together. Soak white paper in resulting solution and dry. For use, moisten a strip of the paper, place the wires upon it, ½ inch apart. A red spot at one of the wires indicates this wire is negative.

Light-Sensitive Paper

To get a paper that is sensitive to light immerse white paper in the following solution:

Potassium iodide .... 8 gm.
Dissolved in water which is then diluted to make 100 cc.

The paper is then removed, dried without removing wrinkles or curls, and, in the dark room, immersed in a solution of:

Lead nitrate .... 8 gm.
Dissolved in water and then diluted to make 100 cc.

The paper is then removed, dried so that it will be flat. It is now coated with lead iodide, which is sensitive to the light, and should be handled only in the dark room. To use it, any desired design or object is laid upon the paper which is exposed to the light with the object in place. The paper is then developed by immersing it in a solution of ammonium chloride (sal ammoniac), 10 gm. dissolved in about 100 cc. of water.

Frosted Designs on Paper

A paper that has a frosted design can be made by using a saturated solution of Epsom salts (magnesium sulphate) in water. The solution is saturated when no more of the salt will dissolve in the water.

The liquid is brushed on a good grade of paper, bristol board or cards, placed in a horizontal position to dry. If thin papers are used, it is well to tack them to a drawing board so that they will not roll.

When the paper is dry, a frosted and crystallized deposit will be found on the surface. If it is wished to color these crystals, add a trace of dye or colored ink to the salt solution before applying it.

Paper Weather Forecaster

Specially prepared paper may be used in forecasting the weather. Dissolve ½ gram of cobalt chloride (not the nitrate) in 50 cc. of water and add 5 grams of gelatin. Heat slowly to dissolve and use the mixture to coat a sheet of blotting-paper. Normally the color of this paper will be pink, but it changes to blue in very dry weather and to a violet tone in moist weather.

Blueprint Paper

Small blank bristol cards, obtained at almost any stationery store, make good blueprint paper. Paper which is sized or glazed does not work as well.

The paper is coated with the following solution by means of a wide, soft brush, as evenly as possible; this should be done overnight, and the paper will be dry in the morning. It is printed under a bright, fairly dense negative to give the best results, in sunlight; and when the details in all parts of the print are distinctly visible as dark blue on the original dark green, the print is taken from the frame and placed in cold water; at once the picture becomes more distinct, and is bright blue—hence the name blueprint paper. Give the print several changes of water until the whites are quite pure and free from yellowness; a drop of hydrochloric acid added to the last washing water assists the purity of the whites. The print after washing is quite finished, and may be dried. The paper should be kept in a tin before use, for the sake of dryness.

Prepare the solution as follows: Five gm. of ferric ammonium citrate (green scales) are dissolved in 30 cc. of water. In another glass dissolve 5 gm. of potassium ferricyanide in 30 cc. of water. These two solutions are now mixed together and poured into a tray, but before doing this darken the room and have only a very dim light or use a red light.

Brown-Print Paper

Dissolve 4 gm. of uranium nitrate in 40 cc. of water. This is brushed over the paper—good quality notepaper will answer well—and when coated, each sheet is pinned up to dry in the dark. If printed under a vigorous negative, in sunlight, we get in a few minutes an orange-colored image which, though faint, can be *developed* by soaking the print in a solution of:

Potassium ferricyanide .... 1 gm.
Water .... 30 cc.

This gives a brown picture. It should be removed, washed in running water for a few minutes, and pinned up to dry.

PERFUMES

Use of Denatured Alcohol

The making of perfumes at home probably will not pay the compounder, but there is a certain satisfaction in making a perfume that is really a good one, even if the cost is a bit more than that for which a similar substance could be purchased.

In the following formulas, alcohol is an ingredient. The alcohol for perfume making should be denatured according to the Federal Prohibition Bureau in its formula #40, which calls for 3 ounces of brucine sulphate and ½ gallon of either U.S.P. acetone or isopropyl alcohol to be added to every 100 gallons of grain alcohol. Of course when denatured alcohol is purchased, denatured according to formula #40, these items will be present. They are harmless for perfumes and toilet preparations. Denatured alcohols by formulas 39B and 39C can also be used. That commonly sold contains 96% alcohol.

To Make Oil of Mirbane

Oil of mirbane (nitrobenzene) is used in many formulas given in this book, and although stocked by many chemical stores, the following procedure is offered for those wishing to make the oil. It is used as a scenting material.

Make a mixture of 150 cc. ordinary concentrated sulphuric acid, and

75 cc. ordinary concentrated nitric acid. Let it cool to the ordinary temperature. Put the vessel containing it in water, and add about 15 cc. to 20 cc. benzene, a few drops at a time, waiting each time until the reaction is complete. Shake well until the benzene is dissolved; then pour slowly into about a liter of cold water. A yellow oil will sink to the bottom. This is nitrobenzene or oil of mirbane. Pour off the acid and water; wash two or three times with water; separate the water by means of a pipette, and dry by adding a little granulated calcium chloride (chloride of lime). After standing for some time, pour off from the calcium chloride, and distill from a proper sized distilling flask, if an exceptionally pure product is desired.

Simple Colognes

#1—Orange flower extract . 50 parts
Oil of citron .... 15 "
Oil of orange .... 15 "
Oil of neroli .... 9 "
Oil of bergamot ...... 5 "
Oil of rosemary ...... 3 "
Alcohol (#40 den.).... 900 "

#2—Oil of bergamot ...... 10 parts
Oil of neroli .... 15 "
Oil of citron .... 5 "
Oil of cedrat .... 5 "
Oil of rosemary ...... 1 "
Tincture of ambergris .... 5 "
Tincture of benzoin .. 5 "
Alcohol ....1,000 "

#3—Oil of bergamot ..... 8 gm.
Oil of lemon .... 4 "
Oil of neroli .... 1 "
Oil of rosemary ..... 1 "
Oil of origanum ..... 6 drops
Orange flower water. 50 gm.
Alcohol (#40 den.) . 600 "

#4—Oil of lavender ...... 1 dr.
Oil of bergamot ...... 1 "
Oil of lemon .... 2 "
Oil of rosemary ...... 2 "
Oil of cinnamon ..... 8 drops
Oil of cloves .... 8 "
Alcohol (96%) ...... 1 pt.

#5—Oil of bergamot ..... 1 gm.
Oil of lemon .... 2½ "
Oil of rosemary ...... 1 "
Oil of neroli .... 1⅕ "
Orange flower water .. 75 "
Alcohol (96%) ...... 300 "

#6—Dissolve ½ ounce of each of the oils of lemon, lavender and bergamot, ½ dram each of the oils of cinnamon and cloves in 1 quart of the best deodorized alcohol; add 2 quarts of filtered water and bottle. This is a dilute cologne.

#7—Oil of bergamot ...... 3 oz.
Oil of lemon .... 1 "
Fine oil of lavender ... ¼ "
Oil of cloves .... ¼ "
Oil of sandalwood .... ½ "
Alcohol .... 2 gal.
Water .... 3 pt.

#8—Take essences of bergamot and citron, of each 5 drams, essence of lemon, 4 drams, essence of rosemary, 2½ drams, essence of orange flower, 3 drops, alcohol, 1 quart; mix together.

#9—Oil of lavender ...... 2 oz.
Oil of bergamot ..... 1 "
Oil of orange .... ½ "
Oil of neroli .... ½ dr.
Oil of cassia .... 1 "
Oil of caraway .... 15 min.
Oil of spearmint ..... 15 "
Tincture of benzoin... ½ oz.
Alcohol .... 1 pt.

Mix, then add 6 pints water.

#10—Elder Flowers.

Terpineol	25.5	gm.
Vanillin	0.75	"
Oil of jasmine	20	drops
Geraniol	10	"
Palmarosa oil	10	"
Oil of bergamot	20	"

Dilute to desired strength with alcohol.

#11—Honeysuckle.

Oil of neroli	12	minims
Oil of rose	10	"
Oil of bitter almond	8	"
Tincture of storax	4	oz.
Tincture of vanilla	6	"
Essence of cassie	16	"
Essence of rose	16	"
Essence of tuberose	16	"
Essence of violet	16	"

#12—Mignonette.

Geraniol	2	gm.
Oil of neroli	2	"
Oil of jasmine	2	"
Balsam tolu	2	"
Oil of orange	15	drops

Dilute with alcohol.

#13—Ylang-ylang.

Ylang-ylang oil	10	minims
Oil of neroli	5	"
Oil of rose	5	"
Oil of bergamot	3	"
Alcohol	10	oz.

#14—Heliotrope.

Heliotrope	2.3	gm.
Vanillin	0.4	"
Coumarine	0.25	"
Tincture of musk	2.5	"
Ylang-ylang oil	20	drops
Geraniol	10	"
Benzaldehyde	2	"

Dilute with alcohol to desired strength.

#15—Verbena.

Oil lemon	16	parts
Oil lemon grass	½	"
Oil orange peel	4	"

#16—Bouquet de Fleurs.

Tincture benzoin	5½	oz.
Oil of bergamot	2	"
Oil of lemon	1	"
Oil of orange	1	"
Rose extract	3	pt.
Tuberose extract	3	"
Violet extract	3	"

#17—Heliotrope Water.

Heliotropin	2	dr.
Oil of rose	15	min.
Oil of bergamot	½	dr.
Oil of neroli	5	min.
Alcohol	10	oz.
Water	6	"

#18—Lilac Water.

Terpineol	2	dr.
Heliotropin	8	gr.
Oil of bergamot	1	dr.
Oil of neroli	8	min.
Alcohol	12	oz.
Water	4	"

#19—Inexpensive Perfume.

Oil of bergamot	7	cc.
Oil of lemon	3½	"
Oil of lavender	3½	"
Alcohol	1000	"

PHOTOGRAPHY

Stock Developers

Pyro-soda developer for tank and tray:

SOLUTION A

Sodium bisulphite	140	gr.
Pyrogallic acid	2	oz.
Potassium bromide	16	gr.
Water to make	32	oz.

SOLUTION B

Water	32	oz.
Sodium sulphite	3½	"

SOLUTION C

Water	32	oz.
Sodium carbonate (desiccated)	2½	"

If trays are used for developing use:
1 oz. each of A, B, and C and add
7 oz. of water. Develop from seven
to nine minutes at 65° F.

For tank development, use:

Solution A .... 9 oz.
Solution B .... 9 "
Solution C .... 9 "
Water to make .... 1 gal.

Develop about 12 minutes at 65° F.

Metol-Hydroquinone Developer

Metol .... 12 gr.
Hydroquinone .... 50 "
Sodium sulphite (cryst.) .. 2 oz.
Sodium carbonate (cryst.). 1½ "
Potassium bromide .... 20 gr.
Water .... 20 oz.

Dissolve chemicals in the order
given. Use at 65° F.

Pyro-Metol Developer

A

Water .... 30 oz.
Metol (or substitutes) .... 1 "
Bisulphite soda .... 75 gr.
Pyrogallic acid .... ½ oz.

B

Water .... 30 oz.
Sodium sulphite .... 4 "

C

Water .... 30 oz.
Carbonate of soda (dry) . 4 "

For use, take:

A .... ½ oz.
B .... ½ "
C .... ½ "
Water ....10-15 "

B and C may be mixed together
and keep well in one solution, which
should be diluted for use with from
6 to 10 parts water.

Edinol Developer

Water .... 20 oz.
Sodium sulphite .... 2½ "
Edinol .... 96 gr.
Sodium carbonate .... 1 oz.

To develop, take 1 oz. of this stock
solution to 1 oz. of water. More
water in warm weather.

Amidol Developer

Amidol .... 2 gr.
Sodium sulphite .... 30 "
Potassium bromide ...... 1 "
Water .... 1 oz.

Chrome Alum Fixing Bath

Dissolve chemicals in order named.

#1—SOLUTION A

Hypo .... 2 lb.
Sodium sulphite .... 2 oz.
Water to make .... 96 "

SOLUTION B

Water .... 32 oz.
Potassium chrome alum .. 2 "
Sulphuric acid C.P. ...... ¼ "

Prepare A and B solutions separately.

When dissolved, pour B into A
slowly, while stirring A rapidly. Use
water at a temperature not higher
than 150° F. (65° C.), for dissolving the chrome alum.

The fixing bath should be renewed
frequently. When using an old or
exhausted bath there is a tendency
for scum to form on the surface of
the plate. Any such scum should be
removed by swabbing the plate with
cotton before drying. Plates should
be left in the fixing bath at least
double the time it takes them to clear.
Wash in running water and dry.

#2—Water (about) ...... 100 oz.
     Sulphuric acid .... 3 dr.
     Sodium sulphite ...... 4 oz.
When dissolved, add:
     Sodium hyposulphite .. 2 lb.
Dissolve, and then add:

Chrome-alum, from 1 to 2 oz., previously dissolved in 20 oz. of water. Then add water to make 160 oz.

The quantity of chrome-alum may be increased in warm weather. Leave film and plates in twice as long as it takes them to clear. They will require 25 minutes' washing.

Ordinary Fixing Bath

Hypo .... 5 oz.
Water .... 20 "

to which, after the hypo is dissolved, should be added ½ oz. of potassium metabisulphite.

Hypo-Acid Fixing Bath

Hypo .... 16 oz.
Water .... 64 "

Dissolve, then add the following hardening solution:

Water .... 5 oz.
Sodium sulphite .... ½ "
Commercial acetic acid (25 per cent) .... 3 "
Powdered alum .... ½ "

Intensification

Intensification of films or negatives is employed if the film or plate has been underexposed or underdeveloped. In either case, the film or plate is bleached in a solution, and then blackened with another solution, the two solutions comprising the intensification process. Some formulas for this operation are:

Mercuric chloride (corrosive sublimate) .... 1 oz.
Water (hot) .... 16 "
Cool and add hydrochloric acid .... 300 min.
Wash well for twenty minutes in running water.

Blacken in following solution:
#1—Potassium oxalate neutral .... 5 oz.
Water (hot) .... 20 "
Cool this solution and use clear supernatant liquid only.

#2—Iron sulphate .... 5 oz.
Sulphuric acid .... 30 min.
Water .... 20 oz.

For use make bath by pouring one part #2 into three parts #1. Wash well. Repeat entire operation if more intensification is desired.

Another intensifying solution consists of:

SOLUTION #1

Bichloride of mercury .... 200 gr.
Bromide of potassium .... 100 "
Water .... 10 oz.

SOLUTION #2

Sulphite of sodium .... ¼ oz.
Water .... 4 "

Place the negative in Solution #1 until bleached, then wash well and place in Solution #2 until entirely cleared; after which the plate must be well washed. This operation may be repeated if there is not sufficient intensity gained by first treatment.

Uranium intensifying solution:

Water .... 100 cc.
Uranium nitrate .... 1 gm.
Potassium ferricyanide .... 1 "
Glacial acetic acid .... 7 cc.

After intensifying wash in three changes of water. This intensifier may be completely removed by prolonged washing in ordinary tap water or by a bath of ammonium carbonate.

Potassium bichromate ..... 100 gr.
Hydrochloric acid .... 50 min.
Water .... 10 oz.

Bleach in the above solution. Wash thoroughly. Redevelop in metol hydroquinone or amidol developer.

Reducing Solutions

#1—SOLUTION A

Water .... 32 oz.
Potassium permanganate .. 1¾ "

SOLUTION B

Water .... 32 oz.
Sulphuric acid, C.P. ...... 1 "

For use, take solution A, 1 part, solution B, 2 parts, water 64 parts. When the negative has been sufficiently reduced, immerse in a plain hypo solution, or in a fresh acid fixing bath for a few minutes, to remove yellow stain, after which wash thoroughly. If reduction is too rapid, add more water.

#2—SOLUTION A

Potassium ferricyanide .... 1 oz.
Water .... 16 "

SOLUTION B

Sodium hyposulphite ...... 1 oz.
Water .... 16 "

Keep solution A in brown glass bottles, as it is affected by the light. Take a sufficient quantity of B to cover the plate in a tray, and add to it a small quantity of A; immerse the plate and observe. If the solution contains enough of A the reduction will proceed rapidly.

#3—STOCK SOLUTION

Water .... 32 oz.
Ammonium persulphate .. 2 "
Sulphuric acid, C.P. ...... ¾ dr.

For use, take one part of stock solution and two parts of water. When reduction is complete, immerse in an acid fixing bath for a few minutes, then wash.

Rapid Drying of Negatives

#1—After fixing and washing, harden film for five minutes in:

Water .... 100 cc.
Formalin (40%) .... 5 "
Dry by heating.

#2—Soak the well-washed negative for three minutes in two successive baths of alcohol and fan until dry.

#3—Immerse the well-washed negative (after removal of surface water with moist chamois leather) in:

Water .... 100 cc.
Potassium carbonate ...... 90 gr.

Keep it there for five minutes. Remove and wipe with clean dry cotton wool pad.

Mounting Paste

Paste for mounting photos in albums or to stiff backed boards is made as follows:
Powder 1 oz. of white gum arabic and mix with 4½ oz. of dextrine, add 1 pint of boiling water, a little at a time, and then boil the mixture in an enameled pan for about 15 minutes. Allow to cool; add ammonia, 10 drops.

Restoring Faded Photographs

If mounted, remove the picture from its mounting by sponging with water and immerse in:

Hydrochloric acid .... 2 parts
Sodium chloride .... 8 "
Potassium bichromate .... 8 "
Distilled water .... 250 "

The above mixture bleaches the photograph, after which the picture should be developed again using a diluted developer.

Short Stop

A good short stop formula for films and plates is:

28% acetic acid .... 3 oz.
Potassium chrome alum .. 3 "
Water .... 48 "

This is placed in a tray between the developing tray and fixing tray and stops further action of the developer.

Removing Pyro Stains

Rub the fingers with bleaching powder and water, then without rinsing, rub crystals of oxalic acid, tartaric acid, or citric acid over the stains.

Flashlight Compositions

#1—Potassium perchlorate . 3½ parts
    Potassium chlorate .... 2 "
    Barium nitrate .... 5 "
    Powdered magnesium metal .... 4 "

#2—Potassium perchlorate . 3½ parts
    Barium nitrate .... 16 "
    Sulphur, powdered ... 3½ "
    Aluminum powder .... 5 "

#3—Magnesium .... 1 part
    Potassium chlorate ... 2 parts

#4—Aluminum .... 4 parts
    Potassium chlorate ... 10 "
    Sugar .... 1 "

#5—Barium peroxide (fresh) 1 part
    Potassium permanganate .... 2 parts
    Magnesium metal .... 2 "

Pictures on Copper

Pictures may be made upon sheet copper or brass by first cleaning the sheet with strong nitric acid, then washing with water and polishing with rouge or a metal polish. The sheet is then immersed in soapy water to remove the grease and sensitized in a darkened room by immersing it in copper (cupric) chloride solution, made by dissolving 10 gm. of the chemical in water and diluting the solution to 100 cc. with water (10%

solution). It is immersed for 10 seconds. A thin white film of cuprous chloride is formed upon the surface, and using a gentle stream of water, this is washed to remove the adhering copper chloride. It can be bathed in alcohol after washing with water, then dried. Contact prints can be made from ordinary negatives by using an arc lamp as the source of light, the exposure under this condition being about one minute. The light converts the cuprous chloride film into cuprous oxide. The image is fixed by washing the sheet in a solution of sodium hyposulphite (photographer's hypo), or a solution of common salt. Potassium bromide can also be used to fix the image. After fixing, the picture should be washed with water and dried. For a permanent effect it is advisable to varnish the picture with a clear spar varnish, or a colorless lacquer.

Photographing on Silk

The following has been suggested for making photographs upon silk. The silk is immersed in a solution of:

Salt (not iodized) .... 4 gm.
Arrowroot starch .... 4 "
Acetic acid (30%) .... 15 "
Water (distilled) .... 100 cc.

To this is added, after mixing, a solution of 4 gm. of tannic acid in 100 cc. of water. The silk should remain in the mixture formed by the above two solutions for three minutes, removed and dried, stretching to eliminate wrinkles. After drying it is immersed in a sensitizing mixture which is made of:

Silver nitrate .... 9 gm.
Nitric acid .... 0.1 "
Distilled water .... 75 cc.

The silk, already sized, is soaked in the above solution for one minute, and then removed and dried, without washing, in a dark room. The silk is now used as contact or printing paper, the negative being placed upon the silk, using sheets of glass to make good contact. The whole is then exposed to the light, allowing the light to shine through the negative as in the usual printing process. The silk is then developed, washed and fixed and then washed, after which it is dried.

Sensitizing Paper

#1—The paper should be floated or brushed with a soft brush, using an 8% potassium iodide solution (dissolve 8 gm. of the iodide in water and then add enough water to make 100 cc.). The paper is removed without washing, and dried. It is then floated on a solution of lead nitrate, this operation being performed in a darkened room. The paper is then dried, taking care that it will lie flat during this process. By this process, the paper is coated with lead iodide which is responsive to light. Print with the paper, in the usual manner of employing printing paper, judging the time of exposure by the change in color of the sheet. This is easily ascertained by experiment. The paper is then developed in a solution of ten grams of ammonium chloride dissolved in water, the solution then being diluted to about 100 cc. with water.

#2—Uranium nitrate ...... 16 gm.
Copper sulphate ...... 4 "
Dextrine .... 4 "
Distilled water ...... 100 cc.

The above solution is made up and protected from the light in amber glass bottles. Cards and paper, sensitized with the solution by floating face down and then dried, are ready for exposure. For bringing out the picture, the exposed surface is washed with or floated on a solution of:

Potassium ferricyanide .... 4 gm.
Distilled water .... 100 cc.

The paper should then be washed and dried. Black-gray tones result. Greenish tones can be secured by using a 2% solution of cobalt-nitrate.

To Make Printing Paper

Two types are readily made, albumen and arrowroot paper.

#1—Albumen paper.
Paper is coated with a clear (strained) mixture of 8 parts white of egg and 2 parts of a 10% solution of ammonium chloride.

#2—Arrowroot paper.
Three and a half parts arrowroot flour are thoroughly mixed with 100 parts of a 3% solution of common salt, and the strained liquid is coated on paper.
The paper, treated by either of these processes, is then floated on, or coated with, 1 part of silver nitrate dissolved in 10 parts of water. The paper thus prepared, this operation being performed in the dark, contains silver albuminate, silver chloride, or silver nitrate, according to the process used in the first bath. After drying the paper when removed from the silver nitrate solution, it is used in a manner similar to that of ordinary photographic printing paper.

Blueprint Papers

Any well-sized paper may be at once sensitized, or a paper may be sized by floating on the following bath for half a minute, draining and drying:

Arrowroot flour .... 2 gm.
Glucose .... ½ "
Water .... 100 cc.

Mix the arrowroot flour and glucose to a creamy paste, stir in the water, boil in jacketed pan (enamel) or in water-bath, cool and strain.

Sensitizing Bath

(a) Potassium ferricyanide. 3 gm.
Water .... 30 cc.
(b) Ferric ammonium cit-
rate (green) .... 7.5 gm.
Water .... 30 cc.

Mix in equal proportions as required and filter; apply with a sponge or brush to the paper in weak light.

After printing, develop in a dilute solution of citric acid (0.2%), and wash in water.

Blue Lines on White

The following is Pellet's process for producing blue lines on white ground:
Solution 1. 20% gum arabic solution.
Solution 2. 33% iron ammonium citrate solution.
Solution 3. 33% ferric chloride solution.

Coat a well-sized paper with a mixture of Solution 1, 20 cc., Solution 2, 8 cc., Solution 3, 5 cc. (allow to stand till cloudiness which forms has disappeared).

In printing, the image appears as yellow on a darker ground. Develop with a 20% aqueous solution of potassium ferrocyanide by brushing on with a brush, avoiding excess of developer. When image is fully developed, wash and soak in dilute hydrochloric acid (1:10). Finally wash well.

Another process is as follows:

Salt .... 3 oz.
Iron chloride .... 8 "
Tartaric acid .... 3 "
Gum acacia .... 25 "
Water .... 100 "

Dissolve the gum in half the water and dissolve the other ingredients in the other half; then mix. Proceed as in other formulas, using potassium ferricyanide solution to develop.

Fixing and Toning Bath

Two liters water, 500 gm. hypo, 55 gm. ammonium thiocyanate, 15 gm. alum, 15 gm. citric acid, 20 gm. lead acetate, 20 gm. lead nitrate, 150 cc. ½% gold chloride. Allow to stand two days and filter before use.

Removing Film from Negatives

The following mixture will be found quickly to remove the emulsion from old negatives so that the glass may be used for other purposes.

Sodium fluoride .... 4 gm.
Sulphuric acid .... 4 cc.
Water .... 600 "

If the emulsion is allowed to settle in the above bath, after being stripped from the plate, the clear supernatant solution can be poured off and used again.

A dilute solution of ammonium hydroxide or household ammonia will also be found to remove the emulsion from old negatives.

Line Drawings from Photographs

To make a line drawing from a photograph, ink over the important outlines with India ink. This of course is entirely practical if the photograph is one of a building, machine, or other object, but for figures or faces, considerable skill will be required in tracing the outlines. When the ink has dried immerse the photograph in a solution of one part of tincture of iodine in about five parts of water. Allow to remain for about five minutes, stirring the solution. Remove, wash in water, and then in a solution of photographers' hypo, which bleaches the entire print, leaving only the inked outlines. The print is then washed thoroughly in water and dried flat.

SOLDER AND ITS USE

Tinning Iron and Steel

When iron or steel is to be soldered to brass, copper, or other rather easily soldered metal, difficulty is experienced in causing the solder to tin or flow on or attach itself to the iron or steel. This is especially true if the iron is not galvanized. A good method of tinning the iron or steel is by immersing it in molten solder. The procedure to be taken is to scratch brush the iron to remove scale, and then if necessary, clean with emery cloth. The material is then brushed with a solution of zinc chloride, or killed muriatic acid; that is, muriatic acid cut with zinc scrap. The iron or steel object is then heated and immersed in molten solder that can be conveniently heated in a ladle or iron cup hammered out from sheet iron. The solder will flow onto the iron by this treatment, effecting a coating that is without bare spots, if the iron has been cleaned thoroughly.

One or more dippings of the iron can be made, heating so that when it is inserted in the molten solder, it will not chill the solder. The iron, which is now tinned, can be soldered to another piece of iron similarly tinned, or to copper or brass.

Several small lumps of zinc chloride thrown upon the surface of the molten solder during the process will effect a more rapid tinning. The excess of solder can be shaken off the tinned portion if only a thin coating of tin is desired.

Soldering Fluids

#1—Dissolve two tablespoons of zinc chloride in a pint of denatured alcohol, and keep in a tightly stoppered bottle.

#2—In 1 pint of muriatic acid dissolve all the zinc metal that will be eaten away, and then add 1 ounce of sal ammoniac.

#3—Zinc chloride	2 parts
Sal ammoniac	16 "
Sodium fluoride	2½ "
Laundry blue	2 "

The above is a British composition.

| #4—Alcohol .... | 1 part |
| Strong phosphoric acid solution .... | 1 " |

#5—Lactic acid	1 part
Glycerin	1 "
Water	8 "

#6—Zinc chloride	10 parts
Glycerin	5 "
Alcohol	5 "
Water	25 "

The zinc chloride can be purchased under the name of white vitriol.

Soldering Paste

Soldering pastes sometimes consist of mixtures of tallow and rosin fortified with sal ammoniac or zinc chloride. The following will produce a good paste:

Tallow	4 parts
Olive oil	5 "
Rosin	2.5 "

Gently heat the above and while it is then cooling, stir in about 1¼ parts of sal ammoniac, beating the liquid with the paste to make a thorough incorporation.

Soldering paste for iron is composed of 5 parts olive oil and 5 parts powdered sal ammoniac. Soldering paste for aluminum is made by melting together equal parts of rosin and tallow, half the quantity of zinc chloride being added to the mixture.

Self-Solders

A soldering substance which is used directly on the cleaned surfaces of the metals to be united, and then heated with a match or other small flame to effect the soldering, consists of soldering paste with solder filings thoroughly incorporated within it. Such a preparation, which will unite many metals, among them being tinned iron, consists of equal parts of sal ammoniac and vaseline and solder shavings.

A mixture which also serves the same purpose consists of about 40 parts of solder shavings or filings, 8 parts of vaseline or petroleum jelly, and 1 part of phenylenediamine.

Zinc Chloride from Killed Acid

The home mechanic frequently can use zinc chloride crystals instead of a solution, in soldering operations. Such a need is in the making of soldering pastes in which sal ammoniac or zinc chloride is rubbed up with vaseline, or petroleum paraffin. To prepare zinc chloride crystals or powder, killed acid must first be made. This is the usual soldering fluid made by dissolving zinc in muriatic (hydrochloric) acid, until the acid will dissolve no more. The acid is then said to be killed. Evaporation of this killed acid, which is merely a solution of zinc chloride, yields zinc chloride crystals, or powder, according to the heat applied in evaporating and length of time in which the crystals form. The crystals recovered should be kept well stoppered. It is best to filter the zinc chloride solution through asbestos before filtering, or allow the particles of carbon, lead, etc., to settle out before crystallizing.

Alcoholic Soldering Flux

A better flux for the home workshop than the ordinary killed spirits may be made by dissolving stick zinc chloride in alcohol. The stick zinc chloride is sold in sealed glass tubes containing 1 oz., for about twenty-

five cents. One ounce is dissolved in 6 or 8 oz. of denatured alcohol, according to the strength desired. The latter proportion is quite satisfactory. This makes a cheap flux which has two great advantages over the regular acid solution. It can be applied with greater ease to the exact spot on the metal which is to be soldered and it will cover the area with a thin level coating, which dries almost instantly and leaves the intervening spaces bare. It also not only performs the office of flux more efficiently, but it does not chill the soldering iron as much as the other solution. A good test of its value may be made by applying the solution to a piece of hacksaw blade without brightening the surface. The solder will instantly take hold when applied with the soldering iron.

For Tinned Iron

#1—Rosin dissolved in linseed oil makes a good soldering fluid for tinned iron such as roofing metal which is to be painted later. The linseed oil which is left upon the tin, even if wiped superficially, will not prevent the paint which is later applied from adhering.

#2—Tallow .... 3 parts
     Rosin .... 5 "
     Olive oil .... 3 "
     Sal ammoniac .... 1 "

Heat all, but do not burn. Beat while cooling to get the sal ammoniac in suspension.

#3—Rosin .... 1 part
     Alcohol .... 5 parts
Dissolve.

Soldering Without an Iron

#1—A tablet of urotropin will serve as the source of heat in soldering wires together. The twisted wires must be cleaned and fluxed.

#2—A soldering paste used without an iron consists of a mixture of vaseline, sal ammoniac and ordinary solder filings.

#3—This resembles aluminum and is sometimes called aluminum solder. It is easily applied by heating the article or by slightly heating the solder. Sticks to metal, wood or glass. Heat one pound of sulphur in a can and add 1 ounce borax and 1 ounce aluminum flake. Place on a slow fire and melt, stirring with a metal rod or spoon until the mass resembles molten metal. Pour off into suitable molds.

Zinc Soldering Flux

Zinc dissolved in muriatic acid yields the commonest of fluxes. It should be allowed to settle after the zinc has disappeared into the acid, and the flecks of carbon and lead which settle to the bottom removed by pouring off the clear supernatant solution above.

Müller soldering liquid, so-called, is prepared by mixing 1 part of a solution of phosphoric acid with 1 to 1½ parts of alcohol (denatured).

Low Melting Soft Solder

Soft pewter and other low melting metals are easily soldered with a soft solder consisting of 5 parts (by weight) of bismuth, 3 of tin, and 2 of lead. It melts at approximately 212° F. Care must be taken in soldering easily fusible metals together to be sure that the solder melts at a lower temperature than the metals to be united.

Hard Solder for Metals

An ordinary hard solder, which is fairly easy running and makes a strong joint, consists of 70 parts of copper, 22 parts of zinc, and 8 of tin. A solder for iron, steel, and the bronzes consists of 53 parts of copper, 43 parts of zinc, 1 part of tin and a trace of lead.

Solders for Aluminum

The following directions are from Circular #78 of the Bureau of Standards:

Aluminum solders, consisting usually of mixtures in various proportions of zinc, tin, and aluminum, are usually applied in the following manner: The surfaces to be soldered are carefully cleaned with a file or with emery, and are then tinned or coated with a layer of the solder by heating the surface and rubbing the solder into it. The joint between the tinned surfaces may then be made in the usual manner with a soldering iron and the solders. A flux is not generally used. Evidently the efficiency of the joint depends upon the adhesion between the aluminum and the initial layer of solder.

A flux is sometimes recommended for use with commercial solders, consisting of stearic acid, rosin, zinc chloride, soap, sugar, paraffin, or mixtures of these. Tests made at this bureau have showed that their use is not advantageous.

All metals or combinations of metals used for aluminum soldering are electrolytically electropositive to aluminum. A soldered joint is therefore rapidly attacked when exposed to moisture and disintegrated. There is no solder for aluminum of which this is not true.

Joints should therefore never be made by soldering unless they are to be protected against corrosion by a paint or varnish, or unless they are quite heavy, such as repairs in castings, where corrosion and disintegration of the joint near the exposed surface would be of little consequence.

Solders are best applied without a

flux or by using paraffin as a flux, after preliminary cleaning and tinning of the surfaces to be soldered. The composition of the solder may be varied within wide limits. It should consist of a tin base with addition of zinc or of both zinc and aluminum, the chief function of which is to produce a semifluid mixture that would be within the range of soldering temperatures.

The higher the temperature at which the "tinning" is done, the better the adhesion of the tinned layer. By using the higher values of the recommended zinc and aluminum percentages, the solder will be too stiff at lower temperature to solder readily and the workman will be obliged to use a higher temperature, thus securing a better joint. A perfect union between solder and aluminum is difficult to obtain.

The joint between previously tinned surfaces may be made by ordinary methods and with ordinary soft solder. Only the tinning mixture need be special for aluminum.

Aluminum Solders

#1—Flower of sulphur ..... 5 lb.
       Aluminum flake (bronze) 4 oz.
       Borax .... 1 dr.

The whole is heated over the fire, the sulphur melting and allowing the aluminum dust to be distributed through it. The mass should be stirred with an iron rod. It is cast into sticks and used with as low a temperature in doing your soldering as possible.

#2—Take 5 parts of tin and 1 part of aluminum. Solder with the iron for light metals, or jeweler's blowpipe or gas-air torch if the objects are massive.

An aluminum solder can be made of 2 parts of silver, 9 parts of aluminum phosphide, 39 parts of tin,

and 50 parts of zinc. This solder requires no flux.

Hard Soldering

Hard soldering is the uniting of silver, gold, steel, or hard metals with a solder that cannot be melted with the heat from a soldering iron. A small flame, usually obtained from a chemist's or jeweler's blowpipe, is used in soldering jewelry or other small parts.

The parts to be soldered must be well cleaned. In jewelry soldering, the work is usually clean when received, and nothing more is done than to apply the flux, which is usually borax and solder.

A typical example in hard soldering is in making a gold or silver ring smaller in size. The ring is first cut at the back with a pair of side cutting pliers, and then a portion is cut out to reduce it to the new size. The edges are then carefully filed, using jeweler's files, or in want of these, magneto files. The parts must fit nicely at their separated edges, or else considerable building up with solder will be necessary.

The flux, which may be fused borax, borax as purchased, or a solution of borax in water, is applied to the cut or joint. Apply the heat by the blowpipe, using a blue flame. The borax will melt down to a glassy film. The solder is now placed on the cut a small piece at a time and the flame again applied. The solder will melt into a ball and run onto and fuse with the work. The solder will travel to the hottest part of the work, and this rule can be followed, together with intelligent placing, to ensure the solder uniting with the metal exactly where it is desired. After soldering, the flux is removed by boiling the ring in weak sulphuric acid, if a signet ring or ring without a stone has been soldered.

The ring is now slicked up, using a fine-grained Carborundum stone or a piece of well-worn emery cloth. Some pieces of emery cloth are kept for such a length of time that they seem to be entirely devoid of abrasive material, although they are excellent for putting a final polish on the soldered joint.

Soft Soldering

Use a good iron. Clean the iron by rubbing its faces upon a brick, the concrete floor, or a stiff wire brush, and then heat until the iron readily melts small globules of solder but does not color the flame a vivid green when the iron is again introduced into the heat.

For heating, a blue flame should be used. If a Bunsen burner is employed, allow the flame to play on the middle portion of the copper head. A flame spreader attachment on the Bunsen burner will distribute the heat along the copper head, thus materially reducing the length of time needed for heating the iron.

A small box, or preferably lump, of sal ammoniac should be at hand, upon which rests small globules of solder that are picked up by the tinned iron.

A soldering iron can be conveniently cleaned preparatory to tinning by thrusting it for an instant into a solution of sal ammoniac. The rapid cooling of the copper will cause a contraction of the scale of copper oxide which will drop off the iron, and the sal ammoniac, undergoing partial decomposition by hydrolysis, will form hydrochloric acid gas which effectively lays bare the metal. Upon withdrawing and touching the point of the iron to drops of solder, the solder will form in a smooth surface over the entire end portion of the iron. The iron is thus tinned.

The work to be soldered must be cleaned of grease. Gasoline, alcohol,

benzol, or toluene is good for this purpose. After wiping with one of these liquids remove the surplus liquid with a dry cloth. Scrape the parts at the spot at which the union is to take place, laying bare the bright metal. Apply the soldering fluid or flux and touch the cleaned surface with the tinned iron, applying the stick of solder to the joints at the same time, if a large area is to be soldered.

The solder will soon run and flow into the crevices, thus uniting the metal. Add more metal if the joint is to be built up, but allow it to sweat or thoroughly flow over the metal by holding the iron upon the work. If the solder becomes sticky or pasty, the iron is not hot enough and should be reheated.

After soldering, the fluid or flux should be washed off to prevent corrosion by the active ingredients of the flux.

Soft Solders

Soft gold solders, suitable for the blow torch or blowpipe:

#1—This is composed of 4 parts gold, 1 of silver, and 1 of copper. It can be made softer by adding brass, but the solder will be likely to oxidize.

#2—18 k gold:

Gold	15 pwt.
Silver	2 "
Copper	2 "

#3—18 k for rings:

Gold coin	19.5 parts
Copper	3 "
Silver	1.5 "

#4—16 k:

Gold	1 oz.
Silver	7 pwt.
Copper	5 "

#5—20 k:

Fine gold	....	1 oz.
Fine silver	....	2 pwt.
Fine copper	......2 pwt.	4 gr.

#6—

Bismuth	....	5 parts
Tin	....	2 "
Lead	....	3 "

Melts at about 374° F.

Black Solder

Brass	....	20 parts
Zinc	....	1 "
Tin	....	6 "

Metal Foil

To solder small articles moisten the surfaces of the metals to be soldered with a solution of sal ammoniac, and fit the joint with tinfoil cut to the exact size. Then heat the metals sufficiently to melt the tinfoil. When cold the surfaces will be found firmly soldered together.

Silver Solders

#1—

Silver	....	9 parts
Copper	....	1 "

#2—Common:

Silver	....	6 parts
Copper	....	4 "

#3—

Silver	....	1 oz.
Brass	....	10 pwt.
Tin	....	2 "

#4—For gold:

Silver	....	1 oz.
Copper	....	5 pwt.
Brass	....	5 "

Brass Solders

	Copper	Zinc	Tin
Very strong	58	42	...
Strong	53	47	...
Medium	50	50	...
Easily fusible	34	66	...
White solder	57	28	15

The first solders in the list melt at higher temperatures than others.

German Silver Solders

#1—

Copper	....	38 parts
Zinc	....	50 "
Nickel	....	12 "

Melt in order given, gas-air blast being necessary. Roll, and melt again. Also called steel solder.

#2—

German silver	....	5 parts
Zinc	....	4 "

Solder for Nickel

#1—

Brass (white)	....	3 parts
Silver	....	1 "

#2—

Brass	....	15 parts
Zinc	....	4 "
Silver	....	5 "

Melt the silver, then add the brass and when molten add the zinc, using borax as a flux.

#3—Use silver solder as a solder for nickel.

Hard Soldering Fluxes

Powdered borax can be used without any preparation, but the following forms are more satisfactory in most instances:

#1—Dissolved in *hot* water to make a saturated solution.

#2—Mixed with water to make a thick paste.

#3—Fused borax mixed with alcohol. This must be kept in a closed container to prevent evaporation.

If there is a tendency for the flux to run off the joint during the soldering, add from $\frac{1}{10}$ to $\frac{1}{2}$ boracic acid to the borax. This makes the flux thicker and gummy but raises the melting point somewhat.

For stainless steels and other metals forming oxides difficult to remove, use a paste, 1 part borax, 1 part boracic acid with zinc chloride solution (muriatic acid killed with zinc).

Borax flows at about 1400° F. This is a good guide in estimating the temperature of the parts to be soldered.

Solders for Iron, Steel, Copper

#1—Silver and brass, equal parts.

#2—Silver	2 parts
Copper	3 "
Zinc	1 "

#3—Silver	6 parts
Brass	6 "
Zinc	5 "

Flux for hard soldering above:

#1—Cryolite (powdered)..	2 parts
Phosphoric acid	1 "

#2—Borax	1 part
Sodium bi-fluoride	1 "

#3—Borax used alone is a satisfactory flux.

Ordinary Half and Half

#1—Tin	1 part
Lead	1 "

Melts at about 372° F.

#2—Lead	2 parts
Tin	1 "

Melts at about 442° F.

#3—Lead	1 part
Tin	2 "

Melts at about 340° F.

Bismuth solder consists of 2 parts or more of tin solder and 1 part of bismuth. It is more fusible than tin solder, and for this reason is used on pewter, repairing toy soldiers, etc.

Iron, steel, cast iron, wrought iron, carbon steels, can all be soldered with any grade of silver solders. They can be joined to copper, brass, nickel-silver and other non-ferrous metals. Borax or a mixture of boric acid (boracic acid) and borax in equal parts are satisfactory fluxes for hard soldering iron and its alloys.

To Hide Soldering

When brass objects are soft soldered with the usual lead-tin solder, the solder is readily seen at the union. If the work has not been sweated, this will not show as much as one in which the seam has been copiously flowed with solder, but the contrast between the solder and the copper or brass is often very striking. To color the solder and make it resemble the copper or brass, dissolve some copper sulphate (bluestone) crystals in water and paint the solder with the solution. Some artisans use an iron wire, but this plates out the copper on the wire more so than the brass or copper itself. The wire is rubbed along the solder, using it to apply the copper sulphate. A mixture of copper sulphate, zinc chloride, and water rubbed on with a battery zinc will also give the solder the characteristic brassy or coppery color.

TESTS FOR MATERIALS

Does It Contain Wood Alcohol?

If the alcoholic liquid is colored or contains sugary bodies or flavoring material, it should be distilled and the distillate used in the tests for wood alcohol.

Dilute the distillate or the straight alcohol until it is about 5% of alcohol by volume. Take 5 cc. of this and add 2 cc. of a solution containing 3 grams of potassium permanganate and 15 cc. of 85% phosphoric acid per 100 cc. Allow to stand 10 minutes. Add 2 cc. of a solution containing 5 grams of oxalic acid dissolved in 100 cc. of 1:1 sulphuric acid (pure concentrated sulphuric acid 1 part, water, 1 part by volume). When the solution is clear (20 minutes may be needed), add 5 cc. of modified Schiff's reagent. The characteristic blue color develops in

10 minutes if there was wood alcohol in the original sample.

Modified Schiff's Reagent: Dissolve 0.2 (one fifth) of a gram of pure rosaniline hydrochloride in 120 cc. of hot water. Cool and add 2 grams of anhydrous sodium sulphite (not sulphate!) dissolved in 20 cc. of water, followed by 2 cc. of strong hydrochloric acid. Dilute this to 200 cc. with water and store in a glass-stoppered amber glass bottle.

Another test, which also calls for the use of a distillate, follows:

Dilute the alcohol to be tested to 20% and place 5 cc. of the dilution in a test tube. Then add 2 cc. 3% potassium permanganate solution and 3 cc. sulphuric acid and allow the mixture to stand for 5 minutes. Now add by drops sulphurous acid until the precipitated manganese hydroxide has redissolved. Five cc. of the clear mixture are next heated to 25° C., some fuchsine-sulphurous acid (0.5 gm. fuchsine, 11.2 gm. sodium sulphite, 20 cc. hydrochloric acid and water to make 500 cc.) is added, followed by sulphuric acid while the mixture is kept cold. Pure grain alcohol is said to show no pink or violet coloration. (Modified U. S. P. test.)

In the following test a distillate of the alcoholic liquid is used:

To two drops of the alcohol under examination 20 drops of decinormal potassium permanganate solution are added, followed by 5 cc. of concentrated sulphuric acid added drop by drop. The almost colorless liquid is mixed with one drop of 5% oxalic acid solution and to the still hot mixture a few milligrams of potassium sulphoguaiacolate are added. The mixture is shaken well and is then cooled. In the absence of wood alcohol the liquid remains colorless, or at most assumes a yellow color, while in the presence of wood alcohol a reddish-blue color is produced, the intensity varying with the amount of wood alcohol present.

An approximate decinormal potassium permanganate solution is made by dissolving 3 gm. of potassium permanganate in water and diluting the solution to 1000 cc. with water.

Testing Alcohol for Acetone

The alcohol must be colorless. If this is not the case, it must be distilled, using the distillate in making the test.

Dilute the sample until it contains about 10% of alcohol by volume. Place 5 cc. in a test tube and add half a gram of pure ammonium sulphate. Shake until the salt has been dissolved and add 3 drops of a 10% solution of sodium nitro prusside. Shake, and stratify or add without shaking, ammonium hydroxide. A violet ring forms at the junction between the two liquids if one drop of acetone is present in 100 cc. of alcohol.

The following test as given by B. T. Effinger in *The Chemist-Analyst* can be used to detect acetone:

Place in a small flask or beaker 20 cc. of the alcohol, 4 cc. of water, 4 cc. of benzaldehyde and 5 cc. of a 10% solution of NaOH. Boil the mixture gently for five minutes. In the absence of acetic aldehyde the solution becomes light yellow in color if acetone is present. To confirm this test cool the solution in running water. If a precipitate is formed filter off the crystals and recrystallize them from a small amount of hot alcohol. Determine the melting point. Dibenzalacetone crystallizes in yellow scales and melts at 111°-112° C.

Acetic aldehyde seems to be the only substance commonly found in alcohol that interferes with this test. This is easily detected beforehand by the coloring of sodium hydroxide solutions yellow.

This benzaldehyde reaction is sensitive enough to detect and confirm the presence of acetone with little difficulty in cases where the concentration is less than 1%.

Tests for the Purity of Alcohol

The following tests have been set forth by the U. S. Pharmacopeia as standards for grain alcohol, and it should be assumed, therefore, that any ethyl alcohol (grain alcohol) which is to be used for beverage purposes should also meet these requirements.

It should not affect the color of blue or red litmus paper previously moistened with water.

If 50 cc. of alcohol be evaporated in a clean vessel, no color or weighable residue should remain.

If 10 cc. of alcohol be mixed with 5 cc. of water and 1 cc. of glycerin, and the mixture allowed to evaporate spontaneously from a piece of clean, odorless blotting paper, no foreign odor should become perceptible when the last traces of the alcohol leave the paper (absence of fusel oil constituents).

If 25 cc. be allowed to evaporate spontaneously in a porcelain evaporating dish, carefully protected from dust, until the surface of the dish is barely moist, no red or brown color should be produced upon the addition of a few drops of colorless, concentrated sulphuric acid (absence of amyl alcohol, or non-volatile carbonizable, organic impurities, etc.).

If 10 cc. of alcohol be mixed in a test tube with 5 cc. of potassium hydroxide test solution, the liquid should not at once assume a yellow color (absence of aldehyde or oak tannin).

If 20 cc. of alcohol be shaken in a clean glass-stoppered vial with 1 cc. of silver nitrate test solution, the mixture should not become more than faintly opalescent, nor acquire more than a faint brownish tint when exposed for six hours to diffused day-light (limit of organic impurities, amyl alcohol, aldehyde, etc.).

Artificial or Blended Whiskey

Whiskeys are often made and sold by diluting alcohol with water and adding flavoring substance and coloring matter. Various bead oils, which contain organic compounds, such as soap extract, are also added.

John F. Williams, writing in *Industrial and Engineering Chemistry,* has developed a unique test by which the amount of alcohol in a whiskey can be determined. At the same time, the test shows whether the whiskey is artificial or has been "cut."

The test is simple and consists of making a solution that will abstract the alcohol and coloring matter from the liquor. The solution used is composed of:

Amyl alcohol (fusel oil)...	70 cc.
Toluene, chemically pure...	28 "
Tartaric acid solution (50%)	2 "

The tartaric acid solution is made by dissolving 50 gm. of pure tartaric acid in water and diluting the resulting solution to 100 cc. The quantities used should be accurately measured and thoroughly mixed. Only pure chemicals should be used.

To make the test, a glass cylinder of about 25 cc. capacity and graduated in tenths of cubic centimeters should be used, and exactly ten cubic centimeters of the whiskey, wine, or other liquor to be tested is placed in the tube. Exactly ten cubic centimeters of the testing solution is also placed in the graduated tube and the whole shaken. The mixture is allowed to settle, again shaken, and allowed to settle. The chemical mixture abstracts the alcohol from the liquor, and leaves the water which the liquor contains at the bottom of the graduated cylinder. The depth of this lower water layer is read off on the graduations of the tube, and compared with the following table:

Lower Layer, in cc.	Alcohol, Per Cent by Volume.
10.2	0
9.9	5
9.6	10
9.3	15
8.9	20
8.5	25
8.05	30
7.4	35
6.8	40
6.7	41
6.6	42
6.5	43
6.15	45
5.9	46
5.7	47
5.25	49
5.1	50
4.4	53
3.9	55
3.3	57
2.3	60
1.5	62
0.6	64

Thus, if the lower layer reads 5.1 cc., then the portion of liquor taken for the test contains 50% alcohol by volume. The test cannot be used to estimate the alcoholic content of liquids containing less than 10% nor more than 64% alcohol.

This test is also useful in determining if coloring material has been added, which will of course give a strong indication that the whiskey has been blended or is artificial. It has been observed that if the top upper layer of liquid becomes colored then the whiskey has been aged in wood, for the coloring material of the charred barrel passes into this top layer. If the coloring material has been added, such as caramel, then the lower layer, which is used to determine the percentage of alcohol, becomes colored.

If the whiskey has been cut, or contains real aged-in-the-wood whiskey to which water and coloring matter have been added, then both top and bottom layers will be colored, the depth of coloring indicating the relative amounts of the two substances used.

The temperature of the ten cubic centimeter sample and the ten cubic centimeter portion of the testing reagent should be 20° C. for accurate results. The presence of sugar and glycerin in the amounts usually added to blended liquors do not interfere with the test.

Testing Gasoline

Perhaps the simplest test that can be used to determine an important characteristic of gasoline is that for the detection of sulphur. On a corrosive basis, a gasoline having less sulphur than another is superior to the gasoline having a greater quantity. The corrosion (copper-strip) test of motor gasoline is usually made by submerging in it a strip of polished copper for three hours and holding the temperature at 122° F. There are other variations of this, such as making the time one-half hour and temperature 200° F. or time three hours and temperature 200° F. The three hours at 200° F. is the most rigid of the three.

In interpreting the results of a corrosion test, more than extremely slight discolorations of the polished copper strip is called "positive," sulphur being present in a harmful degree, the depth of stain increasing with the corrosiveness.

Another simple method for detecting the presence of sulphur in gasoline is as follows:

A 100-cc. sample of the gasoline is placed in a clean 4-ounce bottle and 1 cc. of metallic mercury added. The bottle is shaken uniformly for two minutes, and the gasoline decanted off and filtered at once through an 8-inch qualitative filter paper. The filter paper is then dried by an electric fan or by natural evaporation.

The intensity of the black precipitate on the paper is a measure of the corrosiveness of the gasoline. A clean paper or one that is only slightly discolored indicates that the gasoline will pass the copper strip test.

Testing Artificial Vinegar

Sodium tungstate .... 3 gm.
Sodium phosphate .... 2 "
Molybdic acid .... 0.05 "

Dissolve in 25 cc. of warm water, cool, and make exactly neutral to litmus paper, with dilute nitric acid. Add hydrochloric acid to 10 cc. vinegar sample, and 1 cc. of above reagent. If real, the vinegar will become violet colored. Artificial vinegars will not give this violet color because of the absence of tannins.

Test for Copper in Alloys

The metal or alloy should be dissolved in dilute acid and portions of the filtered liquid tested by the following method. Solutions of copper produce a deep blue color on adding excess amounts of ammonium hydroxide (household ammonia).

One part of copper in a million may be detected by the deep blue precipitate formed with dilute solutions of ammonium or potassium thiocyanate and 1% alcoholic solution of benzidine, or 1 part in 10 millions if a 0.5% alcoholic solution of guaiac resin is substituted for the benzidine solution, and 1 part in 200 millions by the blue color developed by adding a 0.5% alcoholic solution of guaiac resin to a water solution of the copper chemical.

Qualitative Test for Rosin

Shellac may be adulterated with rosin, which is less expensive than shellac. The following method will readily indicate the presence of this substance in shellac.

The Hicks Test is as follows: Treat a fragment of the sample placed in a cavity of an ordinary porcelain dish with about 1 to 2 cc. of a solution of 1 part by volume of phenol dissolved in 2 parts of carbon tetrachloride. Stir the mixture. Place in another dish 1 or 2 cc. of a solution of 1 part by volume of bromine and 4 parts by volume of carbon tetrachloride. Cover the whole dish with an inverted clock glass. If rosin is present the bromine fumes very soon develop an indigo blue color which persists for some time. This test is satisfactory when applied to shellac but can not be relied upon in the presence of other resins.

How to Test Hard Water

The great difficulty in the use of home water-softening methods is determining the quantity of softening agent required. This can not be done accurately without knowing the degree of hardness of the water. The addition of too little washing soda or other softening agent for the amount of hardness does not remove it all, whereas the addition of too much renders the water more alkaline and may sometimes be advisable. Accurate determinations of hardness are made at all water laboratories, and from their results calculations of the correction needed can be made. However, the following method will give a general idea of the condition of the water:

Make a solution of a good white soap in denatured or wood alcohol. This should be as strong as it is possible to make it without a jelly forming upon standing. Fill a small glass bottle about half full of water. Fit it with a tight cork or stopper and mark the level of the surface of the water by scratching the glass lightly with a file or by using a label. Add the soap solution drop by drop (counting the drops) until, when the bottle is shaken violently and placed upon its side, the suds form an unbroken layer over the top of the water and remains that way for 1 minute by the clock. Repeat until the exact number of drops necessary to form the suds has been determined, being careful to use the same quantity of water each time. Compare the quantity of soap needed with that required for producing similar suds in fresh rain water. The difference is due to the hardness of the water. Vary the quantity of softening agent used each week per tub of water and repeat the above test. When the softened water requires no more soap than the rain water, record the quantity of softening agent placed in each tub of water and thereafter add that same amount.

Is It Wrought Iron or Steel?

Wrought iron is iron in which slag is incorporated, the slag making it malleable and easily welded. The slag streaks, formed when the iron is drawn out or rolled, line themselves longitudinally with the metal and often, by casual inspection, they can be seen running lengthwise of the iron.

In order to distinguish these slag streaks more clearly, the iron should be etched in either of the two following mixtures of acids, the acids eating away the iron and leaving the slag in streaks, due to its resistance to the acid.

After removing all marks of the cutting-off tool, and making sure that the end of the pipe is smooth, suspend it so it will dip into a solution of 10 per cent hydrochloric acid, 30 per cent sulphuric acid, and 60 per cent water; or 25 per cent nitric acid and 75 per cent water. After the pipe has been immersed about an hour, wash off the acid, and dry quickly with a soft rag. The end will show ridges or rings, indicating the slag content of wrought iron. In case of dispute, make microscopic examination and chemical analysis to assist in determining whether the material is wrought iron or steel.

In the chemical examination, if the phosphorous content is greater than 0.1%, then it is considered wrought iron, especially if the manganese content is less than 0.1%, as the manganese content of most steels is seldom under 0.3%.

Ammonium persulphate, 1 gm., dissolved in about ten cubic centimeters of water can also be used to etch the material.

The etching is best carried out by means of a cotton swab which has been soaked in the solution. The swab is rubbed over the face of the specimen, considerable pressure being used. A fine polish of the specimen is unnecessary; usually it is sufficient to finish the face on fine emery paper. The dark oxide film that often forms on the freshly etched face of the specimen can be easily removed by a fresh application of the etching solution on the cotton swab. An etching period of from one to two minutes is usually sufficient.

One of the advantages of this method of etching is the readiness of control of the process. The surface is constantly under observation and the etching can be stopped at any instant when the structure is distinctly revealed, by holding the specimen in a running stream of water.

Testing Metals for Tin

Dissolve the substance in water, or hydrochloric acid if it is a metal or insoluble in water. Add a piece of zinc which is known to be free from tin. Stir the mixture with a test tube filled with water. Place the test tube used as the stirring rod in the blue flame of a Bunsen burner. If tin is present, a characteristic blue colored flame will be formed, probably due to the formation of tin hydride. As little as 0.004% of tin can be detected in this manner.

Testing Beeswax for Adulteration

The adulteration of beeswax with mineral wax or with paraffin can be detected by placing a small piece of the suspected wax in a test tube and cautiously pouring fuming sulphuric acid into it until half full. On being heated, the beeswax will dissolve, and the mineral wax and paraffin will float on the surface when the acid cools.

Testing Pure Wool Fabrics

The presence of cotton or other adulterants in wool fabric may be determined by simple tests. Pull out an individual yarn or thread and hold it to the flame of a match until it ignites. Wool catches fire with difficulty and burns with the characteristic odor of burning hair. Cotton and linen, upon the other hand, ignite readily and burn with little odor. Since certain mixtures contain one wool yarn alternating with one or more cotton threads, this test should be applied to several fibers in both warp and woof.

The boiling lye test is more troublesome but is the classic method for detecting, and determining the amount of, an adulteration of wool. Count the number of yarns or threads in a small square of the cloth and then immerse it for exactly ten minutes in a gently boiling, five per cent lye solution. If the tester lacks a balance for making up this solution by weight, he can make one of approximately the right strength by dissolving one teaspoonful of strong lye in twenty teaspoonfuls of water. At the end of ten minutes, what is left of the square of cloth is removed from the solution, washed, and the remaining threads are counted. The woolen yarns in the mixture will have been entirely dissolved, while cotton or linen threads will be uninjured. Wool is the only common textile fiber dissolved by this treatment, so the analyst cannot go wrong. The quotient obtained by dividing the number of remaining threads by the original count, multiplied by one hundred, gives the percentage of threads other than wool used in adulterating the mixture.

Testing Quality of Paint

A good ready-mixed paint is one that has been well ground and that can be mixed readily with a smooth brushing consistency with a paddle. It should dry within 18 hours to a full oil gloss, without sagging, streaking, running, or chalking. The weight per gallon of a ready-mixed red, green, or white paint of good body should be at least 12 lb., and of a black paint at least 9 lb.

The tests for fineness, drying, and film characteristics are made in the following way: Using a good grade of brush, paint two or three clean, dry, 4 by 5 in. tin panels. Note whether the sample works well under the brush and has good hiding power. Examine the wet film from an angle. A poorly ground pigment betrays its presence by particles and specks which give a rough appearance to the surface. Leave the panels in a vertical position in a well ventilated room for 18 hours. At the end of this time a good paint should be fully dry and have a smooth, glossy surface, free from defects.

To test for lead apply the paint to two 1 by 2 in. tin panels. The next step is to make hydrogen sulphide, which is the form of sulphur that blackens lead paint. This can be done conveniently by placing about one tablespoon of either dry lithopone, ultramarine blue pigment or ordinary bluing washing compound (or any other dry sulphide) in the bottom of a quart mason fruit jar and adding a tablespoon of water and a similar amount of muriatic acid or oil of vitriol. When the gas starts bubbling off suspend one of the small paint panels by a thread inside the jar, out of reach of the liquid in the bottom. Stopper the jar so that the gas can have plenty of opportunity to attack the paint. The other panel should be placed in a sulphide-free room. At the end of 18 hours, open the jar and compare the panel with the other one. The panel which was in the jar should not be darker than the one not so exposed, if the paint is to be used in a kitchen or bathroom.

Acid Tests for Alloy Steels

Prepare some fine drillings of the steel to be tested. In two of the test tubes place about one-quarter as much water as they will hold; then add about one-third as much sulphuric acid. Drop an ordinary carpet tack (iron or steel) in one tube and an equivalent amount of the drillings in the other. For accurate results, the weights of metal placed in the two tubes should be about the same. Now place the two tubes in a dish of hot water for half an hour, or until both steels are entirely in solution.

The solution of the tack should be almost white in color and free from any black sediment. Hold the two tubes against the light and compare the tints. If the unknown (that is, the steel undergoing test) contained chromium, it will look distinctly green. Even so little as one-third of one percent can be detected in this way. Nickel in steel also produces a green tint, but of a lighter, less distinctive shade. Now discard the solution containing the tack.

If the unknown contained tungsten, molybdenum, or any amount of phosphorus, a black, insoluble residue will remain in the bottom of the tube. The next step is to add ten drops of nitric acid very cautiously, as the solution is apt to boil out of the tube if the acid is added too rapidly. Then let the tube stand for five or ten minutes. A precipitate due to molybdenum or phosphorus will disappear, the latter with the characteristic odor of phosphine gas (also the odor of commercial calcium carbide); but tungsten shows up as a yellowish white sediment, which is easily recognized again when once seen.

In case the solution of the unknown contains tungsten, allow it to settle, and then carefully pour off the clear liquid above it into two other test tubes, dividing the solution equally between them. Into one pour an equal amount of water, and to the other add an equal amount of hydrogen peroxide, so that the liquids in the two tubes are still at the same level. If as little as one-tenth of one percent vanadium was present in the steel, a brick red color will develop in the tube containing the hydrogen peroxide, which can be easily seen by comparison with the color of the other tube. Titanium, occasionally used in alloy steel, develops a yellow tint when the peroxide is added.

A specific test for nickel can be made by combining the two solutions that were used for the vanadium test in a cup or old jelly tumbler; then add ammonia, stirring with a glass rod or a wooden stick until no more red-brown precipitate forms. The ammonia precipitates all the metals likely to be present except nickel. Let the solution stand for about an hour to settle, and pour off a little of the clear liquid into a clean test tube. If it is necessary to free the liquid from precipitate and scum, filter it through a piece of cloth held at the mouth of the tube. Add an equal amount of water to another tube and compare colors. If nickel is present, the steel solution will look distinctly bluer than the other. The only metal which would interfere with this nickel test is copper, but it is not likely to be present in sufficient quantity to cause any uncertainty.

Testing Purity of Distilled Water

Two substances, sodium chloride and iron, are undesirable in distilled water used for battery purposes. To test for sodium chloride pour one-quarter of a glass of the water into a clean jelly glass and add a few drops of silver nitrate. If sodium chloride is present a milky opalescence will appear when the water is stirred. To test for the presence of iron, again pour one-quarter of a glass of the water into a clean jelly glass and add one drop of thioglycollic acid and half a teaspoon of ordinary household ammonia. The slightest trace of iron in the water will cause a tint ranging from pink to lavender to appear.

Testing Gold

The method usually used in ascertaining whether jewelry is gold or brass or other yellow metal alloy is to touch it with a drop of strong nitric acid by means of a glass rod. If brass, or yellow metal alloy, or the gold has worn off revealing the yellow metal alloy, the drop will form copper nitrate which shows its appearance by a stain, coloring of the acid, and evolution of red gas. Gold, whether plated upon the article or if the article be solid, will produce neither of these reactions.

Test for Real Pearls

If natural pearls are placed with cultivated ones in a solution of methyl iodide, all the pearls float; but if monobromide naphthaline is added drop by drop, only natural pearls keep floating, while the cultivated ones fall to the bottom, owing to the difference of density. This method proved efficacious on 50 or more types.

Test for Acids or Alkalies

The juice of the chokeberry can be used as an indicator for bases or acids. A water infusion of the berries will turn green when alkalies are added to it and light red when mixed with an acid. It has been found to be as sensitive as phenolphthalein. Phenolphthalein is used in alcoholic solution. Infusion of the leaves of purple cabbage can also be used.

How to Make Solutions

In making a percentage solution dissolve the chemical in less than the desired amount of water, and afterwards add sufficient water to make up to the proper amount. For instance, if a ten percent solution is desired, dissolve 10 parts of the chemical in water, and then add enough water to this solution to make a total quantity of 100 parts.

In some formulas such an expression occurs as, "Water enough to make one gallon." In these formulas there is usually a substance present which is to be dissolved in a part of the one gallon of water. After dissolving, and continuing the instructions, the resulting mixture is then mixed with a further quantity of water until the whole mixture has a volume of one gallon.

The expression "parts" can be interpreted as meaning grams, ounces, pounds, etc., and not liquid ounces, pints, or liters, as all formulas are given in parts by weight. The majority of the formulas will produce good working products; also some formulas should only be taken as a guide to be used in the particular process, elaboration being sometimes necessary according to the actual working conditions, which are variable.

Testing Quality of Lacquer

The *spray test* is used to determine the quality of spraying lacquer. To perform this test, dilute the lacquer with thinner to the right consistency and then adjust the spray gun to deliver a fine mist. Spray a cleaned 24 by 30 in. tin panel and, as the panel is drying, examine it carefully for rough spots resembling the outside of an orange peel.

If it is necessary to use the lacquer in a cold or damp place, its resistance to blushing or whitening is important. In this case, spray the panel under the same conditions in which the actual work will be done and then, after an hour's drying, examine carefully for white spots. A first-class lacquer should neither roughen nor blush.

The *brushing test,* which is used on types of lacquer that are applied with a brush, forecasts the effect of the lacquer on the old, underlying coat of stain, paint, or varnish on a previously finished piece. An old mahogany stained chair leg and a board covered with old varnish furnish ideal surfaces for the test.

First, scrub the surfaces with gasoline and allow them to dry. Then apply the lacquer to both types of surfaces in rapid strokes with a well-filled brush.

After the work has dried, examine it for the following defects: First, lack of smoothness; second, particularly on the varnished board, blisters caused by the softening and raising of the underlying coat by the solvent in the lacquer; and third, a defect technically called bleeding, which should be looked for on the stained chair leg. Bleeding is a disfiguring stain in the lacquer due to the color of the old mahogany coat, which is dissolved in the solvent of the lacquer.

The test for corrosive and acid properties should be made on any lacquer which is to be used on metal. These damaging properties can be caused by the presence of sulphur compounds in the lacquer solvent or from the decomposition of the nitrocellulose in the lacquer itself.

To make the test, cut and polish a $\frac{1}{2}$ by 6 in. strip of sheet copper and place it in about half a cup of the the lacquer. Stand the cup and strip in a warm and well-ventilated place, as outdoors in the sun, for an hour or two and replenish the lacquer as it evaporates. Corrosive sulphur compounds are betrayed by brown stains on the copper, while acid causes a green discoloration in the liquid around the metal.

It is the nature of nitrocellulose to curl and wind itself into a knot. To control this tendency, the lacquer makers have added materials called plasticizers, which in the better grades of lacquer wholly eliminate the tendency of the lacquer to pull away from its base.

The test for the proper amount of plasticizer in a lacquer is called the *curling test*. Procure from a stationery store a 6 by 8 in. card of the grade known as "velvo." Apply the lacquer to this card and dry it under the same conditions as those under which the actual work will be done. Lack of plasticizer evidences itself by a pronounced curling of the edges of this card after the lacquer has dried.

A good way to ascertain the strength and flexibility of different brands of lacquers is to remove the dried films from their test panels. This can be done in the following way: Tin plates are cleaned and then amalgamated by rubbing a drop of mercury over them with a soft rag. The excess mercury is rubbed off and each panel is sprayed with a different lacquer. Allow these to dry in a nearly vertical position.

At the end of four hours remove the lacquer films by carefully running a knife blade around the edges and then peeling the material off. A good film will be flexible, even in color, smooth surfaced, and strong enough to resist a considerable tearing pull exerted with the fingers. If the same amounts of lacquer, all properly thinned, have been applied to the different panels, the strongest and toughest of the samples will be the one whose film offers the most resistance to the tearing test. This test, however, should be applied as soon as the film is removed from the panel.

Testing Soil for Acid

The few simple tests given here are useful in determining whether a soil is acid or alkaline. Thus you are able to determine if the soil needs lime, and if certain plants such as rhododendrons, laurel, azaleas, etc., will tolerate the soil in which they are to be planted.

The litmus paper test requires the use of both red and blue paper. To make the test, mix the soil sample with enough water to make a stiff mud, roll into a ball, break the ball open and place a strip of the litmus paper between the two halves. Allow to stand five or ten minutes, then note the change in color, if any. Acid soil turns blue litmus red; alkaline soil turns red litus blue. Care should be taken in handling the litmus paper. Do not allow contact with the fingers as the acid of the perspiration will turn it pink or red.

The Truog Test

This test is made by using a definite amount of soil (10 gm.) which is measured in a small vial. This is placed in an Erlenmeyer flask and Truog's mixture (barium chloride and

zinc sulphide) and distilled water are added. The flask is then shaken to mix the materials. It is then heated to boiling over a flame, and after boiling one minute a strip of lead acetate paper is laid over the top of the flask and the boiling continued for two minutes. If the soil is acid the paper strip will be darkened. The more acid the soil, the darker the paper becomes.

The Thiocyanate Test

This test is used considerably by county agents and agricultural extension workers. It is a convenient field test and quite reliable if good materials are used. The equipment consists of a 4 percent solution of potassium thiocyanate in alcohol, one or more small test tubes, or vials, and, if desired, a wooden block with holes to hold the test tubes or vials. About equal volumes of soil and the solution are put in the container and shaken vigorously, after which it is set aside until the soil settles and the liquid on top clears. If the soil is acid the upper liquid layer will be red; the deeper the red, the more acid the soil.

VARNISH AND SHELLAC

Water Varnishes

#1—Shellac .... 6 oz.
    Borax .... 1½ "
    Water .... 1 pt.

Dissolve the borax in the boiling water and then add the shellac which, if possible, should be finely powdered. The color of the finished product will depend on whether yellow or bleached shellac has been used, the latter producing a varnish that is very clear. Being water mixed, dyes, such as Easter egg or clothing dyes, can be used to impart any desired color to the varnish. The varnish can be used on paper or cloth, and dries hard.

#2—Dried egg albumen.... 1 oz.
    Salicylic acid .... a pinch
    Water .... 1 pt.

The salicylic acid is added to act as a preservative. The varnish will have a slight tint of yellow, depending upon the grade of albumen used.

#3—Shellac .... 3¼ oz.
    Gum sandarac .... ¾ "
    Gum mastic .... 40 gr.
    Castor oil .... 1 dr.
    Denatured alcohol .... 30 oz.

The castor oil is added as a plasticizer, to make the varnish somewhat flexible. The varnish is almost clear.

#4—Shellac .... 1½ oz.
    Castor oil .... 20 drops
    Alcohol (den.) .... 20 oz.

#5—Shellac .... 1 oz.
    Alcohol (den.) .... 20 "
    Oil of lavender .... 2 dr.

#6—Glucose .... 1 lb.
    Gum arabic .... 1 "
    Water .... 3 pt.

Soak the gum arabic in the water until soft. At this time the foreign matter, such as sticks and stones which are usually found incorporated with the gum, can be removed by straining through a coffee strainer or folded wire screen. Heat will hasten the solution of the gum. The glucose is added afterward. The product when applied and hardened produces a glossy surface. A variation of this formula would substitute glycerin for the glucose as a plasticizer.

#7—Borax .... 2 oz.
    Shellac .... 6 "
    Water (hot) .... 1 pt.

Dissolve the borax in the hot water and then add the shellac.

Varnish for Paper

#1—Shellac, bleached ..... 1 part
    Household borax ..... 1 "
    Alcohol, den. .... 20 "

The borax and shellac will dissolve slowly in this mixture, which is useful in applying to paper where a water-proof surface is desired. The solution darkens the shade of the paper somewhat, but if this is objectionable, replace the shellac with gum sandarac.

#2—Bleached rosin .... 1 part
    Gum sandarac .... 1 "
    Benzol .... 20 "

#3—Gum sandarac .... 1 oz.
    Gum mastic .... 2½ "
    Camphor .... ½ "
    Denatured alcohol .... ½ pt.

Varnish for Maps and Charts

Lay the chart or map flat upon a table and fasten securely by means of thumb tacks at the edges, allowing only the heads to hold the paper to the table. Flow on a solution of collodion, using a straight edge such as ruler, or, if preferred, a fine camel's-hair brush. Ventilate the room in which the work is done, and take the usual precautions as regards to the inflammability of the mixture.

The following solution can also be used:

Collodion .... 1 pt.
Castor oil .... ½ oz.

The oil here acts as a plasticizer, preventing cracks in the dried varnish surface.

Dammar Varnish

Dammar gum .... 5 lb.
Turpentine .... 1 gal.

True to the characteristics of dammar varnishes, the product will be turbid, owing to incomplete solubility.

VARNISH AND SHELLAC 219

Celluloid Varnish

Celluloid (scrap photo film)	1 part
Amyl acetate	5 "
Acetone	5 "

Dissolve. Inflammable!

Shellac-Ammonia Varnish

Dissolve 1 oz. of flake shellac in ¾ pt. of strong ammonium hydroxide (not household ammonia). The shellac will require some time to dissolve, and the container should be well stoppered during this interval.

Borax-Water Varnish

One oz. of borax dissolved in 12 oz. of water, add 2 oz. of shellac. Boil until dissolved.

Battery Top Varnish

An inexpensive varnish for filling rough surfaces with a liquid that has a rather stiff body can be made by dissolving in alcohol the colored compound obtained from the tops of dry batteries. The compound must be freed from bits of paper and the actual activating battery compound. Sealing wax also can be used, and in either case, denatured alcohol is the solvent.

Shellac Varnish

#1—The following yields a somewhat flexible product, due to the castor oil acting as a plasticizer:

Shellac	2 to 3 lb.
Castor oil	½ "
Denatured alcohol	1 gal.

Cut (dissolve) the shellac and then mix in the castor oil.

#2—Shellac	4 parts
Borax	2 "
Glycerin	2 "
Anilin black	5 "
Water	50 "

Dissolve the borax in the water, heat and add the shellac until dissolved then incorporate the rest.

Violin Varnish

#1—Gum mastic	10 parts
Gum dammar	5 "
Linseed oil	5 "
Turpentine	100 "

#2—Gum sandarac	125 parts
Gum mastic	62 "
Shellac	62 "
Gum elemi	31 "
Turpentine	62 "
Alcohol	1000 "

White Hard Varnish

Gum sandarac	2½ lb.
Gum mastic	½ "
Alcohol	1 gal.

Place all in a jug and keep stoppered in a warm place for several days, shaking at intervals. When liquefied, strain and keep tightly stoppered.

Special Metal Varnish

A varnish for metal is prepared by dissolving sufficient asphaltum in benzol to make a solution of creamy consistency. The addition of a teaspoon of boiled linseed oil to an ounce, or one ounce of the oil to about one half pint of asphaltum varnish, makes a more durable and flexible varnish useful both on metals and on glass.

Dead Black Varnish

Alcohol	8 oz.
Lampblack	½ "
Liquid shellac	1 "

Inexpensive red varnish, for use on magnet coils or wood, can be made by dissolving red sealing wax in warm alcohol. Due to filler being present in the sealing wax, the dissolved wax should be shaken before using to mix the settled-out filler with the dissolved portion of the wax. It is best to use this varnish by applying thin coats.

Waterproof Varnish

Gum copal	450	parts
Sandarac	75	"
Turpentine	40	"
Castor oil	5	"
Alcohol	800	"

Preparing Colorless Shellac

To remove wax, pigment, sand, wood, and other impurities from shellac, dissolve 2 tablespoons of sodium carbonate in 2 qt. boiling water and add 6 heaping tablespoons of flake shellac. Cool the solution. The wax and other impurities will float upon the surface in a solidified mass, which may be removed by filtration. Carefully acidify the solution by adding slowly a few drops of hydrochloric acid while constantly stirring the liquid. This operation must be carried on in a glass or porcelain vessel. The granular light brown or yellow precipitate is collected on a filter and is melted in boiling water to remove excess water and to leave the shellac harder.

Anti-Rusting Varnish for Tools

#1—Dissolve paraffin wax in benzene or gasoline and immerse the warmed tools in the solution.

#2—Immerse the tools in an alcoholic solution of shellac that has been diluted with an equal volume of denatured alcohol.

#3—Tallow	2 oz.
Rosin	1 "

Melt the tallow, which can be mutton tallow as obtained in small tin cans at drug stores, and then add the rosin, working it in with a knife blade. For a softer paste, use more tallow.

#4—Penetrating oil	1 part
Straight gasoline	1 "

This mixture can be used for tools that are to be laid away in places not protected from moisture. The mixture will fill all crevices.

Four-Hour Varnish

#1—Nevindene (indene resin)	81 lb.
Limed rosin (5%)	13 "
No. 1 fused lead resinate	6 "
China wood oil	25 gal.
No. 1 cobalt drier	1 "
No. 1 manganese drier.	⅜ "
Mineral spirits	44 "

Heat the wood oil to 400° F. and add 13 lb. of limed rosin and 40 lb. of nevindene. Run the batch so as to get to the top heat of 565° F. in approximately 30 minutes. Hold at 565° F. until a few drops spun on glass pick up 12 to 15 inches before breaking. Chill with the lead resinate and balance of 41 lb. of nevindene to cool around 495° F. Hold here for a syrupy body but do not string the varnish. As soon as the desired body is obtained add enough mineral spirits completely to check the batch. Add the liquid driers at 350° F. Water and alkali resistant.

#2—The following formula is more elastic than #1:

Nevindene (indene resin)..	81 lb.
Limed rosin (5%)	10 "
No. 1 fused lead resinate..	9 "
China wood oil	32 gal.
Bodied linseed oil	3 "
No. 1 cobalt drier	1½ "
No. 1 manganese drier	½ "
Mineral spirits	56 "

The method of cooking is virtually the same as described for No. 1 except that the China wood oil is heated to 565° F. with all of the limed rosin and 50 lb. of nevindene, and that the body is not carried quite as far at 565° F. At the top heat, the varnish is chilled as soon as a few drops spun on glass pick up about 6 inches. After checking to 490° F. on the way down the varnish may be held for the appearance of a slight string to the very last drops from the kettle stirring rod, provided the linseed oil has not been added and is available as a final chill back. This will insure a heavy body. In the event that it has been necessary to use the linseed oil, the final checking may be done by adding mineral spirits in a thin stream.

The following product gives a more flexible varnish than the first two:

#3—Nevindene (indene res-
    in) .... 81 lb.
    Limed rosin (5%) ... 12½ "
    No. 1 fused lead res-
    inate .... 6½ "
    China wood oil .... 22 gal.
    Bodied linseed oil .... 3 "
    No. 1 cobalt drier ..1-1/16 "
    No. 1 manganese drier ⅜ "
    Mineral spirits .... 44 "

Heat the wood oil to 400° F. and add the limed rosin and 40 lb. of nevindene. Run the batch so as to get to the top heat of 565° F. in approximately 30 minutes. Hold at 565° F. until a few drops spun on glass pick up 12 to 15 inches before breaking. Chill with the lead resinate and enough nevindene to cool to around 495° F. Hold here for a syrupy body but do not string the varnish. As soon as the desired body is obtained, add any remaining nevindene and enough mineral spirits completely to check the batch. Add the liquid driers at 350° F.

#4—Neville hard resin .... 100 lb.
    China wood oil (tung
    oil) .... 10 gal.
    Mineral spirits .... 25 "
    No. 1 cobalt drier .... 1¼ "

Heat the wood oil to 400° F. and add 30 lb. of hard resin. Run the batch so as to get to the top heat of 565° F. in about 35 minutes. Hold at 565° F. until a few drops spun on

glass pick up about 24 inches before breaking. Chill with the balance of 70 lb. of hard resin. The batch should not show a string at any stage. If desired, just enough of the resin may be added to chill to 490° F. and the kettle held here for a final stout body. The resin must all be in solution when the kettle has cooled to 425° F. The mineral spirits should be added as soon as all of the resin has dissolved. Add the liquid drier at 350° F.

#5—Umber .... 12 oz.
    Asphaltum .... 2 "
    Boiled linseed oil .... ½ pt.
    Rosin .... 2 oz.
    Turpentine .... 1½ pt.

Melt the asphaltum and rosin together, add the warmed oil, stir thoroughly, and then mix the turpentine.

Driers for Paints and Varnishes

#1—Rosin, water white .. 100 lb.
    Lead acetate white crys-
    tal .... 45 "

Melt rosin to 300° F. and add the acetate slowly. Raise the temperature to 500° F. and hold there until all acetic acid fumes have been driven off. Pour into cooling pan.

This resinate contains approximately 20% lead metal.

#2—Rosin, water white .. 100 lb.
    Refined linseed oil .... 100 "
    Cobalt acetate .... 16 "
    Mineral spirits .... 35 gal.

Heat rosin and linseed oil to 350° F. and add cobalt acetate slowly. Keep the temperature rising. When nearly all the acetate has been added, the mixture may crystallize but in raising the temperature to 500° F. it will again become liquid. Add the balance of acetate if not already added and hold at 500° F. until all acetic acid fumes have been eliminated. Cool to 390° F. and add mineral spirits.

#3—Rosin, water white .. 100 lb.
    Refined linseed oil .... 100 "
    Manganese acetate ....15½ "
    Mineral spirits ...... 35 gal.

The procedure in making this drier is the same as in #2.

Ground Glass Varnish

Gum sandarac .... 2¼ oz.
Gum mastic .... ½ "
Ether .... 24 "
Benzol ....6 to 18 "

Varying the amount of benzol (benzene) used will vary the density produced upon the glass. For a heavy varnish, use the smaller quantity.

Various Liquid Shellacs

#1—Ordinary liquid "three pound cut" shellac:
Denatured or wood alcohol 1 gal.
Pure flake or fine ground
    orange shellac .... 3 lb.

Put in jug and shake frequently until "cut" or dissolved. Apply liquid with brush. Do not put in metal containers as the metal turns the liquid black.

#2—White Lead .... 20 lb.
    Pure fine ground or
    flake shellac ...... 10 "
    Denatured or wood al-
    cohol .... 3 gal.
    Lampblack .... ¼ lb.

Put in a jug or other closed receptacle and shake till solution results. This is very elastic. Shake or stir before using. The color is black.

#3—Flake shellac .... 3 lb.
    Denatured alcohol .... 1 gal.
    Vermilion red .... 1 lb.

Red ochre can be used instead of vermilion red. The color is red.

How Japanning is Done

Many articles of metal, papier maché, plaster, or even wood, have been japanned in the past, but in recent years, the better enamels, lacquers, and spraying methods have somewhat displaced the japanning art. Briefly, japanning consists of applying a coat of colored varnish on metal, plaster, wood, or other materials, and baking the varnish on at a temperature between 250° and 300° F. The process is not difficult to carry out, and amateurs have good success at the work.

The needs of the japanner are not many. A good oven and a baking or oven thermometer and some good varnishes and pigments will produce good enamel, or japanned films.

In the heating operation, the colored varnish is baked on, thus promoting a firmer bond between the varnish and the pigment and the work. All brush marks are eliminated, for with the mild heat used at first, the varnish thins out and flows. On further heating, the vehicle hardens, the thinner is volatilized, and the pigment is left in a film closely adherent to the work.

The formulas given here have been used with success, are relatively simple to make, and easy to apply.

Red Japan Varnish

Use a good copal or clear varnish and use, for a deep red, powdered vermilion. Burnt umbers and the various oxides of iron, especially those found naturally, are used for the varying shades of brown and red.

Flexible Black Japan

Asphaltum .... 2 oz.
Burnt umber .... 4 "
Linseed oil .... 2 qt.
Japan drier .... 1 oz.

The asphaltum is dissolved in the linseed oil, the japan drier added and the umber worked in.

Shellac (shellac varnish), when mixed with lampblack or ivory black produces a good black japan.

A good varnish, worked up with zinc white, will produce a good white japan.

Transparent Japan

Oil of turpentine	8 oz.
Oil of lavender	6 "
Camphor	1 dr.
Gum copal	2 oz.

Dissolve, using gentle heat. This is used for japanning tin or copal can be used alone without the other ingredients.

Yellow Japan

Turmeric or saffron dissolved in alcoholic shellac varnish makes a good yellow japan.

A small amount of dragon's blood added to the varnish for yellow japan results in a beautiful and rich salmon-colored varnish, and by these two mixtures all the shades of flesh-colored japans can be produced.

Green Japan

Use the green chromic oxide with a clear varnish. As in the other color formulas, the pigment must be thoroughly worked into the varnish before being applied. Grinding in a mortar until a slurry is formed is a good method of mixing the pigment with the varnish when small amounts of the japan are desired.

Blue japan is made with a very clear varnish and Prussian blue.

WOODWORK AT HOME

Fireproofing Wood

Phosphate of ammonia is used without admixture with other substances in the fireproofing of a large amount of wood for structural purposes and interior finish. The process generally employed is quite similar to that used in impregnating wood with creosote and other preservatives. The wood usually is treated with steam in an autoclave to remove the resins, a vacuum is then drawn, and the solution of ammonium phosphate is run in. Pressure is applied and the solution is forced into the wood under a pressure of anywhere from 200 pounds per square inch to 1,000 pounds or perhaps more, depending upon the character of the wood and its susceptibility to penetration. Different woods require different amounts of ammonium phosphate, but as a general rule, from 5% to 7% of ammonium phosphate on the weight of the dry wood is sufficient to give good resistance to burning.

Sodium tungstate solution has been used to render wood fireproof. Although deep impregnation of the wood by the chemical is necessary to make it a perfect non-combustible substance, the tungstate solution, even if only penetrating a short distance into the fibers, will retard combustion so that only a slow smouldering occurs.

Phosphates, such as ammonium phosphate and also the ammonium tungstate, have been used to impregnate wood for this purpose.

Another process consists of impregnating the wood with a solution of iron sulphate or zinc sulphate, and then immersing it in a solution of calcium chloride. This will cause the highly desirable precipitation of non-combustible calcium sulphate (gypsum) in the wood fibers. The iron chloride or zinc chloride will also be formed within the fibers and as the wood is allowed to dry, will crystallize out. The zinc chloride, which is formed if zinc sulphate (white vitriol) is used, will also impart to the wood decay-resisting properties, and it would seem therefore that zinc sulphate would be the better of the two for the purpose.

Borates, such as borax, have also been used in conjunction with ammonium phosphate for fireproofing.

Water-glass solution will penetrate the wood, especially if applied warm, and thus give it a certain degree of fireproofing qualities. Garages, barns, or attics can be conveniently painted with such a solution, thus rendering them more immune to actual burning.

Orthophosphoric acid	2 parts
Manganese chloride	3.5 "
Magnesium carbonate	1 "
Boric acid	1 "
Sal ammoniac	2.5 "

Mixed and dissolved in 100 cubic centimeters of water, this solution, it has been claimed, will effectively fireproof wood.

#1—The following can be used as a paint:

Water-glass powder	35 parts
Shredded short fiber asbestos	35 "
Water	100 "

It is mixed with water before using. According to the brand and make of the water-glass, the time required for dissolution will vary.

#2—Ammonium phosphate 100 gm.
     Boric acid .... 10 "

Dissolve in one liter (1,000 cc.) of water and impregnate the wood by sinking beneath the warm solution.

#3—Borax .... 15 parts
     Ammonium sulphate .. 135 "
     Boric acid .... 5 "

All dissolved in 1,000 cc. of water.

Fire-Resistant Wood

Wood may be made fire-retardent by injecting, under pressure, solutions of certain chemicals such as ammonium sulphate, ammonium phosphate, ammonium chloride, or sodium borate. If a sufficient quantity is injected, the wood after drying becomes so fire-resistant that it will not support combustion. If held in a hot flame it will char and in time fall to pieces, but it does not burn with a flame and will stop burning almost immediately after being removed from the flame. There are two objections to this method of fireproofing wood. One is that the cost of the chemicals and the expensive nature of the apparatus used for injecting them make the treatment expensive. This eliminates the method from consideration as a means by which you can economically fireproof a small amount of material for your own use.

A second objection to the use of the chemicals mentioned above is the fact that they are all soluble in water, and if the wood is used where it will be exposed to the action of water the chemicals will be washed out in time and the wood will lose its fire-resisting qualities. A method of treatment has been developed, however, by which this objection is overcome.

This method consists essentially in treating the air-dried wood or shingles with a solution of borax in water. The wood is then kiln dried to about 10 per cent moisture and given a second treatment with a zinc chloride solution. The wood is again dried and is then ready for use. The solutions must be applied under heavy pressure, and retorts capable of withstanding high pressure are necessary, together with pressure pumps, measuring tanks, and other comparatively expensive equipment. Theoretically, the process depends upon the formation of an insoluble salt by the zinc chloride and the borax. This salt is practically insoluble in water and the treated wood can, therefore, be used in exposed situations. Under the action of heat the salt fuses, coating the cell walls and rendering them resistant to fire.

A fire-resistant paint of which zinc borate and linseed oil are the principal ingredients has been found to give good protection.—From "The Fireproofing of Wood"—Forest Products Laboratory, U. S. Dept. Agriculture.

To Prevent Decay in Wood

The following substances are beneficial in preventing the decay of wood posts and lumber.

Mercuric chloride (corrosive sublimate) is a white powder that makes an effective wood preservative when dissolved in water. It has been successfully used in wood-preserving plants, especially in Europe, for many years. Because it is a deadly poison and is also corrosive to iron and steel, mercuric chloride can not be recommended for general use.

Sodium fluoride is a white powder which, dissolved in water to make a 2 to 4 per cent solution, is effective in preventing decay. A zinc chloride solution is also useful.

Good results in preventing decay can not, in general, be expected from paint, linseed oil, whitewash, or similar materials when used on fence posts or other timbers in contact with the ground. They do not penetrate the wood deeply, and as a rule are not poisonous to wood-destroying fungi.

To Preserve Posts in Ground

For posts set in the ground, the best preservative is creosote. This can be applied by boring a small slanting hole in the base of the post just above the ground and filling the cavity formed with this liquid. The hole then is stoppered with a small plug. Three or four days later more creosote is added and the hole again plugged. At the end of a week a final addition

is made and the plug permanently fastened in place.

Bleaching Out Wood Stains

While wood stains can be taken out partially by bleaching, the bleaching process is applied only on work that is stained in patches. One method is to use 3 oz. of oxalic acid crystals (about 25 cents' worth) in 1 qt. of warm water. This will bleach many stains and remove ink marks and rust stains from any surface.

Walnut Stain for Wood

#1—Magnesium sulphate . 1 part
    Potassium permanganate .... 1 "
    Water .... 25 parts

Apply the above while hot. A small amount of red rosin dye will improve the color.

#2—Potassium bichromate . 1 oz.
    Sal soda .... 6 "
    Water .... 1 gal.
    Vandyke brown ...... 10 oz.

Boil for about 10 minutes and apply with a brush to the wood.

#3—Water .... 1 qt.
    Washing soda .... 1½ oz.
    Vandyke brown ...... 2½ "
    Bichromate of potash . ¼ "

Boil for 10 minutes and apply with brush, using either a hot or cold solution.

#4—Take 2 gal. of shellac, burnt sienna, 2 lb., burnt umber, 2 lb., lampblack, ½ lb.; shake all together and mix well. Apply 1 coat with a brush, dry; sandpaper smooth, and apply a coat of common varnish or shellac to give a gloss, or rub with oil. This formula is for pine.

Ebony Stain

For ebony black, first coat the wood with a strong alkaline solution of extract of logwood, using about 1 part of potash to 3 parts of the extract in 6 parts of water. When dry, coat with a strong solution of vinegar and iron.

Basic Stain and Colors

In staining new interior wood a very thin coat of shellac, particularly if the wood is soft, should first be applied to make an even foundation for the stain. If this precaution is not taken, the stain will strike in here and there, appearing dark in some spots and light in others. When the shellac is dry, the stain selected can be applied over it.

Raw linseed oil, or flatting
oil .... 2 qt.
Turpentine .... 2 "
Japan drier .... 1 "

With the above base the following colors, ground in oil, can be used to produce the desired stain:

Mahogany:

Burnt sienna .... 2 lb.
Rose lake .... 1 "
Dropblack .... ¼ "

Vary the proportion of dropblack to the depth desired for this stain.

Light Oak:

Raw sienna .... 2 lb.
Raw umber .... ½ "

If the raw sienna is inferior in staining power, omit the raw umber and use three pounds raw sienna.

Cherry:

Burnt sienna .... 2 lb.
Raw sienna .... 1 "

If the burnt sienna has more of a brown than a fiery red tone, omit the raw sienna but use three pounds of burnt sienna instead of two.

Dark Oak:

Raw sienna .... 2 lb.
Raw umber .... ¾ " ·
    Small amount burnt sienna.

Walnut. A mixture of dropblack and burnt sienna.

Ebony. To prepare a fine ebony stain applicable especially to walnut boil 40 parts of gall nuts, 4 parts of logwood chips, 5 parts each of sulphate of iron and verdigris with water, strain through cloth and apply the warm fluid to the wood, and then give it 3 coats of a warm solution of iron acetate.

Satinwood:

Gamboge .... 3 oz.
Turmeric .... 6 "
Alcohol .... 1 qt.

Steep the gamboge and turmeric in the alcohol for a day or two and filter. Use several coats to produce the desired depth of stain.

Stain for Shingles

Work the desired colored pigment, ground in oil, in:

Raw linseed oil .... 2 volumes
Turpentine .... 2 "
Coal tar creosote .... 2 "
Japan drier .... 1 "

Black Stain for Wood

#1—Brush the wood with a hot solution of logwood chips, and while still moist, rub in with a rag a solution of ferrous sulphate. By this manner, iron tannate, which is black, is precipitated into the pores of the wood.

#2—To 1 pint of boiling water add ¾ ounce of copperas and 1 ounce logwood chips. Apply to the wood. When the surface has dried, rub in a solution of paraffin wax, or beeswax in gasoline.

For Other Colors

Gray: Use dilute solution of alcoholic cochineal.

Brownish red: A decoction of Brazil wood.

Rose: A solution of cochineal with some alum water.

Light Brown: Sulphate of copper dissolved in water, then solution of potassium ferrocyanide in water with an addition of some hydrochloric acid.

Dark Brown: Soak the wood in a solution of potassium permanganate, using the following solution:

Potassium permanganate .. 1 oz.
Water .... 1 qt.

After removing, the wood should be thoroughly dried. It can then be oiled if a glossy appearance is desired. It is not recommended for children's toys.

Yellow: Mix turmeric powder, 1 oz., and alcohol, 1 pt. Digest for 4 days, shaking occasionally. Strain off for use. Apply to the wood by brushing it over 3 or 4 times, taking care that the first stain is dry before the second is applied.

Red Coloring:

#1—Dragon's blood .... 1 oz.
      Denatured alcohol .... 1 pt.

#2—Brazil wood .... 1 oz.
      Cochineal .... 1 "
      Dragon's blood .... 1 "
      Saffron .... 2 "
      Alcohol .... 2 qt.

Steep ingredients in the alcohol and stain.

Bronze for Wood

A suitable varnish for the aluminum or gold bronze to be applied to wood is:

Shellac .... 4 oz.
Gum benzoin .... ½ "
Alcohol .... 1 pt.

The alcohol used is the solvent, dissolving the two adhesives to form the vehicle. The whole should be allowed to dissolve by standing several days. It is mixed with the bronze powder when wanted and applied.

Easy Dyes for Wood

Iron salts such as iron acetate form compounds having a dark-brown color when applied to certain woods such as oak, mahogany, and chestnut. Potassium or sodium bichromate gives brown or red stains on certain woods such as oak, ash, and walnut.

Use a solution of picric acid crystals in water; gives a yellow stain.

Easter egg dyes can be dissolved in water and the resulting dye solution applied to wood. The colors will not be lasting, and are unfit for outdoor use.

A dark red stain is obtained with potassium carbonate, 1 ounce, logwood chips, ½ pound, water 2 quarts. Boil the logwood chips in the water till it becomes a very dark red color; then add the carbonate, and boil for 2 more hours. The decoction must be applied to the wood boiling hot.

To Darken the Stain

When wood is stained using substances that are dissolved in water (water solvent stains), the penetration is not great on hard woods, which often results in a color just a trifle lighter than the one desired. Strong ammonia has been used on hard woods to effect a darkening in color but this caustic is liable to raise the grain of the wood. Potassium bichromate is also useful as well as potassium permanganate, in securing a darkening of the hard wood by simple immersion or painting on.

If the wood is soaked in or painted with a warm solution of:

Ferrous sulphate .... 3 oz.
Logwood chips .... 4 "
Water .... 2 qt.

it will be given a color much resembling that of oak. This treatment is satisfactory, but by an application of a solution of a handful of iron or steel filings which has been allowed to remain in a pint of vinegar for several days, the wood will be stained darker and much deeper. The stain produced is also more lasting.

Stains Made with Logwood

The cheapness of logwood chips makes them ideal for use in staining woods. The logwood contains an active principle which is dissolved out by boiling water. The resulting decoction is applied to the wood which is afterwards immersed in certain chemical solutions. Acting as an indicator, the decoction changes color for many chemicals which are added to it, and a list of the colors which are produced by the addition of the chemical, which is dissolved in water and used for the second bath, are given here. Thus if the wood is soaked in a solution of, or painted with, the logwood decoction, and afterwards painted with or soaked in a weak solution of hydrochloric acid, the wood will be stained red, and if removed and dried, the operation will be complete. The natural coloring of the wood itself will make some difference in the shade which is produced, but the following table gives the approximate color:

Concentrated hydro-
    chloric acid ......reddish-yellow.
Dilute acids ....reddish.
Ferric nitrate ......black.
Potassium chromate.black.
Stannous chloride ..violet.
Tartaric acid ....gray-brown.
Sulphate of copper .dark gray.
Tannin ....yellow-red.
Sal ammoniac .....yellow.
Sugar of lead ......gray brown.
Potassium perman-
    ganate ....light brown.
Potassium iodide ...red-yellow.

Pyrogallic acid .....yellow-brown.
Cupric chloride ....red to brown.
Sulphate of iron ....gray to black.
Alum ....brown.
Potassium carbonate.yellow-brown.
Magnesium sulphate.brown.
Cupric nitrate ......violet.
Potassium sulphocya-
    nide ....red.
Zinc chloride ....red-brown.

Bleaching Dark Wood

Wood that has darkened can be bleached by applying a thin layer of calcium hypochlorite mixed to a thin paste with water. Allow this to dry and then moisten with dilute hydrochloric acid made by mixing one part of acid to three parts of water. Brush the wood clean after a few hours. If the wood is still too dark, repeat the process.

Wax Polish for Wood

#1—Melt over a low fire 1 lb. of yellow beeswax and ¼ lb. of rosin, and after removing the vessel from the fire add ¼ pt. of oil of turpentine. Allow the mixture to cool with constant stirring, and apply it to the wood with a rag, rubbing thoroughly.

#2—Beeswax .... 8 oz.
    Spermaceti .... 2 "
    White Venice turpentine 2 "

Mix all together and use warm.

Artificial Wood

An artificial wood for making pressed moldings and imitation carvings can be prepared as follows: Boil together equal parts of hide glue and sawdust with water. Then macerate or steep in water a quantity of newspaper until it is soft, and add sufficient of this to the glue and sawdust to form a soft mass. The glue can be made reasonably waterproof by adding potassium bichromate and exposing the mixture to the light. If desired, a trace of formaldehyde also may be added to the mixture.

Wood Filler Putty

This is a good wood putty but should not be used to imbed window glass into frames as it will not stand up under outside weathering.

#1—Diatomaceous earth, or
    chalk .... 2 parts
    Burnt sienna .... 15 "
    Burnt umber .... 10 "
    Whiting .... 60 "
    Powdered glue ...... 20 "

The above is mixed with water, preferably warm, and allowed to set until the glue has soaked up and spread into the rest of the mixture. It is then applied to cracks and allowed to dry. The sienna and umber are coloring agents as well as fillers.

#2—Powdered slaked lime.. 1 part
    Rye flour .... 2 "
    Linseed-oil varnish .... 1 "

Color with burnt umber.

#3—Gum arabic .... 1 part
    Water .... 2 "
    Potato starch ......3 to 5 "

Color to match the wood, using sienna or umber.

#4—Very fine sawdust is made into a paste by moistening with linseed-oil varnish and kneading. This very plastic mass forms an excellent putty.

#5—Water .... 20 parts
    Glue .... 1 "

Finest sawdust as much as may be required to make stiff paste. The glue is first dissolved by boiling it in the water, and the sawdust is then gradually stirred in.

#6—Boil linseed oil with enough starch to make a very thick paste— add a little japan drier and reduce to proper consistency with turpentine.

Add no coloring for oak or white ash; for other wood add enough color to mask the white of the starch. For dark ash and chestnut use little raw sienna; for walnut, burnt umber and a very little Venetian red. Apply the filler with brush or rags. This will not harden until overnight.

#7—Beeswax .... 4 oz.
    Turpentine .... 10 "

Alkanet root, enough to color. Melt all and strain. Useful on varnished woods.

#8—Glue .... 2 parts
    Cement .... 7 "
    Sawdust ....3 to 4 "

Mix with water before using.

#9—Casein .... 7 parts
    Water .... 7 "
    Ammonia water ...... ¾ "
    Burned lime .... ½ "

Prepare just before using.

For woods already stained or color-varnished use one of the following:

#1—Beeswax .... 4 oz.
    Rosin .... 1 "
    Turpentine .... 2 "

Heat, then add beeswax and add alkanet root until the desired color and consistency is produced.

#2—Corn starch .... 5 lb.
    Japan drier .... 1 qt.
    Magnesia .... 2 oz.
    Linseed oil .... 1 qt.
    Turpentine .... 3 "

#3—Whiting .... 6 oz.
    Linseed oil .... 12 "
    Japan drier .... 8 "
    Turpentine .... 8 "
    Corn starch .... 1 "

Mix well, rubbing up the starch and whiting in small amounts at a time.

WORKING ON GLASS

For Making Glass

Glass is a fused mixture of sodium or potassium silicates with one or more of the insoluble silicates with varying proportions of other substances which produce color, or give to the glass some especial characteristic such as certain refractive indexes or tolerance to reagents. The silicate is derived from the sand (silicon dioxide, silica, quartz) used, and in practice is mixed with potassium or sodium carbonate and the other ingredients, and fused, the silica entering into chemical combination with the carbonate or base to form the glass.

Window glass is made by fusion of a mixture of sand, sodium carbonate or sodium sulphate, and calcium carbonate (limestone) in fire clay pots.

Flint and lead glass are made from ground flint, lead oxide, and potassium carbonate, with or without the addition of saltpeter, and is very fusible. Ordinary household articles such as drinking tumblers, vinegar jugs and decanters, are made from this quality of glass.

Bottle glass is green due to the iron it contains, and arsenious oxide (white arsenic) is often added to counteract this green color by oxidizing the iron.

Common and Colored Glass

Common glass:

Sand	17	parts
Soda ash	4	"
Borax	2	"

White bottle glass:

Sand (white)	64	parts
Lime	6	"
Sodium carbonate	23	"
Sodium nitrate	5	"

The sodium nitrate acts as a decolorizer.

Green bottle glass:

Sand	63	parts
Sodium carbonate	26	"
Lime	11	"

Common Flint:

Quartz sand	110	parts
Minium	110	"
Soda ash	33	"

Blue glass:

White sand	10	parts
Potassium carbonate	3.5	"
Borax	1	"
Red lead	15	"
Cobalt (ic) oxide	.4	"

Green glass:

#1—Sand	50	parts
Soda ash	15	"
Calcium carbonate	5	"
Saltpeter	1	"
Ferric oxide	5 to 10	"
Copper (ic) oxide	3 to 10	"

#2—Sand	100	parts
Potash	66	"
Hydrated lime	8	"
White arsenic	6	"
Pyrolusite	5	"
Iron oxide	5	"
Cobaltic oxide	5	"

Violet glass:

Sand	55	parts
Soda ash	15	"
Saltpeter	2	"
Chalk	5	"
Pyrolusite	10	"
Ferric oxide	2	"

Red glass:

Sand	100	parts
Red lead	200	"
Copper oxide	6	"
Stannic oxide	6	"

Turquoise glass:

Sand (quartz)	100	parts
Potassium carbonate	40	"
Saltpeter	11	"
Copper oxide	½	"

Yellow glass:

Sand	65 parts
Soda ash	25 "
Chalk	3 "
Wood charcoal	1 "

Water-glass:

Mix well 20 parts of fine sand, and 60 of potassium carbonate. Fuse in a crucible large enough to take care of foaming. Carbonic acid escapes; the silica and potassium combine and form glass. Pour out the glass, which is potassium silicate, on an iron plate. The compound formed in this manner is potassium water-glass and is soluble in water.

To Stain Glass

Substances used to stain or color glass are: For amethyst, oxide of manganese; blue, oxide of cobalt; for brown, oxide of iron; for green, black oxide of copper; for purple, oxide of gold; for ruby red, oxide of copper; for white, oxide of tin; for yellow, oxide of silver. These substances, well powdered, are either added to the melted contents of the glass-pot, or are applied to the surface.

Silvering on Glass

The glass should be made absolutely clean by swabbing with dilute nitric acid, then with soapy water. The soapy water is then washed off, and either of the following processes carried out with the glass lying face up or face down. Other acids such as chromic acid can be used to first clean the glass of organic matter, or it may be scoured with whiting or rouge, after which it is cleaned with soapy water, the last traces of soap removed with large amounts of water. The glass surface which is to be silvered is not to be touched after cleaning. The following formulas and processes are suggested. Distilled water should be used in the making of the solutions.

#1—Silver nitrate	....	40 gm.
Distilled water	....	500 cc.
Ammonia.		

Enough ammonia should be used to dissolve the precipitate first formed and form a clear solution, then a few drops of silver nitrate solution should be added and the bulk made up to 1000 cc. (36 oz.). The reducing solution is 0.5 to 1.0 cc. of a mixture of equal volumes of 10 percent solution of chloral hydrate and 40 percent formaldehyde to every 50 cc. of the silver-ammonia solution.

#2—Silver nitrate	....	12 gr.
Rochelle salts	....	12 "
Distilled water	......	8 oz.

The salts are added to the boiling water, allowed to boil for six minutes, then cooled and filtered.

#3—Silver nitrate	......	35 gr.
Strong ammonia water	....	enough
Distilled water	.....	8 oz.

Dissolve 19 grains of the silver nitrate in 1 ounce of distilled water, and add enough strong ammonia water to make the solution permanently clear. Then add the balance of the silver nitrate, 16 grains, and dissolve it; then add rest of the distilled water, and filter, using glass funnel.

Mix equal parts of the solutions, #2 and #3, and pour onto the middle of the glass to be silvered. Flow over the surface of the glass, which must be perfectly level; any untouched portions of the glass may be wetted with the aid of a clean glass rod. Allow the glass to remain untouched until the silver precipitates. Allow the water to drain, dry with the aid of a gentle heat, and coat with a varnish, using a soft brush.

#4—Sugar .... 5 gm.
   Tartaric acid .... 0.6 "
   Distilled water ...... 50 cc
   Boil, cool and add
Alcohol .... 10 cc.
Distilled water to make ... 100 "

Of this 2 to 3 cc. should be mixed with 2 cc. of 10 per cent chloral hydrate solution and added to 50 cc. of the silver solution. The glass to be silvered should be first cleaned with strong nitric acid by the aid of a swab of cotton on a stick or the like, or immersed for 5 minutes in 16 per cent chromic acid acidulated with sulphuric acid. The glass may be silvered face up or face down, the mixture applied, the dish rocked till the solution turns reddish. It should then be thrown away and 100 cc. of the ammoniacal silver solution, without any reducer, poured over it with rocking till the desired thickness of silver is attained. This takes but a few minutes, according to temperature.

Silvering Mirrors

Solution 1: Silver nitrate, 175 grains; distilled water, 10 oz. Solution 2: Nitrate of ammonia, 262 grains, distilled water, 10 oz. Solution 3: Pure caustic potash, 1 oz. (avoir.); distilled water, 10 oz. Solution 4: Pure sugar candy, ½ oz.; distilled water, 5 oz. Dissolve and add 50 grains tartaric acid, boil in a flask for 10 minutes and add 1 oz. alcohol and 10 ozs. distilled water. Take equal parts of solution 1 and 2 and mix together. In another glass mix equal parts of Nos. 3 and 4. Then mix the resulting solutions. Lay the glass on a table, perfectly level, and pour the liquid on the glass, as much as it can hold without running over, and let stand several hours until all the silver is deposited on the glass. Drain and dry; then varnish with a camel's-hair brush.

Here is another silvering process:

Solution No. 1—In 4 oz. of distilled water dissolve 1½ oz. of nitrate of silver. When dissolved, add 26-degree ammonia, drop by drop, until the precipitate formed is just dissolved. Then add 45 oz. of distilled water, allow to stand 12 hours and then filter.

Solution No. 2—In 5 oz. of distilled water dissolve 69 gr. of nitrate of silver. In another 5 oz. of distilled water dissolve 6 gr. of potassium hydroxide. In a third 5 oz. of distilled water dissolve 50 gr. of Rochelle salts, and when all the chemicals are well dissolved, mix the three solutions, allow to stand for 12 hours and then filter. When ready to silver, take 4 oz. of Solution #1 and 1 oz. of Solution #2 for each square foot of glass, mix them, stir quickly, and apply.

To Silver Glass Globes

Melt together and mix well the following: lead, 6 oz.; tin, 4 oz.; bismuth, 10 oz. This alloy is used for silvering globes. A small quantity is put in the globe, which is then exposed to a gentle heat and turned so as to distribute the alloy evenly. The temperature required is about 200° F.

Solution #1—In 4 oz. of distilled water dissolve 39 gr. of nitrate of silver. When dissolved, add 26-degree ammonia, drop by drop, until the solution turns the color of coffee. Continue adding ammonia, stirring all the while, until the color clears up. (Note—About 10 to 12 drops of ammonia as a total will be enough.) Stir thoroughly. The liquid should now be almost clear. If not, add a few more drops of ammonia. Dissolve 33 gr. of nitrate of silver in 12 oz. of distilled water. Mix this with the solution just made, allow to stand for 12 hours and filter.

Solution #2—In 1 pt. of distilled

water dissolve 24 gr. of Rochelle salts. Boil for exactly one minute, very gently, in a clean enamel-ware vessel. Then add 24 gr. of nitrate of silver and allow to simmer for exactly five minutes. Allow to cool, let stand for 12 hours and filter.

To silver, take 2 oz. of Solution #1 and 2 oz. of Solution #2 for each square foot of glass to be silvered, mix them, stir quickly and at once apply.

Varnish for Mirrors

After silver plating glass, the mirror so produced should be preserved from attack by hydrogen sulphide and other sulphur gases which are present in the air. A good backing varnish is made as follows:

Asphaltum .... 1 lb.
Benzol or benzine .... 1 pt.
Spar varnish .... ½ "

Dissolve the asphaltum in the benzol or the benzine and when solution is complete, add the varnish and stir well. This is applied to the back of the metallic silver surface and allowed to dry. Asphaltum varnish can be used alone, but the addition of the spar varnish gives further protection.

Etching on Glass

Although not stocked by many chemical supply houses in the smaller towns, hydrofluoric acid can be purchased and used as is for etching glass. The glass should be exposed to the acid, the latter being marketed in ceresine wax bottles.

Hydrofluoric acid gas can be generated by heating a fluoride, such as sodium fluoride, in an old saucer or dish, with strong sulphuric acid, the glass to be etched or frosted held above the dish in the vapors. A dish hammered from sheet lead can be used if the process is to be employed regularly. If the glass is waxed care must be taken that the wax does not melt from the heat applied to the acid and fluoride. A damp cloth on the underside of the glass plate will keep it cool.

The following mixture can be acted upon by strong sulphuric acid to produce hydrofluoric acid gas:

Ammonium fluoride .... 1 part
Barium sulphate .... 1 "

To roughen the surface of glass put a little Carborundum powder on the surface of the glass. Moisten with a drop of water. Lay on a fragment of a sheet of glass and rub, moistening when necessary.

To mark glass, permanent etching is obtained by writing the letters and numbers on the glassware using sodium silicate and a steel pen.

Frosting on Glass

Epsom salts crystallize out on glass under certain easily reproduced conditions to give the leafy plates that closely resemble hoar frost. The crystals are made by covering the glass with

Epsom salts .... 6 oz.
Dextrine, white .... 2 "
Water, about .... 20 "

The dextrine is added to the warm water in which the Epsom salts has been previously dissolved. The dextrine acts as an adhesive.

To Pulverize Glass

Heat the glass to a red heat, and while in this condition plunge it into cold water; then dry and pulverize it. It becomes more friable by the sudden cooling. This operation is often used in making enamels.

Transferring Photos to Glass

Glycerin .... ¼ oz.
Gelatin .... 4 "
Water .... 8 "
Alcohol .... 3 "

Dissolve the gelatin in the water, over a very slow fire, add the glycerin, and pour the whole into the alcohol, very slowly, so as to mix thoroughly. Clean the glass, flow on the solution, lay the photo face down on the glass, and pour on more of the solution. Remove the excess so that no air bubbles remain and allow to dry. When dry, the photo will be transparent and may be colored with oil paints. The pictures used must be unmounted and their back must be free of printing or writing.

Making Picture Mirrors

A picture mirror is a novelty that serves as a glass to protect a photograph mounted behind it and also as a mirror. It is a plain sheet of glass when a light behind the picture is turned on and an ordinary mirror when the light is off. It is made as follows:

#1—Heat 4 ounces of distilled water to the boiling point, add 3 grains of silver nitrate and 3 grains of Rochelle salts, and boil for 8 minutes. Cool and filter through cotton or filter paper, using a glass or rubber funnel.

#2—Into a tablespoonful of distilled water place 5 grains of silver nitrate and agitate until dissolved. The solution may be slightly cloudy. Add ammonia water, drop by drop, until the solution becomes muddy, then clears. Next add 4 grains more of silver nitrate, dissolve, and add distilled water to make 4 ounces. Filter as with solution No. 1.

Thoroughly mix equal parts of solutions 1 and 2, and immediately pour the mixture on the glass. The liquid should flow to all edges. Watch the glass and when the lettering on a piece of newspaper placed under the glass is just barely visible beneath the silver film, pour off the excess solution, rinse the delicate silver coating in clear water, and dry.

If the silvering is sufficient, spray a coat of lacquer or clear varnish over the silver film, and the mirror is ready to use. Further silvering, if necessary, can be done by repeating the process.

Place the mirror in a frame, a picture behind it, and a sheet of clear glass at the rear, and fasten them in the usual manner with brads or old phonograph needles. Then add a reflector and electric bulb, and the picture mirror is complete.

Electroplating Glassware

The article to be plated is well cleaned. It is then placed in a receptacle of just sufficient diameter to accommodate it and covered with a 50 per cent water solution of hydrazine hydroxide. To this is added, drop by drop and with constant vigorous shaking, a 5 per cent solution of copper sulphate until a deep golden suspension of colloidal copper is obtained. One or two drops of excess are then added and metallic copper is deposited as a thin film upon the surface of the article and the walls of the container. This film may serve as a support and conduction pathway for a subsequent layer of electrolytically deposited copper.

Marking Glassware

The following method of etching glass, using one's own rubber stamp for a stencil, will appeal to many. It is due to J. W. Robbins and appeared in *The Chemist-Analyst*.

1. Take a quantity of the oxide and place in a dish and warm slightly over a flame to remove traces of moisture. Break up all lumps to a fine powder. Either litharge or red lead give satisfactory results.

2. The glass to be etched must be free of finger prints, moisture, and grease.

3. An ordinary rubber stamp having the desired lettering, and an ordinary stamp pad, are used. Stamp the wording on the part to be etched, shake a small quantity of litharge over the wording, and brush off the excess lead with a camel's-hair brush. The ink acts only as a binder for the oxide.

4. Run through the flame, such as a small Bunsen flame, until the oxide has a glossy appearance. In some cases the wording may become black due to the formation of a higher oxide of lead by the use of the oxidizing part of the flame. This higher oxide may be removed by holding in the extreme upper part of the flame, and burning the oxide off, leaving a clear etching.

5. Care must be taken not to use too hot a flame as this has a tendency to spread the lead.

TABLES AND USEFUL INFORMATION

Care of Storage Batteries

The following tables and useful information will be found of great help in using the formulas set forth in the preceding pages. They should be studied carefully and frequent reference made to them to be sure the formulas are being properly compounded and to assist you in checking the results.

Only chemically pure acid (CP) should be used. *Kempe's Engineer's Year Book* recommends the following tests for impurities:

Tests for impurities:—

Hydrochloric Acid (Chlorine).—To a small quantity of dilute electrolyte add a few drops of nitric acid, then add 3 drops of silver nitrate. The formation of a white, cloudy precipitate indicates the presence of chlorine in some form.

Nitric Acid.—Mix a solution of diphenylamine in concentrated sulphuric acid, and add it to the sample under test. Nitric acid will be indicated by a blue color.

Iron.—Fill a test-tube with dilute electrolyte and heat to boiling point; add several drops of concentrated nitric acid and boil again. Repeat two or three times. When solution is cold add a few drops of potassium sulphocyanide, which will color a deep red if iron is present.

Copper.—Add common ammonia until the resultant mixture gives an alkaline reaction; a deep blue indicates the presence of copper.

Arsenic.—Add an equal quantity of hydrogen sulphide solution; a yellow precipitate indicates arsenic.

Chemically pure reagents only must be used.

Easily Fusible Alloys

Alloys of use where a low melting point is desired, including a number that melt below the boiling point of water, are given by the following tables from *Kempe's Engineer's Year Book*:

MELTING POINTS OF ALLOYS

Bismuth	Lead	Tin	Melting Point	
			° F.	° C.
50	31.2	18.8	201	94
47	35.5	17.7	208	98
42.1	42.1	15.8	226	108
40	40	20	235	113
36.5	36.5	27	243	117
33.3	33.3	33.3	253	123
30.8	38.4	30.8	266	130
28.5	43	28.5	270	132
25	50	25	300	149
23.5	47	29.5	304	151
22.2	44.4	33.4	289	143
21	42	57	289	143
20	40	40	293	145

236 TABLES AND USEFUL INFORMATION

Bismuth	Lead	Tin	Melting Point °F.	Melting Point °C.
19	38	43	298	148
18.1	36.2	45.7	304	151
17.3	34.6	48.1	311	155
16.6	33.2	50.2	316	158
16	36	48	311	155
15.3	38.8	45.9	309	154
14.8	40.2	45	307	153
14	43	43	309	154
13.7	44.8	41.5	320	160
13.3	46.6	40.1	329	165
12.8	49	38.2	342	172
12.5	50	37.5	352	178
11.7	46.8	41.5	333	167
11.4	45.6	43	329	165
11.2	44.4	44.4	320	160
10.8	43.2	46	318	159
10.5	42	47.5	320	160
10.2	41	49.8	322	161
10	40	50	324	162

The addition of cadmium gives alloys of still lower melting point.

The following table includes the best known of these:

Testing Oil for Watches and Clocks

To test the fitness of oils for lubricating watches and clocks, pour a drop of the oil to be tested upon different metal plates, as iron, brass, tin, lead, etc.; keep them in a place free from dust, and examine the drops during 8 to 14 days in regard to their liquidity. Oil remaining liquid after the lapse of this time can be safely used.—*Kempe's Engineer's Year Book.*

To Weigh with Coins

A half-dollar = 12½ grams
A quarter = 6¼ grams
A dime = 2½ grams
In avoirdupois:
A half-dollar = 200 grains
A quarter = 100 grains
A nickel = 80 grains
A cent = 50 grains
A dime = 40 grains
1 oz. = 437½ grains

Therefore, 2 half-dollars (400 grains) and a dime (40 grains) combined are near enough to serve as a 1-oz. weight.

Alloy	Cadmium	Lead	Tin	Bismuth	Melting Point °F.	Melting Point °C.
Fusible alloy	12.5	25	12.5	50	149	65
Lipowitz's alloy	10	26.6	13.3	50.1	158	70
Woods' alloy	15.4	30.8	15.4	38.4	160	71
Fusible alloy	34.5	27.5	10	27.5	167	75
" "	6.2	34.5	9.3	50	171	77
" "	25	25	50	...	187	86
" "	16.6	...	33.3	50.1	203	95
" "	11.1	...	33.3	55.6	203	95
" "	25	...	25	50	203	95

Popular, Archaic, and Trade Names of Chemicals

Common Name	Chemical Name
Alcohol, grain ...	Ethyl alcohol
Alcohol, wood...	Methyl alcohol
Alum, common...	Potassium aluminum sulphate
Aqua regia......	Nitric and hydrochloric acids mixed
Baking soda	Sodium bicarbonate
Baryta water	Barium hydroxide solution
Bleaching powder	Calcium hypochlorite
Bluestone	Copper sulphate
Blue vitriol	Copper sulphate
Boracic acid	Boric acid
Borax	Sodium borate
Brimstone	Sulphur, molded in sticks
Calomel	Mercurous chloride
Caoutchouc	Rubber
Carbolic acid	Phenol
Carbonic acid gas	Carbon dioxide
Caustic potash ..	Potassium hydroxide
Caustic soda	Sodium hydroxide
Chalk	Calcium carbonate
Copperas	Ferrous sulphate
Corrosive sublimate	Mercuric chloride (bichloride of mercury)
Cream of tartar..	Potassium bitartrate
Epsom salt	Magnesium sulphate
Flowers of sulphur	Sulphur, crystals
Glauber's salt....	Sodium sulphate
Green vitriol	Ferrous sulphate
Hartshorn	Ammonium hydroxide
Hypo	Sodium thiosulphate
Laughing gas	Nitrous oxide

Common Name	Chemical Name
Limewater	Calcium hydroxide solution
Litharge	Lead oxide, PbO
Liver of sulphur.	Potassium sulphide
Lunar caustic ...	Silver nitrate, cast in thin sticks
Lye	Potassium hydroxide
Meerschaum	Magnesium silicate
Minium	Lead oxide, Pb_3O_4
Muriatic acid ...	Hydrochloric acid
Oil of vitriol	Sulphuric acid
Oleum	Fuming sulphuric acid
Orpiment	Arsenic sulphide, As_2S_3
Oxone	Sodium peroxide
Plumbago	Graphite
Potash alum	Potassium aluminum sulphate
Quicklime	Calcium oxide
Quicksilver	Mercury
Realgar	Arsenic sulphide, As_2S_2
Red lead	Lead oxide, Pb_3O_4
Red prussiate of potash	Potassium ferricyanide
Rochelle salt	Sodium potassium tartrate
Sal ammoniac ...	Ammonium chloride
Sal soda	Sodium carbonate
Sal volatile	Ammonium carbonate
Saleratus	Sodium bicarbonate
Salt (common) ..	Sodium chloride
Salt (rock)	Sodium chloride
Saltpeter (Chile).	Sodium nitrate
Saltpeter (Bengal)	Potassium nitrate
Salts of lemon ..	Potassium acid oxalate
Salts of sorrel....	Oxalic acid
Slaked lime	Calcium hydroxide
Soda ash	Sodium carbonate

Common Name	Chemical Name
Spirits of harts-horn	Ammonium hydroxide (ammonia water)
Spirits of salt ...	Hydrochloric acid
Sugar of lead....	Lead acetate
Tartar emetic....	Potassium antimony tartrate
Yellow prussiate of potash	Potassium ferrocyanide
Washing soda....	Sodium carbonate
Water-glass	Sodium silicate
White vitriol	Zinc sulphate

Elements and Their Symbols

Aluminum	Al
Antimony	Sb
Arsenic	As
Barium	Ba
Bismuth	Bi
Boron	B
Bromine	Br
Cadmium	Cd
Calcium	Ca
Carbon	C
Chlorine	Cl
Chromium	Cr
Cobalt	Co
Copper	Cu
Fluorine	F
Glucinum	Gl
Gold	Au
Helium	He
Hydrogen	H
Iodine	I
Iridium	Ir
Iron	Fe
Lead	Pb
Lithium	Li
Magnesium	Mg
Manganese	Mn
Mercury	Hg
Molybdenum	Mo
Neon	Ne
Nickel	Ni
Nitrogen	N

Osmium	Os
Oxygen	O
Palladium	Pd
Phosphorus	P
Platinum	Pt
Potassium	K
Selenium	Se
Silicon	Si
Silver	Ag
Sodium	Na
Strontium	Sr
Sulphur	S
Tantalum	Ta
Thorium	Th
Tin	Sn
Titanium	Ti
Tungsten	W
Uranium	U
Vanadium	V
Zinc	Zn
Zirconium	Zr

Converting Metric to English Measurements

The following condensed tables, taken from the *Smithsonian Physical Tables,* are to be recommended for quick and accurate figuring, without the necessity of tedious multiplication.

A number of more than one figure may be converted by changing one figure at a time (viz., units, tens, hundreds, and decimals) and adding all terms, having taken care as to the correct placing of decimal points.

LINEAR

	Meters to Inches	Meters to Feet	Meters to Yards	Kilometers to Miles
1	39.3700	3.28083	1.093611	0.62137
2	78.7400	6.56167	2.187222	1.24274
3	118.1100	9.84250	3.280833	1.86411
4	157.4800	13.12333	4.374444	2.48548
5	196.8500	16.40417	5.468056	3.10685
6	236.2200	19.68500	6.561667	3.72822
7	275.5900	22.96583	7.655278	4.34959
8	314.9600	26.24667	8.748889	4.97096
9	354.3300	29.52750	9.842500	5.59233

CAPACITY

	Milliliters or Cubic Centimeters to Fluid Drams	Centiliters to Fluid Ounces	Liters to Quarts	Decaliters to Gallons	Hectoliters to Bushels
1	0.27	0.338	1.0567	2.6418	2.8378
2	0.54	0.676	2.1134	5.2836	5.6756
3	0.81	1.014	3.1701	7.9253	8.5135
4	1.08	1.353	4.2268	10.5671	11.3513
5	1.35	1.691	5.2836	13.2089	14.1891
6	1.62	2.029	6.3403	15.8507	17.0269
7	1.89	2.367	7.3970	18.4924	19.8647
8	2.16	2.705	8.4537	21.1342	22.7026
9	2.43	3.043	9.5104	23.7760	25.5404

CUBIC

	Cubic centimeters to cubic inches	Cubic decimeters to cubic inches	Cubic meters to cubic feet	Cubic meters to cubic yards
1	0.0610	61.023	35.314	1.308
2	0.1220	122.047	70.269	2.616
3	0.1831	183.070	105.943	3.924
4	0.2441	244.094	141.258	5.232
5	0.3051	305.117	176.572	6.540
6	0.3661	366.140	211.887	7.848
7	0.4272	427.164	247.201	9.156
8	0.4882	488.187	282.516	10.464
9	0.5492	549.210	317.830	11.771

SQUARE

	Square Centimeters to Square Inches	Square Meters to Square Feet	Square Meters to Square Yards	Hectares to Acres
1	0.1550	10.764	1.196	2.471
2	0.3100	21.528	2.392	4.942
3	0.4650	32.292	3.588	7.413
4	0.6200	43.055	4.784	9.884
5	0.7750	53.819	5.980	12.355
6	0.9300	64.583	7.176	14.826
7	1.0850	75.347	8.372	17.297
8	1.2400	86.111	9.568	19.768
9	1.3950	96.875	10.764	22.239

WEIGHT

	Quintals to pounds av.	Milliers or tonnes to pounds av.	Kilograms to ounces Troy
1	220.46	2204.6	32.1507
2	440.92	4409.2	64.3015
3	661.39	6613.9	96.4522
4	881.85	8818.5	128.6030
5	1102.31	11023.1	160.7537
6	1322.77	13227.7	192.9045
7	1543.24	15432.4	225.0552
8	1763.70	17637.0	257.2059
9	1984.16	19841.6	289.3567

Note: For those accustomed to direct multiplication, some useful conversion factors are:

1 centimeter	=	0.39370 in.
1 meter	=	3.2808 ft.
1 cubic centimeter	=	0.0610 cu. in.
	or =	0.00176 pt.
	or =	0.03520 fl. oz.
	or =	0.28157 fl. dr.
1 liter	=	1.057 liq. qt.
	or =	33.815 fl. oz.
1 gram	=	15.4324 gr.
	or =	0.03527 av. oz.
1 kilogram	=	2.205 av. lb.

(Unnecessary decimal figures may be dropped as desired.)

WEIGHT

	Milligrams to Grains	Kilograms to Grains	Hectograms to Ounces Avoirdupois	Kilograms to Pounds Avoirdupois
1	0.01543	15432.36	3.5274	2.20462
2	0.03086	30864.71	7.0548	4.40924
3	0.04630	46297.07	10.5822	6.61387
4	0.06173	61729.43	14.1096	8.81849
5	0.07716	77161.78	17.6370	11.02311
6	0.09259	92594.14	21.1644	13.22773
7	0.10803	108026.49	24.6918	15.43236
8	0.12346	123458.85	28.2192	17.63698
9	0.13889	138891.21	31.7466	19.84160

To convert temperature in degrees Centigrade to degrees Fahrenheit, multiply by nine-fifths and then add 32.

INDEX